THE AMERICAN GIRLS

17  74

FELICITY, a spunky, spritely colonial girl,
full of energy and independence

18 24

JOSEFINA, an Hispanic girl whose heart and
hopes are as big as the New Mexico sky

18 54

KIRSTEN, a pioneer girl of strength and
spirit who settles on the frontier

18 64

ADDY, a courageous girl determined to be
free in the midst of the Civil War

19  04

SAMANTHA, a bright Victorian beauty, an
orphan raised by her wealthy grandmother

19  34

KIT, a clever, resourceful girl facing the
Great Depression with spirit and determination

19 44

MOLLY, who schemes and dreams on the
home front during World War Two

1934

KIT
LEARNS
A LESSON
A School Story

By VALERIE TRIPP

ILLUSTRATIONS WALTER RANE

VIGNETTES SUSAN MCALILEY

American Girl™

SCHOLASTIC INC.

New York Toronto London Auckland Sydney
Mexico City New Delhi Hong Kong Buenos Aires

ISBN 0-439-39583-6

PICTURE CREDITS
The following individuals and organizations have generously given
permission to reprint images contained in "Looking Back":
pp. 62-63—Courtesy of the Wood family (classroom photo); courtesy of Frances Pederson
Hall (report cards and merit pins); *Palmer Method Handwriting*, McGraw-Hill Companies;
cover, *Ohio Valley Pioneers* by Harry Edmund Danford; cover, *Stories in Trees* published by
Lyons & Carnahan; cover, *Tales & Travels*, Simon & Schuster; pp. 64-65—Records of Soil
Conservation Service/National Archives, NA 114-SD-5089 (farm); Library of Congress (family
in car and girl with cotton sack); *Chicago Daily News*/Illinois State Historical Society (protesting
teachers); © Bettmann/CORBIS (single woman protester); pp. 66-67—*The Cincinnati Post* (teacher
and headline); from the book *Public Schools in Hard Times*, published by Harvard University
Press, photo by Marion Post Wolcott (crowded classroom); Brown Brothers (breadline);
courtesy of Frances Pederson Hall (rhythm band).

Edited by Tamara England and Judith Woodburn
Designed by Myland McRevey, Justin Packard, Ingrid Slamer, and Jane S.Varda
Art Directed by Laura Moberly and Ingrid Slamer
Cover Background by Mike Wimmer

12 11 10 9 8 7 6 5 4 3 2 1   2 3 4 5 6 7/0

Printed in the U.S.A.   23

First Scholastic printing, September 2002

FOR JILL DAVIDSON MARTINEZ,
WITH LOVE

Table of Contents

DAD
*Kit's father, a
businessman facing
the problems of the
Great Depression.*

MOTHER
*Kit's mother, who takes
care of her family and
their home with strength
and determination.*

KIT
*A clever, resourceful
girl who helps her family
cope with the dark days
of the Depression.*

CHARLIE
*Kit's affectionate and
supportive sixteen-
year-old brother.*

UNCLE
HENDRICK
*Mother's wealthy and
disapproving uncle.*

MRS. HOWARD
*Mother's garden club
friend, who is a guest in
the Kittredge home.*

STIRLING
HOWARD
*Mrs. Howard's son,
whose delicate health
hides surprising
strengths.*

RUTHIE
SMITHENS
*Kit's best friend, who
is loyal, understanding,
and generous.*

ROGER
*A know-it-all boy
in Kit's class.*

MESSAGES

"Hey, Kit, wake up."

Kit Kittredge opened one eye and saw her brother Charlie at the foot of her bed. She put her pillow over her head and groaned, "Go *away*."

"Can't do that," said Charlie cheerfully. "Not till I'm sure you're up and at 'em." He turned on the lamp. "Come on, Squirt. Time to get to work."

Kit groaned again, but she sat up. "I'm awake," she yawned.

"Good," said Charlie. He tilted his head. "What's that funny sound?"

Kit listened. *Plink. Plinkplinkplink!* "Oh," she said. "The roof leaks."

1

"Why don't you ask Dad to fix it?" asked
Charlie. "I'm sure he could."

"Well, it only leaks when it rains," said Kit.

"No kidding," said Charlie.

"Besides, I like the plinking sound," Kit said.
"It's like someone's sending me a message in a secret
code that uses plinks instead of dots and dashes." In
the adventure stories Kit loved to read, people often
sent messages in secret codes, and Kit was a girl who
was always on the lookout for excitement.

"*Plinkplinkplink*," said Charlie. "That means 'Get
up, Kit.'"

"Okay, okay!" laughed Kit as she got out of bed.
"I get the message!"

"At last," said Charlie. "See you later." He
waved and disappeared down the stairs. Charlie had
to leave very early every day to get to his job loading
newspapers onto trucks, but he always woke Kit and
said good-bye before he left.

It was cold in the attic this rainy November
morning. Kit shivered and dressed quickly. Mornings
got off to a fast start at the Kittredge house these
days. Because of the Depression, Kit's dad had lost
his job back in August. To bring in money, Kit's

family had turned their home into a boarding house. The boarders paid money to rent rooms and have meals there. Mother was *very* particular about having their breakfast ready on time.

As Kit hurriedly tied her shoes, she saw that someone had moved her typewriter from one side of her desk to the other. *I bet Dad used my typewriter,* she thought. *He probably wrote a letter to ask about a job.* Kit sighed. Before Dad lost his job and they started taking in boarders, Kit used to love to type newspapers that told Dad what had happened at home while he was away at work. She promised herself that the day he got a new job, she'd make a newspaper with a huge headline that said, 'Hurray for Dad! Bye-Bye, Boarders!' Kit could not *wait* for that day. She did not like having the boarders in the house *at all*.

The thought of that headline cheered Kit as she went downstairs to the second floor to face her morning chores. Her first stop was the bathroom, where she fished three of Dad's socks out of the laundry basket. Teetering first on one foot, then on the other, Kit put a sock over each shoe. She put the third sock over her right hand like a mitten. Then Kit propped the laundry basket against her hip and peeked out the door to be sure the coast was clear. It was. Kit took a running start, then *swoosh!* She skated down the hallway, dusting the floor with her sock-covered feet and giving the table in the hall a quick swipe with her sock-covered hand.

Kit skated fast. She could already hear the boarders rising and making the annoying noises they made every morning. As she skated past Mr. Peck's room, she heard him blowing his nose: *Honkhonk h-o-n-k! Honkhonk h-o-n-k!* It sounded to Kit like a goose honking the tune of "Jingle Bells." The two lady boarders were chirping to each other in twittery bursts of words and laughter. Next door to them, in what used to be Kit's room, Mrs. Howard was bleating and baaing over her son Stirling like a mother sheep over her lamb. *A chirp, chirp here and a baa, baa there! It's like living on Old MacDonald's Farm, for Pete's sake!* Kit thought crossly. She skated to the top of the stairs, sat, peeled off the socks, and put them back in the laundry basket. Then she climbed onto the banister and polished it by sliding down it sideways.

She landed with a thud at the foot of the stairs and
found a surprise waiting for her: Mother.

"Oh! Good morning, Mother!" said Kit.

Mother crossed her arms over her chest. "Is that
how you do your chores every day?" she asked.
"Skating and sliding?"

"Uh . . . well, yes," said Kit.

"No wonder the hallway is always so dusty. Not
to mention Dad's socks," said Mother. She sighed a
sigh that sounded weary for so early in the morning.
"Dear, I thought you understood that we've all got
to work hard to make our boarding house a success.

Your chores are not a game. Is that clear?"

"Yes, Mother," said Kit.

"I'd appreciate it if you would dust more carefully from now on," said Mother. She managed a small smile. "And so would Dad's socks."

Kit felt sheepish. "Should I dust the hall again now?" she asked.

"I'm afraid there's no time," said Mother. "I'll try to get to it myself later. Right now I need your help with breakfast. The boarders will be down any minute. Come along."

"Okay," Kit said as she followed Mother into the kitchen. To herself she groused, *The boarders! It's all their fault. Mother never scolded me about things like dusting before they came, because I never had boring chores to do!* Kit knew her skate-and-slide method of dusting was slapdash, but she'd thought that nobody had noticed the dust left in the corners—except maybe persnickety Mrs. Howard. She should've known Mother would see it, too.

Mother wanted everything to be as nice as possible for the boarders. She insisted that the table be set beautifully for every meal. She went to great pains to make the food look nice, too, though there wasn't much of it. Dad went downtown nearly every day and brought home a loaf of bread and sometimes cans of fruits and vegetables. But even so, Mother had to invent ways to stretch the food so that there was enough. This morning Kit watched Mother cut the toasted bread into pretty triangles. Then, after Kit spooned oatmeal into a bowl, Mother put a thin slice of canned peach on top.

"That looks nice," said Kit. "The toast does, too."

"Just some tricks I've learned," Mother said. "Cutting the toast in triangles makes it look like there's more than there really is. And I'm hoping the peach slices will distract our guests from the fact that we've had oatmeal four times this week already. But it's cheap and it's filling."

"Humph!" said Kit as she plopped oatmeal into another bowl. "Oatmeal's good enough for *them*."

"Hush, Kit!" said Mother. She glanced at the door to the dining room as if the boarders might have heard. "You mustn't say that. We've got to keep our boarders happy. We need them to stay. In fact, we need more."

"*More* boarders?" asked Kit, horrified. "Oh, Mother, why?"

"Because," said Mother, sounding weary again, "even with Charlie's earnings and the rent from the boarders, we don't have enough money to cover our expenses. We need at least two more boarders to make ends meet."

"But where would we put them?" asked Kit. "No one would pay to share my attic. The roof leaks! And Charlie's sleeping porch is going to be freezing cold this winter."

"Yes," agreed Mother. "The sleeping porch should be enclosed, but we don't have any money for lumber."

sleeping porch

"Anyway," said Kit, "it'd be silly to go changing the house all around and filling it with boarders when I bet Dad is going to get another job any day now. Didn't he say he's going downtown again today to have lunch with a business friend?"

"Mmmhmm," said Mother, taking the oatmeal spoon from Kit.

"Probably it's an interview!" said Kit. She crossed her fingers on both hands. "Oh, I hope Dad gets a job!" she wished aloud.

"That," said Mother, "would be a dream

come true." She handed the heavy breakfast tray to Kit, took off her apron, and smoothed her hair. "Meanwhile, all we have going for us is this house and our own hard work. We must do everything we can to make sure our boarders stay. We can't let them see us worried and moping. So! Shoulders back, chin up, and put on a cheery morning face, please."

Kit forced her lips into a stiff smile.

"I guess that will have to do," said Mother briskly. She put on a smile too, pushed open the door, and walked into the dining room like an actress making an entrance on a stage. Dad and all the boarders were seated at the table. "Good morning, everyone!" Mother said.

"Good morning!" they all answered.

Kit's smile turned into a real one when she saw Dad, who was wearing his best suit and looking very handsome. He winked at her as if to send her a message that said, *It really **is** a good morning now that I've seen you.*

Miss Hart and Miss Finney, the two lady boarders, cooed with pleasure when Kit set their peachy oatmeal before them. Kit was careful not to spill. Miss Hart and Miss Finney were nurses.

"Good morning, everyone!" Mother said.

Their starched uniforms were as white as blank pieces of paper before a story was written on them. *I bet Miss Hart and Miss Finney have plenty of interesting stories to tell about their patients at the hospital,* thought Kit. *Maybe they've had daring nursing adventures, like Florence Nightingale and Clara Barton. What great newspaper headlines those adventures would make!*

Then Kit scolded herself for being curious. Miss Hart and Miss Finney must remain blank pages! Kit did not want to like them. She did not want to be interested in them or in Mr. Peck, either, even though he played a double bass as big as a bear and had a beard and was so tall he reminded Kit of Little John in her favorite book, *Robin Hood.* They would probably all turn out to be dull anyway, just as disappointing as tidy Mrs. Howard and skinny Stirling. They were *not* friends. They were only boarders, and they wouldn't be around for very long. As soon as Dad got a new job, they'd leave. Kit thought back to the wish she'd made and rewrote it in her head. *I should have added the word* **soon***,* she thought. *I hope Dad gets a job* **soon.**

As Kit sat down at her place, she saw Dad slip his toast onto Stirling's plate. Stirling's mother saw, too, and started to fuss. "Oh, Mr. Kittredge!" said Mrs. Howard to Dad. "You're too generous! And Stirling's digestion is so delicate! He can't eat so much breakfast. It's a shame to waste it."

"Don't worry, Mrs. Howard," joked Dad. "Stirling's just helping me be a member of the Clean Plate Club. I'm having lunch with a friend today. I don't want to ruin my appetite."

Stirling, who was Kit's age but so short he looked much younger, didn't say a word. But Kit noticed that he wolfed down his own toast and Dad's, too, pretty fast. *Delicate digestion, my eye,* thought Kit.

"Goodness, Mr. Kittredge," Miss Finney piped up. "Last night at dinner you said you weren't hungry because you'd had a big lunch. Those lunches must be feasts!"

"They are indeed," said Dad.

Just then, Mother brought in the morning mail. She handed a couple of letters to Dad and one fat envelope to Miss Finney, who got a letter from her boyfriend in Boston practically every day. Kit was trying to imagine what Miss Finney's boyfriend had to say to her in those long letters when Mother said,

"Why, Stirling, dear, look! This letter is for you."

Everyone was quiet as Mother handed Stirling the letter. Even his mother was speechless for once. The tips of Stirling's ears turned as pink as boiled shrimp. He looked at the envelope with his name and address typed on it, then eagerly ripped the envelope open, tearing it apart in his haste to get the letter out and read it.

Mrs. Howard recovered. "Who's it from, lamby?" she asked.

Stirling smiled a watery, timid-looking smile. "It's from Father," he answered. His odd husky voice sounded unsure, as if he himself could hardly believe what he was saying.

"My land!" exclaimed Mrs. Howard, pressing one hand against her heart. "A letter at last! What does he say?"

Stirling read the typewritten letter aloud. "'Dear Son, I haven't got a permanent address yet. I'll write to you when I do, and I'll send more money as soon as I can. Give my love to Mother. Love, Father.'" Stirling handed two ten-dollar bills to his mother. "He sent us this."

"Wow!" exclaimed Kit. "Twenty dollars? That's a lot of money!"

Miss Finney and Miss Hart murmured their agreement, and Mr. Peck put down his coffee cup in amazement.

Mrs. Howard was overcome with happiness. In a weak voice she said to Mother, "Margaret, take this," she said as she tried to give Mother one of the ten-dollar bills. "You've been so kind to us. You must share in our lucky day."

"Oh, but—" Mother began.

"I insist," said Mrs. Howard.

Mother hesitated. Then she said, "Thank you." She put the ten-dollar bill in her pocket.

After that, everyone started talking at once about Stirling's startling letter. Everyone but Stirling, that is. Kit saw Stirling read his father's message once more, and then fold the letter very small and hold it in his closed hand.

After breakfast, Dad sat at the kitchen table reading the want ads in the newspaper while Kit and Mother washed the dishes. "Mr. Howard must be doing all right if he can send his wife twenty dollars," Dad said from behind the newspaper. "Maybe Chicago is the place to go. Maybe there are jobs there."

"Chicago *is* a bigger city than Cincinnati," said Mother.

"We'd move to Chicago?" asked Kit. She didn't like the idea of leaving her home and her friends.

"No," said Dad, putting the paper down. "Only I would go."

Kit spun around from the sink so quickly her wet hand left a trail of soapsuds on the kitchen floor. "You'd go without us?" she asked, shocked. "You'd leave us? Oh, Dad, you can't!"

"Now Kit, calm down," said Dad. "It's just an idea. I haven't said I'll go. But if nothing turns up here by Thanksgiving . . ."

"Thanksgiving?" interrupted Kit. "That's only two weeks away!"

"You know how hard your father's been looking for a job here in Cincinnati," said Mother. "Ever since August."

"And he'll find one," said Kit. She looked at her father. "Won't you, Dad? One of those business friends you have lunch with is sure to offer you a job any day now, right?"

"Kit, sweetheart," Dad started to answer, then stopped. He picked up the paper and went back to his reading. "Right," he said. "Any day now."

As Kit turned back to the dishes, she thought, *When I wished for Dad to get a job soon, I didn't mean in Chicago!* In her head, she rewrote the message of her wish again. Now it was: *I hope Dad gets a job **soon**, and **here in Cincinnati**.*

CHAPTER
TWO

PILGRIMS AND INDIANS

As they walked to school that morning, Kit told her best friend Ruthie about changing her wish for Dad. The girls huddled under Ruthie's umbrella. They ignored Stirling, who trailed along behind them like a puny, pitiful puppy. "I didn't realize a wish had to be so specific," said Kit.

"Oh, yes," said Ruthie. "You have to be *very* careful what you say in a wish. Otherwise it'll come true, but not the way you meant it to. That happens a lot in fairy tales." Ruthie had read hundreds of fairy tales because she was interested in princesses. "Also, you usually have to work hard to *deserve* a wish to come true. You have to do something brave or impossible, or make a giant, noble sacrifice. And you have to wait. Wishes take time. Years, in some cases."

"Thanksgiving's only two weeks from now," said Kit. "I'm afraid that if Dad doesn't get a job here by then, he'll go away to Chicago."

"Chicago," repeated Ruthie. "He might as well go to the moon."

"I don't want *Dad* to leave," said Kit. "I want the *boarders* to leave."

Ruthie tugged on one of the straps of Kit's book bag and tilted her head toward Stirling. Kit realized that once again she'd spoken without thinking. She was pretty sure that Stirling already knew she wanted him and the other boarders to leave. Still, it wasn't nice to say so in front of him. Kit wouldn't have if she'd remembered that he was there. He was just so *invisible*.

All morning at school Kit tried not to think about how awful it would be to watch the boarders sitting around the table gobbling Thanksgiving turkey if she knew that Dad was going to leave. She could hardly bear listening to Roger, a show-offy boy in her class, answer a question about the first Thanksgiving that their teacher, Mr. Fisher, had asked.

"The first Thanksgiving was in 1621," said Roger. "The Pilgrims invited the Indians to a feast to celebrate their successful harvest. We have turkey at Thanksgiving because the Pilgrims served the Indians four wild turkeys, and we call it Thanksgiving because the Indians were thankful to the Pilgrims for being generous and sharing their food."

Kit couldn't stand it. She shot her hand up into the air and waved it.

"Yes, Kit?" said Mr. Fisher.

"Roger's got the story backwards," said Kit. "It's called Thanksgiving because the Pilgrims gave the feast to thank the Indians."

Roger snorted.

Kit wasn't the least bit intimidated by Roger. "The Pilgrims would've starved to death if it weren't for the Indians," she said. "The Indians taught the Pilgrims to plant corn and gave them supplies and help. I think that was pretty nice of the Indians, considering that the Pilgrims had barged into their land where they'd been living happily by themselves for a long time." As Kit spoke, she realized that this year, more than ever before, she had tremendous

Kit shot her hand up into the air and waved it.

sympathy for the Indians. She knew how it felt to have a bunch of strangers living with you and eating your food and expecting your help when you didn't want them there in the first place!

"Well!" said Mr. Fisher. "Thank you, Kit."

It made Kit feel a little better to have pleased Mr. Fisher. She liked him, but they had gotten off on the wrong foot the first day of school when Mr. Fisher called on Kit to read aloud in reading group. Kit hadn't known what page they were on because she'd read ahead and was busy thinking up better endings to the stories.

Mr. Fisher was cross with her then, but he was happy with her now. "Kit makes a good point," he said. "The Indians took pity on the Pilgrims and shared what little they had. It's important to help both friends and strangers when times are hard. We see this all around us today, because of the Depression. Who can give me examples of ways that our families and friends and neighbors are helping one another, and strangers, too?"

"When hoboes come to our back door," said Ruthie, "my mother always gives them sandwiches and coffee."

"At our church there's a box of old shoes for people to take if they need them," said a boy named Tom.

"My cousin sent me a winter coat she'd out-grown," said a girl named Mabel.

Kit was surprised to see Stirling raise his hand. He'd almost never done so before. Stirling was new to the class and the school because he had moved into Kit's house only last summer. He didn't know anyone but Kit and Ruthie, and he was so quiet he was easy to forget.

"Sometimes people get kicked out of their house because they can't pay the rent," Stirling said in his deep voice that always surprised Kit, coming as it did from such a pip-squeak. "And friends are nice and invite them to live in their house with them."

"Oh, so that's why you live with Kit," brayed Roger. "I thought you two were married!"

The class snickered as Roger made kissing noises. Stirling slouched in his seat. Kit shook her fist at Roger, but she was mad at Stirling, too. *Stirling should have kept his mouth shut!* she thought.

"That will do, Roger," said Mr. Fisher. "I'll wait

for quiet, boys and girls." He waited until the
snickering stopped, then asked, "Who can give me
more examples of how we're helping one another?"

"Soup kitchens serve free meals to people who
can't buy food," said a girl named Dorothy.
"And some soup kitchens also give people
groceries to take home to their families."

"Yes," said Mr. Fisher. "Now, as you
all know, Thanksgiving is coming soon. I'd like
our class to do its part to help the hungry. So if you
can, please bring in an item of food. It doesn't have
to be anything big. An apple or a potato will do.
I know most of us don't have much food to spare.
But if we all chip in, we can make a Thanksgiving
basket and donate it to a soup kitchen."

The students murmured among themselves,
but without much enthusiasm. They'd all seen
soup kitchens with long lines of people waiting
outside them. Kit had once seen a man in a soup
line faint on the street from hunger. She knew
that soup kitchens were for people who had been
without work for so long that they had no money
or hope or pride left, and who were so desperate
that they had to accept free food.

"My father says that people who go to soup kitchens should be ashamed," said Roger, full of bluster. "They're bums."

"They're not bums," said Ruthie. "Most of them are perfectly nice, normal people who happen to be down on their luck. I think we should feel sorry for them."

"My father says they're just too lazy to work," said Roger. "And now that Franklin Roosevelt's been elected, people will expect the government to take care of them. My father says it'll ruin our country."

Franklin Roosevelt

Kit grew hot under the collar listening to Roger and thinking of how hard Dad was trying to find a job. "People aren't too lazy to work," she said. "They'd work if they could find a job. But jobs are hard to find."

Mr. Fisher nodded. "Right here in Cincinnati," he said, "one out of three workers is unemployed, which means they don't have a job. One out of three. What fraction is that?"

"One-third," said Tom.

"That's correct," said Mr. Fisher.

One out of three? thought Kit. Unemployment was a lot worse than she'd thought! Just for a shivery second, her absolute confidence that Dad would find a job in Cincinnati was shaken a little bit. Maybe he really would have to go to Chicago! Then Kit spoke to herself firmly. *No!* she thought. *Dad is different. He **will** find a job. Any day now. He said so.*

"These are hard times," said Mr. Fisher. "That's why it's especially important to remember the example of the Indians and the Pilgrims. We all have friends or relatives who're struggling to make ends meet. This year many of us will have to do without some of the things we've had in years past."

"But Mr. Fisher," Mabel asked, "we're still going to have a Thanksgiving pageant this year, aren't we?"

"Yes, of course," said Mr. Fisher.

Now the class buzzed with excitement. Everyone loved the pageant!

Mr. Fisher crossed his arms. "I need your attention, boys and girls," he said. The children shushed one another, and Mr. Fisher continued. "The sixth-graders will be the Pilgrims," he said. "The fifth-graders will be the Indians. Our fourth grade is responsible for the scenery." Mr. Fisher held up a drawing. "Here's a drawing of the backdrop we'll paint."

The drawing showed four giant turkeys and a huge cornucopia with fruits and vegetables spilling out. The turkeys' feathers were all different colors, and they were not just painted on. They were made out of bits of paper cut to look like real feathers, and they were glued onto the turkeys.

"That's good!" said Tom.

"Yes, it is, isn't it?" said Mr. Fisher.

"Who drew it?" asked Dorothy.

"Stirling," said Mr. Fisher.

Everyone twisted around to stare at Stirling. For the second time that day, Stirling slouched down in his seat. But this time, no one was snickering. Everyone, including Kit, was gaping at Stirling in astonishment.

At lunch Ruthie said, "Stirling is really good at drawing, isn't he, Kit?"

Kit shrugged. "I guess so," she said. She was still annoyed with Stirling for speaking in class and embarrassing her in front of everybody.

"Shh!" said Dorothy. "Here he comes now!"

Stirling was walking toward Kit, his knickers ballooning out over his spindly legs. Kit and Stirling had to share a lunchbox, and every day Stirling came over to the girls' side of the lunchroom to get his sandwich from Kit. Usually, the girls at the table completely ignored Stirling. But today when he came over, several girls squeaked, "Hi, Stirling."

Stirling blushed pinker than ever. "Hi," he mumbled. He took his sandwich and scuttled back to the boys' side. Unfortunately, Roger had spotted Stirling with Kit. He began to whistle "Here Comes the Bride." Kit glowered at Roger, who batted his eyelashes at her across the lunchroom.

"Hey, Kit," said Ruthie, trying to distract her. "Good news! There's some wood left over from our new garage. My father said that you and I can use it for our tree house."

"That's great!" said Kit. She had been sketching tree houses and hoping to build one ever since she'd read *Robin Hood*. She loved the tree houses that Robin and his men built high in the branches of the trees in Sherwood Forest. Kit knew her family had absolutely no money to spend on something as unnecessary as wood for a tree house. So it was lucky that Ruthie's father, who still had a job, was giving away the leftover wood.

"I was thinking," said Ruthie, "you know how your tree house sketches haven't ever really turned out very well?"

"Yes," Kit admitted honestly.

"Well, why don't we ask Stirling to draw a plan for us?" asked Ruthie.

"No!" Kit said. "Gosh, Ruthie! If we let him plan a tree house for us, then when it's built he'll want to come in it and we'll have to let him. He's already invaded my real house. I don't want him in our tree house, too!"

"Okay, okay," said Ruthie. "Don't get all worked up. The tree house doesn't even *exist* yet!"

"I'll ask Dad to help us," said Kit. "He loves building things."

"Sure!" said Ruthie. She grinned. "And he'll be so busy building our tree house, he'll forget all about going away!"

Kit grinned back. "Right!" she said. "How soon can we get that wood?"

SPILLING THE BEANS

A few days later, Kit's class was on the stage in the school auditorium working on the backdrop for the Thanksgiving pageant. Stirling had drawn the outline on big sheets of paper that were pinned to the curtains at the back of the stage. The boys in the class were painting in the fruits and vegetables and the cornucopia. The girls were cutting out paper turkey feathers. Stirling was standing on a stool, gluing the finished feathers onto the outlines of the giant turkeys.

Mr. Fisher was far away, up in the balcony wrestling with the spotlights, and Roger was taking advantage of his absence by being a general pain. He came over and jabbed Stirling with his paintbrush.

"So, Stirling," he said, "when's the wedding for you and Kit?"

It was as if Stirling hadn't heard Roger. He stepped down off his stool and calmly began brushing glue onto another batch of turkey feathers.

Roger turned his back on Stirling. "Hey, Kit," he said. "What's the matter with your boyfriend? He's awful quiet."

"Stirling is *not* my boyfriend," snapped Kit. "He and his mother *pay* to live at our house. They're *boarders*."

"Oh yeah!" Roger drawled. "That's right." He plopped himself down on the stool that Stirling had been using. Loudly and slowly, so that everyone could hear him, Roger said, "I heard that your family is so hard up you're running a boarding house now." He smirked. "And *you're* the maid."

"I am not!" Kit denied hotly. Of course, she *had* been feeling like a maid lately. But she'd never give Roger satisfaction by admitting it.

"That's not what I heard," Roger taunted. "Here's you." He pretended that his paintbrush was a maid's feather duster and he used it to brush some imaginary dust off his arms. Then he stood up, turned, and started to swagger away.

It was then that Kit saw the giant turkey feathers stuck to the seat of Roger's pants! Kit touched Ruthie's arm and pointed at Roger.

Ruthie chortled when she saw the feathers. "Hey, look, everybody!" she called out happily, pointing to Roger's bottom. "Look at Roger—Mr. Turkeypants!"

Everyone looked. The girls screamed with laughter and the boys whistled and clapped. "Hey, Turkeypants!" Ruthie hooted. "Gobble, gobble!" Kit realized with surprise that Stirling must have sneaked the gluey feathers onto the stool just as Roger sat down so they'd stick to his pants when he stood up.

Roger also realized that Stirling was the one who'd tricked him. "You think you're pretty smart, don't you, Stirling?" he said furiously as he pulled off the gluey feathers. "Sticking your stupid turkey feathers on me. Well, at least *my* father hasn't flown the coop and disappeared like yours has!"

By now the whole class was gathered around Kit, Ruthie, Stirling, and Roger. They all looked at Stirling, waiting to hear what he'd say to Roger.

But Stirling didn't say anything, and his silence exasperated Kit. "For your information, birdbrain," she said to Roger, "Stirling's father sent him a letter from Chicago just a few days ago." She paused for impact. "And it had twenty dollars in it! His mother gave ten dollars to my mother."

Everyone gasped. *"Twenty dollars!"* they whispered in amazement.

"Well," sneered Roger. "That's good news for *your* family then, Kit, since your father doesn't have a job *or* any money. My father says your dad used up all of his savings to pay the people who worked at his car dealership, which was stupid. No wonder no one will offer him a job."

"That's not true!" said Kit, outraged. "My father has job interviews all the time. Almost every day he has big, fancy lunches and meetings about jobs. He'll get one any day now. He said so."

"No, he won't," said Roger. "Nobody wants your father."

With that, Roger shoved his armful of sticky turkey feathers at Kit, who shoved them right back. Kit was so angry and shoved so hard that Roger staggered backward, lost his balance, and fell against a ladder that had a bucket of white paint on it. Everyone shrieked in horror and delight as the can fell over, splattering white paint on the backdrop and clonking Roger on the head! White paint spilled over Roger's hair and face and shoulders and back and arms. It ran in rivers down Roger, striping his legs and his socks and pooling into white puddles around his shoes.

"Arrgghh!" Roger roared. He swiped his hand across his face to clear the paint out of his eyes and lunged for Kit.

But at that very instant, Mr. Fisher appeared. "Stop!" he shouted.

Roger stopped. Everyone was quiet.

Mr. Fisher frowned as he surveyed the white mess. "Who's responsible for this?" he demanded.

"Not me!" said Roger. "Stirling started it. He stuck feathers on me. And then Ruthie called me Mr. Tur—a stupid name—and Kit shoved me into the ladder. *They* did it, not me. They—"

Mr. Fisher held up his hand. "Quiet," he said. "Roger, go to the boys' room and clean yourself up. Boys and girls, I want you to go back to the classroom and sit silently at your desks. Kit, Ruthie,

*Everyone shrieked in horror and delight as the can fell over, splattering
white paint on the backdrop and clonking Roger on the head!*

and Stirling, you three stay here. I want to talk to you."

Roger scuttled past Kit on his way out. *"Now* you're going to get it," he hissed at her, sounding pleased. *"Now* you'll be sorry!"

Kit lifted her chin. "I'm not sorry I shoved you, Roger," she said. "I'd do it again, no matter what the punishment is. I'd shove anyone who says anything mean about my dad!"

"So watch out!" added Ruthie for good measure.

Roger made a face. But for once, he made no smart remark in reply.

When Kit, Ruthie, and Stirling were walking home from school later, the girls agreed that Mr. Fisher's punishment was not too terrible, really. They'd had to clean up the stage, and they were going to have to spend their recess time for the rest of the week helping Stirling redo the backdrop where white paint had spattered on it. Mr. Fisher had also decided that Kit, Ruthie, and Stirling would deliver the class's Thanksgiving basket to a soup kitchen while the rest of the class was watching the Thanksgiving pageant.

"The only bad part of the punishment is missing

the pageant," said Ruthie. "Especially because we have to go to a soup kitchen instead."

"The worst part to me is that loudmouth Roger isn't being punished," said Kit. "It's not fair. He's the one who started the whole fight."

"Don't worry," said Ruthie. "In fairy tales, bad guys like Roger always get their comeuppance in the end. Everyone finds out the truth eventually."

That reminded Kit of something. "Uh, Stirling," she said. "It would probably be better if we didn't say anything about this . . . this situation when we get home. My mother might get a little upset if she found out."

"Mine, too," said Stirling. His voice was serious but Kit saw a little ghost of a smile flicker across his face. She understood. They both knew that Stirling's mother would go into absolute *fits* if she found out her little lamb had been part of a fight. And she'd surely come swooping down to school and insist that he couldn't possibly go to a soup kitchen. Think of the germs!

"You know, Stirling," said Ruthie. "I think you're being pretty nice about this whole thing. After all, it was your drawing that was ruined by all that paint."

Another smile flickered across Stirling's face. "Too bad the first Thanksgiving didn't take place during a blizzard," he said in his low voice. "Then Roger could have been the Abominable Snowman in the pageant."

Ruthie laughed. And Kit did, too.

Stirling knew how to keep quiet. He did not spill the beans about the spilled paint, the fight, or the punishment. So when the day came for the trip to the soup kitchen, Kit and Stirling went off to school as if it were a normal morning. They did bring Kit's wagon with them, but the grownups were too busy to notice.

After an early lunch at school, the rest of the class went to the pageant. Mr. Fisher helped Kit, Ruthie, and Stirling put the Thanksgiving basket into the wagon. It was heavy. Students had brought potatoes, beans, and apples. There were a few jars of preserves and six loaves of bread. Kit and Stirling brought a can of fruit, and Ruthie, whose family still had plenty of money, brought in a turkey that weighed twenty pounds.

"The soup kitchen is down on River Street," said Mr. Fisher. "After you deliver the basket, you may go home." He paused. "Happy Thanksgiving," he said. Then he hurried off so he wouldn't miss the beginning of the pageant.

Kit, Ruthie, and Stirling set out. It was a cold day. The sky was the grayish brown color of a dirty potato, and soon it began to spit rain. Ruthie propped her umbrella up in the wagon to keep the basket dry. Kit's shoes were wet through, and her wrists were wet and chapped because her arms were too long for her coat sleeves. Her shoulders ached from pulling the heavy wagon. But Kit was not the kind of girl who wasted time feeling sorry for herself. Instead, she made up her mind to pretend that she was a newspaper reporter. As she walked along, she imagined how she would write about the people and things she was seeing.

"I'll take a turn pulling the wagon now," Ruthie offered after a while.

"Thanks," said Kit. She smiled at Ruthie, who looked like a damp, overstuffed couch in her new winter coat. "This whole thing is kind of an adventure, isn't it?"

"Sure," said Ruthie, after only the tiniest

hesitation. "We're like the bedraggled princess in 'The Princess and the Pea.'"

Kit grinned. *Good old Ruthie,* she thought. *She has a princess for every occasion.*

"No one who sees us would know that this is a punishment," Kit said. "It doesn't look like one, or feel like one, either."

"No," said Ruthie. "Especially since Roger's not with us."

The girls giggled.

But they stopped giggling when they turned the corner onto River Street and saw the line outside the soup kitchen. It was four people across, and it stretched from the door of the soup kitchen all the way to the end of the block. The people stood shoulder to shoulder, hunched against the rain. The brims of their hats were pulled low over their faces as if they were ashamed to be there and did not want to be recognized. The buildings that lined the street were as gray as the rain. They seemed to slump together as if they were ashamed, too.

"Oh my," said Ruthie quietly.

Stirling didn't say anything, but he moved up to be next to the girls.

Kit prided herself on being brave, but even she was daunted by the dreary scene before her. She squared her shoulders. "Let's go around to the back door," she suggested. "That's probably the right place to make a delivery."

Kit led the way down a small alley and around to the rear of the building. She knocked on the back door. No one answered. Kit lifted the basket out of the wagon. She took a deep breath, pushed the door open, and stepped inside. Stirling and Ruthie followed her. When they went in, they saw why no one had answered Kit's knock. It was very busy.

People were rushing about with huge, steamy kettles of soup, trays of sandwiches, and pots of hot coffee. A swinging door separated the kitchen from the room where the food was served and the groceries were given away.

One lady saw Kit and the others and stopped short. She peered through the steam rising off the soup she carried and asked, "May I help you?"

"We're from Mr. Fisher's class," said Kit. "We have a Thanksgiving basket to donate."

"Oh, yes!" said the lady. "You're expected. Bless you! As you can see, my hands are full. You'll have to unpack the basket yourselves. Leave the turkey and the potatoes and all here in the kitchen. We'll use them to make tomorrow's soup. But bring the canned goods and the loaves of bread out front now. You can give them away."

Kit, Ruthie, and Stirling did as they were told. After they unloaded the basket, they pushed through the swinging door from the kitchen to the front room, which was crowded with people. It smelled of soup and coffee. At round tables in the center of the room, people sat eating and drinking. Some talked quietly. But most of the people kept a polite silence, as if they did not want to call attention to themselves or make themselves known to anyone around them. Along one side of the room, there was a long table with people lined up in front of it. Kit could see only their backs as they stood patiently, holding bowls and spoons, waiting for soup to be served to them. Across the room there was another long table where a lady was handing out groceries and loaves of bread for people to take home. Rather shyly, Kit, Ruthie, and Stirling went over, put their food on the table, and stood next to her.

"Thanks," said the lady. "Please give the bread to the people as they pass by."

Kit, Ruthie, and Stirling kept their eyes on the bread as they handed it out. It was kinder and more respectful not to look into the faces of the people, who seemed grateful but embarrassed to be accepting free food. Most of them kept their eyes down, too. Kit felt very, very sorry for them as they took their bread, murmured their thanks, and moved away. *All of these people have sad stories to tell,* she thought. *They weren't always hungry and hopeless like they are now. How humiliating this must be for them!*

The lady handing out the groceries seemed to know some of the people. "Well, hello!" she said to one man. "You're here a little later than usual today."

Kit handed the man his bread.

"Thank you," he said.

Kit looked up, bewildered.

It was Dad.

KIT'S HARD TIMES

"Kit!" Dad gasped.

Kit couldn't breathe. She felt as if she had been punched hard in the stomach. Shock, disbelief, and a sickening feeling of terrible shame shot through her as she stared at Dad.

Suddenly, Kit could bear no more. She pushed past Ruthie and Stirling and bolted through the swinging doors. She ran through the kitchen and past the stoves with kettles of soup that had billowing clouds of steam rising from them. She burst out the back door into the alley. Once she was outside, her legs felt wobbly, and she sagged against the hard brick wall.

In a moment, Ruthie and Stirling were beside

her. "Kit?" said Ruthie gently. "Are you okay?"

Kit nodded. She looked at Ruthie. "Is my dad still . . ." she began.

"Your dad left," said Ruthie. "He said he'd talk to you at home."

Kit took a shaky breath.

"Come on," said Ruthie. "Let's go." Stirling grabbed the wagon handle, and they started down the alley with the empty wagon rattling and banging noisily behind them. Slowly, miserably, and without talking, the three of them walked together until they came to the end of Ruthie's driveway. They stopped next to the stack of lumber left over from the new garage, and Ruthie turned her sad face toward Kit. "Listen," she said. "Everything's going to be all right."

"All right?" Kit repeated. She shivered. "No, Ruthie," she said. "Everything's *not* going to be all right. My father hasn't been having job interviews. He's been going to a soup kitchen. He had to, just to get something to *eat*, to get food for our *family* to eat." Kit's voice shook. "Dad's not going to get a job here in Cincinnati. Maybe he would have a better chance of finding one in Chicago. I guess . . ." Kit faltered, then went on. "I guess now I hope that he *will* go."

"No, you don't," said Stirling in his husky voice.

Kit frowned. "What do *you* know about what I want?" she asked. "*Your* father is in Chicago, sending you letters with money stuck in them!"

"No," said Stirling. His gray eyes looked straight at Kit. "He isn't."

"What are you talking about?" asked Kit. "I saw the money!"

"That was *my* twenty dollars," Stirling said. "My father gave it to me before he left. He told me to save it for an emergency." Stirling sighed, and then he poured out the whole story. "My mother hasn't been able to pay any rent since we moved in," he said. "I offered her the twenty dollars lots of times, but she always said no. Then, a few weeks ago, she told me that we were going to have to leave your house. I knew it was because she was ashamed to stay any longer without paying. She wouldn't feel so bad if she could help with the housework, but your mother won't let her. I figured if I could trick her into taking the twenty dollars, she might use it for rent. So I made her think it came in a letter from my father."

Kit squinted at Stirling, trying to understand.

"You sneaked the money into the letter?" she asked.

Stirling shook his head. "No," he said. "It's worse than that." He paused. "I wrote the letter myself. I typed it on your typewriter."

"*What?*" Kit and Ruthie asked together.

"The truth . . ." Stirling hesitated. "The truth is, I don't know where my father is," he said. "But I'm pretty sure he's never coming back here to my mother and me. He flew the coop, as Roger said."

"Oh, no," Ruthie sighed.

Kit felt her hands clench into fists.

"So that's how I know that you don't want your dad to go away, Kit," said Stirling earnestly. "No matter what, it's better to have your dad at home. No matter how bad or hopeless things are, you don't want him to leave."

Kit sat down hard in the wagon. She held her head in her hands.

"Stirling," said Ruthie, "you'd better tell your mom what you did."

Stirling nodded. It was as if he'd used up all his words.

Ruthie walked up her driveway backward, waving good-bye until she went inside her house.

Kit stood up tiredly. As she trudged slowly home with the wagon and Stirling behind her, a new thought presented itself. *When Stirling tells his mother about the letter and the money, they'll leave,* she thought. She walked up the steps and opened her front door. *They won't live here in our house anymore.*

Of course, Kit had wanted Stirling and his fussbudgety mother to leave ever since they'd arrived. But now . . . It was very peculiar. Now that it was about to happen, Kit did not feel glad. She stood in the front hall, which smelled of wet wool coats and dripped with umbrellas, and watched Stirling head upstairs to the room he and his mother shared.

"Is that you, lamby?" Mrs. Howard called. "Did you wipe your feet?"

Stirling looked back over his shoulder at Kit, and a quicksilvery smile slipped across his face. Then he turned away and climbed the rest of the stairs.

Slowly, Kit took off her coat and headed upstairs to change out of her school clothes. As she passed by Mother and Dad's room, the door opened.

"Kit," said Dad. "Come in here, please. I'd like to talk to you."

49

Kit went in and sat on the desk chair.

"I've already told your mother about what happened today," said Dad. "I owed her an apology, and I owe you and Charlie one, too. I'm sorry I misled all of you. I should have told you what I was really doing." Dad walked over to the window and looked out. "I've been going to the soup kitchen for weeks now, to eat and to get food to bring home. We've been so short of food. It was the only way I could contribute to the household."

"Are we . . . are we really that poor?" asked Kit, almost in a whisper.

"Yes," said Dad. "We are. But I didn't want any of you to know. That's why I pretended not to be hungry here at home. I'd have lunch at the soup kitchen, and then I could give my breakfast or dinner away to make our groceries stretch further." Dad turned to face Kit. "I shouldn't have led you to believe that I'd find a job here in Cincinnati soon. I guess my only excuse is that I wanted it to be true."

Kit went to stand next to Dad. He put his arm around her shoulder.

"But," said Dad, "it's time for me—for all of us—to face the truth. And the truth is that there's

"It's time for me—for all of us—to face the truth," Dad said.

nothing for me to do here. There's no point in studying the want ads in the newspapers every day for a job that's never going to appear. So your mother and I have decided. I'm going to Chicago."

"Oh, Dad!" cried Kit. "You're not going to Chicago because of that letter from Stirling's father, are you? Because—"

Dad held up his hand to stop her. "I'm going," he said, "because there's really no alternative. We don't have room in the house to take in as many boarders as we need. If I go to Chicago, maybe I can find a job and send a little money home."

"I don't want you to go, Dad," Kit said desperately.

"You'll have to write to me and tell me what happens after I leave," Dad said, smiling a small smile. "It'll be like the old days. Remember the newspapers you used to make for me? I loved them so much. When I'm gone, will you write newspapers and send them to me so I won't feel so far away?"

Kit nodded slowly.

"That's my girl," said Dad. "You were my reporter during the good times. I need you to be my reporter during the hard times, too."

Hard times, thought Kit dully as she left Dad and walked down the hallway. The odor of onions frying rose up from the kitchen, and Kit knew that Mother must be making another one of the odd sauces she made so often nowadays—one that was meant to stretch a small piece of meat to feed a crowd. Kit heard Miss Hart and Miss Finney laughing in their room and Mr. Peck teaching Charlie to play his big double bass fiddle. She thought about the chores waiting for her that absolutely had to be done. Mother needed her to set the table for dinner and scrub the potatoes and put them in the oven to bake. Then there was laundry to iron and fold and put away, all before dinner. *This is it,* Kit thought. *This is the truth of my life now. Maybe forever.*

With heavy, defeated steps, Kit climbed the stairs to the attic. How foolish she had been to think that her life was going to go back to the way it used to be! Kit sank into her desk chair. She cleared a space between her typewriter and a pile of papers and rested her head on her arms. She had been wrong about so many things! Instead of resenting the boarders, she should have been grateful for them.

Instead of wanting them to leave, she should have been trying to figure out a way to fit more boarders in the house. Because . . . Kit felt pinpricks of fear up her spine. Because there was no guarantee that Dad would be able to find a job in Chicago, either. What would become of her family? How would they have enough money for food and clothes and heat? Would they be so poor they'd be kicked out of their house?

Oh, I wish we had room for more boarders! Kit thought passionately. *Then Dad could stay. If Ruthie's right about wishes, and you have to work hard to deserve them, then I promise to work as hard as I possibly can to make this one come true.*

Kit felt a drop of water on her hand. She looked up and saw a new leak in the roof, right above her desk. Drops of water plopped onto the papers next to her. Kit saw that the drops had blurred one of her tree house sketches. *Oh well, what difference does it make?* she thought, shoving the papers aside. *Dad won't be here to build it. There's no use for the sketch or Ruthie's lumber now.* Kit sat bolt upright. *Unless . . . wait a minute! Tree house? Boarding house?*
Suddenly, Kit had an idea.

54

All through dinner Kit was distracted, thinking about her idea. The more she thought about it, the better she liked it. As soon as they were alone in the kitchen, washing the dishes after dinner, Kit presented her idea to Mother.

"Mother," she said, "I've been thinking. Ruthie's father has a stack of lumber left over from their new garage. He said Ruthie and I could have it to build a tree house. But I bet he wouldn't mind if we used the lumber to fix up Charlie's sleeping porch instead. If we made it nice enough, then maybe Mr. Peck would move in with Charlie."

"And then?" Mother asked.

"Then we could put two new boarders in Mr. Peck's room," said Kit.

"We could certainly use the money," said Mother. She sighed tiredly. "But I just don't know if I could handle the extra work that two more boarders would be." Her face looked sad. "Especially after your father leaves."

"How about asking Mrs. Howard to help you with the housework instead of paying rent?" asked

Kit. "I'd still help, too, of course. But Mrs. Howard is a crackerjack cleaner."

Mother shook her head. "I'm not sure she'd agree to that," she said.

"Oh, I think she would," said Kit. "Stirling says she *wants* to help."

Mother was quiet for a thoughtful moment. Then she said, "Kit, dear, it's very ingenious of you to have thought of all this, and it would be very nice of you and Ruthie to sacrifice your tree house lumber. But I'm afraid lumber for the renovation is not our only problem. We don't have money to pay a carpenter. Who'd do the work?"

Kit sighed and sat down at the kitchen table, discouraged. Then, suddenly, she and Mother looked at each other. They'd both had the same idea at the same time. Together they said, "Dad!"

"Dad could do it!" said Kit. "He's great at building things."

"Yes," agreed Mother. "But the idea would have to be presented to him in just the right way. Now that he's decided to go, it'll be hard to change his mind."

Kit grinned from ear to ear. "You leave that to me," she said, full of enthusiasm. "I have a great plan!"

Mother smiled at last. "All right," she said. "Give it a try!"

"Thanks, Mother!" said Kit. She hugged Mother, and then darted out the kitchen door and flew up the stairs two at a time. She couldn't carry out her plan alone, but she knew just whom to ask for help.

Kit knocked on Stirling's door.

"Yes?" said Mrs. Howard. When she opened the door, Kit saw that the room was as neat as a pin.

"May I please speak to Stirling?" asked Kit.

Mrs. Howard began to say no. "He's very tired, and—"

But then Stirling appeared from behind his mother.

"Stirling," said Kit, looking straight at him. "Will you help me?"

"Yes!" said Stirling immediately. It was as though he'd been waiting for Kit's question for a long time.

The next morning, when Dad sat down to breakfast, this is what he saw at his place:

The Hard Times News

SPECIAL THANKSGIVING DAY EDITION

****

Editor: Kit Kittredge
Artist: Stirling Howard
Adviser: ~~Mother~~ Margaret Kittredge

WANTED

Tall bearded man to share sleeping
porch with early rising, agreeable
teenager. Must play double bass and ~~an~~
drink coffee. Call Charlie Kittredge.

 WANTED

Do you have interesting, ~~x~~exciting stories
to tell about adventures in nursing? If so,
I'd like to hear them! Call Kit~~t~~ Kittredge.

WANTED IMMEDIATELY

Talented handy man to fix sleeping porch
so ~~that~~ it will sleep two. Great workingg
conditions! Call the Kittredge family.

WANTED

Neat and tidy lady to help with housekeeping in exchange for room and board.
Call Margaret Kittredge..

WANTED

Kids with wagon to haul away ~~an~~
leftover lumber suitable for use in fixing
sleeping porch. Call Ruthie Smithens.

Kit, Stirling, and Mother sat on the edges of their seats watching Dad read *The Hard Times News.* When he finished reading, Dad glanced at Mother over the top of the paper with a questioning look in his eyes. Mother smiled and nodded, then Dad smiled, too.

"Well!" said Dad, patting the paper. "Look at this! There's a construction job in these want ads. A boarding house needs to expand. It's right here in Cincinnati, close to home." Dad winked at Kit. "In fact, it *is* at home. It's the perfect job for me!"

Kit ran to Dad and hugged him. "So you'll stay, then?" she asked.

"Yes," said Dad. "I'll go talk to Ruthie's father about the leftover lumber today." He handed Kit's newspaper to Mrs. Howard. "I think there's a job here that might interest you, Mrs. Howard," he said.

Mrs. Howard read the want ads and exclaimed, "My land! So there is!" She turned to Mother. "I'd love to help you with the housekeeping," she said. "I'm very good at dusting. I've noticed that the upstairs hallway—"

"That's Kit's job," Mother interrupted politely. "But with two more boarders moving in soon, there'll be plenty to do. I'd be glad to have your help."

"I'll start today!" said Mrs. Howard.

Kit stood next to Dad and looked around the breakfast table as the newspaper was passed from hand to hand. Charlie and Mr. Peck were laughing and talking together about being roommates. Miss Hart and Miss Finney were beaming at her, looking as if they were brimming over with stories to tell. Suddenly, she heard a quiet voice next to her say, "Happy Thanksgiving, Kit."

It was Stirling. His gray eyes were shining. Kit smiled. "Happy Thanksgiving, Stirling," she said.

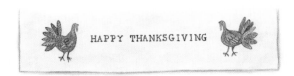

HAPPY THANKSGIVING

Looking
Back
1934

A Peek Into
the Past

When Kit was in school in the early 1930s, students were separated by grade into individual classrooms, just as they are today. They sat in sturdy desks that were nailed to the floor in neat rows, and they stood every morning to recite the Pledge of Allegiance. Boys and girls formed orderly lines to go in and out for recess. Classrooms were quieter and teachers were stricter than they are today.

Children in Kit's time studied many of the same subjects students do today— reading, spelling, arithmetic, geography, and history. Special subjects, such as art, music, and physical education, were taught by teachers who

Report cards in the 1930s often included grades for behavior and attitude.

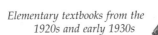

Position
Picture
Number
7

Many teachers of Palmer Method penmanship keep individual progress packs in which are filed once a week exercises including word, sentence and paragraph writing. The examination of these packs by teachers and pupils is an incentive which keeps interest alive and all working industriously towards the goal of ideal muscular movement handwriting.

It is impossible to procure the desired handwriting results with the use of poor materials. The following suggestions will be found helpful and practical:

PAPER: White, of good texture, standard ruling, (⅜ths of an inch), size 8 x 10½ or 7 x 8½ inches.

PENHOLDER: Wood, light in weight, extend beyond the

PENS: Steel, good light

INK:

visited individual classrooms once or twice a week. One of the special weekly subjects in the Cincinnati school that Kit attended was *penmanship*, or handwriting.

However, the Great Depression that had started in 1929 was beginning to affect every part of society, including schools. As the Depression deepened and more people lost their jobs and homes, schools started having serious money troubles, too. By 1932—three years into the Depression and the year Kit's story begins—many schools could no longer afford new books and supplies. In some schools, broken windows were not replaced and roofs started to leak. To save money, school boards canceled special programs, such as kindergartens, and shortened the school year by making school holidays longer and closing schools earlier in the year.

Some states had so little money that the school year lasted only three months! In especially depressed areas—such as the rural South, where a lack of rain caused many farms to fail—schools simply closed down when their money ran out.

Cincinnati students learned penmanship by the Palmer Method and received special merit pins as they improved.

Elementary textbooks from the 1920s and early 1930s

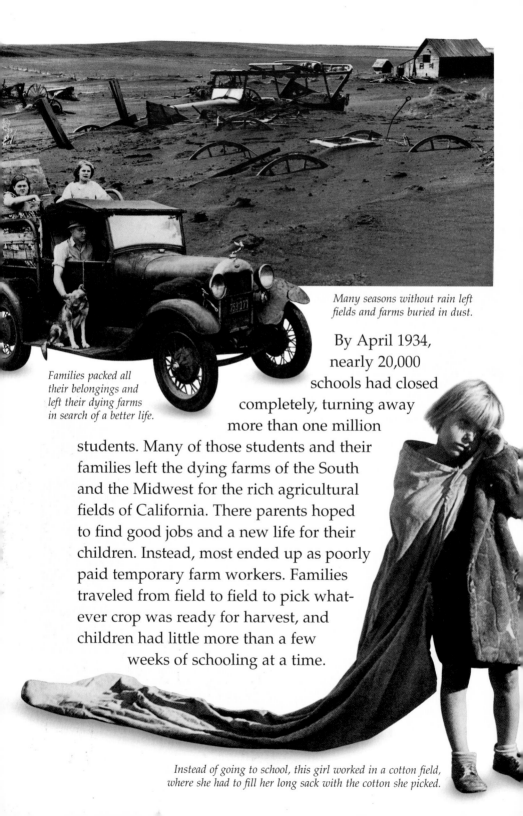

Many seasons without rain left fields and farms buried in dust.

Families packed all their belongings and left their dying farms in search of a better life.

By April 1934, nearly 20,000 schools had closed completely, turning away more than one million students. Many of those students and their families left the dying farms of the South and the Midwest for the rich agricultural fields of California. There parents hoped to find good jobs and a new life for their children. Instead, most ended up as poorly paid temporary farm workers. Families traveled from field to field to pick whatever crop was ready for harvest, and children had little more than a few weeks of schooling at a time.

Instead of going to school, this girl worked in a cotton field, where she had to fill her long sack with the cotton she picked.

Teachers in Chicago protested
salary and school cuts.

Before the Depression hit, the average teacher's salary was about $155 per month, or almost $8 per day. To save money without closing schools, some states cut teachers' salaries. In Iowa, teachers were paid only $40 per month, or about $2 per day.

But even after salary cuts, some schools didn't have enough money to pay their teachers. Many teachers went without pay for months. Schools in some southern states revived the old practice of *boarding round* their teachers—giving them rooms and meals with the families of their students in place of a salary.

To further reduce expenses, principals were dismissed and more students were crowded into each classroom so fewer teachers were needed. Many married women teachers were fired so single women or men with families could have their jobs. When programs were cut, other teachers lost their jobs.

Tragedy struck the Cincinnati schools in 1932, when a penmanship teacher killed himself after learning that the school board had eliminated his citywide handwriting program and most of his salary.

TEACHER ENDS LIFE FEARING CUT IN PAY

Teachers worried when students stopped coming to school, because it often meant that a family was in deep

Crowded classrooms made learning hard for students and discipline a challenge for teachers.

financial trouble or had moved away to look for work. Teachers knew that children sometimes stayed out of school because their shoes and clothes were too worn or they had no money for supplies. They also knew that during the cold winter months, children sometimes took turns going to school because their family had only one presentable coat.

Like Kit's teacher, many teachers coordinated food and clothing drives in their communities. Teachers worked with the Red Cross, the Salvation Army, or local

At a food drive, people sometimes received fresh produce, eggs, and cheese in addition to bread or canned foods.

A bread line in New York City

charities to help those in need. They also contributed to funds that collected money for their students and their students' families. Dedicated teachers did whatever they could to help students get a good education as they coped with the harsh realities of lost jobs, daily hunger, and America's uncertain future.

Teachers went to great lengths to help students forget their troubles for a few hours. This class's teacher made sure everyone in the band had costumes.

More to Discover!

While books are the heart of The American Girls Collection,®
they are only the beginning. The stories in the Collection come
to life when you act them out with the beautiful
American Girls
dolls and their exquisite clothes and accessories.
To request a free catalogue full of things girls love,
send in this postcard, call **1-800-845-0005,**
or visit our Web site at **americangirl.com**.

Please send me an American Girl® catalogue.

My name is _____

My address is _____

City _____ State _____ Zip _____

3802i

My birth date is _____ / _____ / _____ E-mail address _____
                 month   day   year

Parent's signature _____

And send a catalogue to my friend:

My friend's name is _____

Address _____

City _____ State _____ Zip _____

1229i

If the postcard has already been removed from this book
and you would like to receive an American Girl® catalogue,
please send your name and address to:

American Girl
P.O. Box 620497
Middleton, WI 53562-0497

You may also call our toll-free number, **1-800-845-0005,**
or visit our Web site at **americangirl.com**.

Place
Stamp
Here

American Girl ®

PO BOX 620497
MIDDLETON WI 53562-0497

Praise for *Pax Romana*

'Goldsworthy brings a wonderful vitality to his subject; his account possesses an immediacy usually associated with contemporary history. The reader is treated to an enthralling view of a highly complex system of governance. Too often, Rome's brutality has overshadowed the brilliance of her administrators. Goldsworthy gives statecraft its proper emphasis'   Gerard DeGroot, *The Times*

'The best of his many excellent books on ancient Rome for its range and depth ... Adrian Goldsworthy is on top form with *Pax Romana*'   Peter Jones, *BBC History Magazine*

'The latest in the line of tomes about the toga-wearers on the Tiber is Goldsworthy's admirably thorough account of how they conquered then controlled their empire'

John Lewis-Stempel, *Sunday Express*

'The reign of Augustus – when the Romans learned to stop worrying and love the emperors – is the center of Adrian Goldworthy's powerful reassessment of Roman imperialism'

Greg Woolf, *Wall Street Journal*

'For Goldsworthy, the author of a series of excellent books on the Roman world, the idea of empire gets an unfairly bad press. In this refreshing and thoughtful book, he argues that military power alone fails to explain why the Romans managed to rule such a huge domain for so long'

Dominic Sandbrook, *Sunday Times* Christmas Books

'Two lessons for today stand out in the book: First, it is hard to make and keep a peace. Second, the greatest threat to the Pax Romana came not from foreigners but from the internal power struggles of the Romans themselves'

Thomas E. Ricks, *New York Times*

Adrian Goldsworthy has a doctorate from Oxford University. His first book, *The Roman Army at War*, was recognised by John Keegan as an exceptionally impressive work, original in treatment and impressive in style. He has gone on to write seven further books, which have sold more than a quarter of a million copies and been translated into more than a dozen languages. A full-time author, he regularly contributes to TV documentaries on Roman themes.

By Adrian Goldsworthy

FICTION

True Soldier Gentlemen
Beat the Drums Slowly
Send Me Safely Back Again
All in Scarlet Uniform
Run Them Ashore
Whose Business Is to Die

NON-FICTION

The Roman Army at War, 100 BC–AD 200
Roman Warfare
The Fall of Carthage
Cannae: Hannibal's Greatest Victory
The Complete Roman Army
The Men Who Won the Roman Empire
In the Name of Rome
Caesar: The Life of a Colossus
The Fall of the West: The Death of the Roman Superpower
Antony and Cleopatra
Augustus: From Revolutionary to Emperor
Pax Romana: War, Peace and Conquest in the Roman World

PAX ROMANA

War, Peace and Conquest in the Roman World

ADRIAN GOLDSWORTHY

WEIDENFELD & NICOLSON

A W&N PAPERBACK

First published in Great Britain in 2016
This paperback edition first published in 2017
by Weidenfeld & Nicolson
an imprint of The Orion Publishing Group Ltd
Carmelite House, 50 Victoria Embankment
London EC4Y 0DZ

An Hachette UK Company

3 5 7 9 10 8 6 4 2

A CIP catalogue record for this book is
available from the British Library.

ISBN 978 1 4746 0437 6

Typeset by Input Data Services Ltd, Somerset

Printed and bound by CPI Group (UK) Ltd, Croydon, CR0 4YY

www.orionbooks.co.uk

CONTENTS

PART TWO – PRINCIPATE

ACKNOWLEDGEMENTS

A book like this takes a long time to write and many others contribute to the process. As always I must express my heartfelt thanks to the family and friends who have read and commented on various drafts of the manuscript, especially Kevin Powell, Ian Hughes, Philip Matyszak, Guy de la Bédoyère and Averil Goldsworthy. Dorothy King has listened with patience and discussed many of the ideas expressed in this book. Particular thanks must go to my agent, Georgina Capel, for her enthusiasm and for creating the situation allowing me to take the time to write this book properly. Thanks must also go to my editors, Alan Samson in the UK and Steve Wasserman in the USA, and their teams for producing so handsome a volume.

LIST OF MAPS

PREFACE

LIVING IN PEACE

Pax Romana is one of those Latin expressions that journalists and cartoonists still expect their readers to understand without the need for translation, alongside tags such as *mea culpa* and Shakespeare's *'et tu Brute'*. A cartoonist can depict a modern politician in toga, sandals and laurel wreath and invoke Julius Caesar or a generic Roman emperor and know that people will think of a leader betrayed by those close to him, or of one prey to pride and folly like Caligula or Nero. Few schools teach Latin or Greek, but TV documentaries about Rome are common, and dramas appear every so often, tending these days towards ever more lurid pictures of a world of treachery, sex and violence – blood and buttocks rather than the old sword and sandals. Such caricatures tell us little about the ancient past and a good deal about current tastes in entertainment, but it is striking that their makers are confident setting these stories in a Roman context because they feel that the audience will recognise that world.

The Romans continue to fascinate us even though more than fifteen centuries have passed since the collapse of the Roman Empire in the West. In language, law, ideas, place names and architecture they have had a profound influence on Western culture, and much of this has passed on to regions wholly unknown to the Romans. Many leaders and states from Charlemagne onwards have done their best to invoke the spirit of Rome and the Caesars as justification for their own power. Rome often appears in debates in the USA about their country's role in the world and its future, and is used by people of all political persuasions. The use of military force and diplomatic pressure to spread a *Pax Americana* across the wider world is held up as an aspiration by some and depicted as a sinister plot by others.

Empires are not fashionable, and for many anything associated with empires and imperialism must be a bad thing. In this view peace, whether Roman or created by a modern power, is a veil to conceal conquest and domination. This is not a new idea. At the very end of the first century AD the Roman historian Tacitus has a Caledonian war leader tell his men that the Romans 'create a desolation and call it peace'.[1]

The words come in a biography praising Tacitus' father-in-law, Agricola, and precede a dramatic account of a battle in which this man defeats the Caledonian tribes. Both in this work and his others, it is hard to see the author as a devout critic of the Roman Empire, and the overwhelming tone of literature from the Roman period is one of celebration of power and success. Obviously this does not come as a surprise, since it is human nature to want to think well of ourselves. Like most imperial powers, the Romans felt that their domination was entirely right, divinely ordained and a good thing for the wider world. Emperors boasted that their rule brought peace to the provinces, benefiting the entire population.

Yet the Roman Empire was remarkably successful for a very long time, the *Pax Romana* holding sway over much of Western Europe, the Middle East and North Africa for centuries. This area was stable and apparently prosperous, with little or no trace of desolation. Roman Peace does appear to have been a reality, for rebellions and large-scale violence were extremely rare. Even critics of empires must concede this about Rome. By any standards the Roman Empire was unusual, and this – apart from its continuing fascination and appearance in current debates – makes it all the more important to understand what Roman Peace really meant. It matters if it was solely the product of bluntly wielded military power and oppression, or of subtler, more insidious methods of coercion. As important is some understanding of the cost of imperial rule to the subject population and how these felt about being part of a foreign empire. A significant proportion of the world's inhabitants lived in the Roman Empire and that in itself is a good reason to wish to understand what this meant. It is well worth asking how complete and secure the *Pax*

Romana actually was, but from the start we ought to think a little about just what peace means.

I was born in peacetime, the child of parents who had lived through the Second World War. My mother was a small child during the Blitz in Cardiff, and still remembers the air raid siren wailing, the fear of going into the dark and cold air raid shelter in their garden, the different sounds of bombs, land-mines and anti-aircraft guns, the patter of falling shrapnel, the stench after a raid and the houses reduced to rubble, sometimes with people buried underneath. She also speaks about she and her friends staging concerts and collecting pennies to 'buy a Spitfire', of uniforms everywhere and of being unable to cross the street because of the stream of trucks carrying GIs and supplies on their way to the docks to embark for Normandy. The memories are still vivid today and very immediate whenever she talks about those years. My father was an apprentice in the Merchant Navy, did the Atlantic run, and then was in the Mediterranean supporting the landings in Tunisia and Italy. His ship was in the Bay of Naples when Vesuvius erupted in 1944, and he remembered having to clean ash off the deck. Only occasionally would he speak of the constant threat of U-Boats and air attack, of ammunition ships exploding and the sea on fire from burning fuel, with men trying to swim to safety through it. He left the Merchant Navy and was soon old enough to be conscripted into the Army, and served in Palestine under the British Mandate, caught between Jewish and Arab militants and a target for both. His father had served through the First World War on the Western Front, at Gallipoli and in Egypt and Palestine. Neither were professionals. They had 'done their bit' like millions of their contemporaries and then happily returned to civilian life.

The seventieth anniversaries of VE and VJ Days were commemorated in 2015, while I was writing this book, alongside centenaries of events in the First World War, but it still seems natural to speak of 1939–1945 as THE War – a habit picked up from my parents and their contemporaries. My brother and I are among the last to be born for whom active memory of the Second World War was just one generation away. This was not uncommon at our school, where the parents were a little older than the national average, and there were a fair few boys whose fathers had been in the Forces, and at least one Bevan Boy sent to a coal mine. The War still seemed very immediate, and most boys of our age were more or less obsessed with it. There were new dramas being broadcast, and by this time the great flurry of war films produced in the 1940s, 1950s and 1960s were old enough to appear regularly on television. We watched these avidly, read books and comics about it, assembled plastic model kits of fighters, bombers, tanks and warships, and brandished toy guns in imaginary battles where one side was usually the Germans or Japanese, doing our best to mimic the sounds of machine guns and explosions. Sometimes our games instead took us to the Wild West or Outer Space – both staples of television in the 1970s – but more than anything else we relived the Second World War. It was a good war against bad enemies, and 'we' won, led by familiar actors on screen, the heroes of our comics and our dads. To a young boy's mind, it seemed a lot more exciting than school – and in our games no one was hurt, apart from the odd bruise or scratch from running through brambles.

The War was won in 1945, so that I was born and grew up in peacetime. This was the era of the Cold War, the threat of a Third World War there in the background, but not real to a child, and in my memory it was only in the 1980s that the media became obsessed with the prospect of impending nuclear destruction. Then the Cold War ended, suddenly, abruptly and with little or no warning – I have heard more than one person who worked in military intelligence for NATO admit that it caught them by surprise. Politicians spoke of the 'Peace Dividend', which meant slashing the size of the Armed Forces and spending the money on things they thought would win votes. As a student in the early 1990s I served in the Oxford University Officer Training Corps, and there were still classes on identifying Warsaw Pact vehicles, but no longer a sense that there was a likely enemy for a future major war. Another world war was hard to imagine, and by now I was certainly old enough to appreciate how fortunate I was to live at this time. Peace reigned, at least in the sense that there were no ongoing major wars involving Western states. Yet neither then, nor at any stage in my life, has peace meant the complete absence of armed conflict involving Britain, let alone in the wider world.

A few months after I was born, the Troubles flared up in Northern Ireland. For decades, television news showed film of riots and petrol bombs, and the aftermath of explosions and other attacks. It is probably a question of semantics and political beliefs as to when a terrorist campaign becomes a war, but there can be no doubt about the loss of life. Although predominantly focused in a comparatively small geographical area, at times it spread, with PIRA and other Republican paramilitary groups launching attacks on mainland Britain, and on a few occasions in Europe, their targets civilian as well as military. For much of my lifetime there were no rubbish bins on railway stations because it was thought too easy to conceal a bomb in them. In the OUOTC we were specifically banned from wearing uniform outside Yeomanry House if we were not on exercise or parade because of the perceived risk of becoming a terrorist target. It is only comparatively recently that this policy has been reversed in the Army as a whole.

Since 1945 only one year has passed without at least one member of Britain's Armed Forces being killed on active service. Apart from the Korean War, there were all the many conflicts accompanying the withdrawal from empire. In my lifetime there was the Falklands, the First Gulf War and – after the era of the 'peace dividend' – Sierra Leone, Iraq and Afghanistan, not to mention air operations in the Balkans, Libya and elsewhere, or peace-keeping commitments where the peace was not always perfect. Even when the UK is not directly involved, it is rare for newspapers or broadcasters not to be reporting from some conflict zone somewhere in the world. Like famine or earthquakes, wars can too easily be dismissed as the sort of terrible thing that happens in distant lands, while coverage tends to be patchy, as the news cycle moves on to fresh stories.

A list of conflicts since 1945 would be as long as it would be depressing. Nothing has approached the scale of devastation inflicted by the world wars, but that is unlikely to have been any consolation to those caught up in these struggles, which have varied from open wars between states to protracted campaigns of violence involving small communities, militias and other irregulars. Yet for most Westerners, even the conflicts involving their own countries have been distant affairs, prosecuted by professionals, with no direct impact on day-to-day life. Britain has not faced the danger of invasion since the Second World War, the USA for even longer. No conflict since 1945 has posed a serious threat to the very existence of these countries, or threatened to cut off food supplies or other essentials. The Cold War might have escalated to this level, but did not in spite of periods of crisis.

Today the main danger to Western countries is posed by terrorism. This dominates the media at the moment, for I am writing this preface in November 2015, just days after the savage terrorist attacks in Paris which claimed more than a hundred innocent lives and have left others critically, perhaps fatally, injured. Ghastly as this was, an atrocity of this sort will not prevent Paris from functioning as a city, a centre of commerce and government and a home to over two million people. Life will go on, even if it is hard for those who lost loved ones, just as life went on in New York, Washington DC, London, Brussels, Madrid and Sydney after terrorist attacks on them. The numbers involved, the resources and weapons available to terrorists limit the amount of damage they can inflict. During the Second World War it took sustained aerial bombing causing death, injury and destruction on a far bigger scale seriously to disrupt a town or city.

The main aim of terrorists is to gain publicity, spreading fear and enhancing their own reputation. They cannot win a military victory on their own and hope only to shake the countries they attack, changing opinion and achieving some political end. Terrorist movements are very hard to defeat, making it probable that attacks will continue for a long time, more or less sporadically. However effective the security services are in limiting opportunities and making it ever harder for the terrorists to operate, it is doubtful that they will be able to prevent every plot. Statistically the risk of falling victim will remain low, for modern populations are very large, and people will adapt, perhaps more nervous than they were before the threat emerged, but still far more occupied with the concerns of living their lives. The odds are that such attacks generate as much or more anger than fear in the wider population. The vast majority of people in Western countries will continue to feel that they live in peacetime. Most will take the stability, security, wealth and much higher life expectancy of the post-war world as both natural and normal – even as a right. It requires effort to remind ourselves that it is merely a matter of chance when and where we are born.

This is a book about the Roman world and the Roman Empire. I have spoken at such length about my own life and the present day as a reminder that peace is not an absolute, but relative. People can feel that they live in a peaceful world even when organised violence and even large-scale operations are going on. Distance has a great influence on perspective. Anyone serving in the Forces, and especially the combat arms, is likely to have a very different sense of these decades, as will their families. It is vital to remember this when we look at the evidence for the Roman period. We should not be surprised to find evidence for fighting and warfare somewhere in the empire even at the height of the presumed *Pax Romana*. What matters is understanding its scale and frequency, and trying to judge how far it impinged on the lives of the wider population. The answers are unlikely to be simple, but this is the very heart of the question. Even in the modern world peace is a rare and precious thing. If the Romans really did create conditions where most of the provinces lived in peace for long periods, then it is well worth studying this achievement.

I am an historian, and this book is an attempt to understand one aspect of the past on its own terms. It is not meant either as a justification for or condemnation of the Roman or any other empire, but to explain what happened and why. Nor do I intend detailed comparison between the Romans and other imperial powers, still less to draw lessons for the current day. Others are far better qualified to speak of such things – and plenty of people who know little about history or the present day will no doubt make strident assertions that

the Roman experience proves this or that. Lessons can be learned
from history, but it is wise to take great care to understand a period
before drawing any conclusions. This book is intended for that
purpose.

INTRODUCTION

A GLORY GREATER THAN WAR

'For these [the Romans] I set no bounds in space or time; but have given empire without end.' – *the pronouncement of Jupiter in Virgil's* Aeneid, *20s BC.*[1]

THE *PAX ROMANA*

'If a man were called to fix the period in the history of the world, during which the condition of the human race was most happy and prosperous, he would, without hesitation, name that which elapsed from the death of Domitian to the accession of Commodus [i.e. AD 96–180]. The vast extent of the Roman empire was governed by absolute power, under the guidance of virtue and wisdom.'[2]

Edward Gibbon's judgement on the Roman Empire at its height was generous and reinforced the importance of his main theme tracing its decline and fall. From the perspective of the late eighteenth century it was not altogether unreasonable. Europe in Gibbon's day was divided between kingdoms great and small, always competing for power and often at war, while – fairly or not – North Africa and Asia appeared primitive. Under Rome all this area had been united, sharing the same sophisticated Greco-Roman culture. It was a monarchy, lightly veiled by 'the image of liberty', but of universal good when the monarch was a decent, capable man. Monuments to its prosperity – temples, roads, aqueducts, circuses and arches – survived into Gibbon's day. Most remain today, and centuries of archaeology have added greatly to their number and provided many other objects great and small. The empire was prosperous because it was peaceful, warfare banished to the frontiers which were protected by the army. This was the *Pax Romana* or Roman Peace, which allowed the greater part of the known world to flourish.

Many people today are still struck by the technical skill of the Romans, and the apparent modernity of their world. This image of sophistication runs alongside one of decadence, of the underlying cruelty of mass slavery and brutal gladiatorial entertainments, and the whimsical and very personal cruelty of mad and bad emperors. In spite of this there is a sense that the world beyond Rome's frontiers was a bleak, grim place. Rome was the civilized world, its boundaries marked by barriers such as Hadrian's Wall, another great monument which still snakes across the Northumbrian hills as a reminder of a lost empire. In fact Hadrian's Wall was unusual, and such linear boundaries were rare. When Rome collapsed Europe sank into the Dark Ages, literacy and learning all but forgotten, and there was warfare and violence of every sort where once there had been peace.

Peace is almost as rare today as it was for Gibbon and his contemporaries, and if the Romans truly did create a long period of peace over such a wide area then this deserves to be explained. Praise of peace was commonplace for authors in the ancient world, Greek as well as Roman, but they also readily accepted that war would be frequent. The word *pax* came to mean something very close to our 'peace' by the first century BC. Peace was celebrated by poets, and often held up as the most desirable state. Roman emperors boasted of preserving peace, and sometimes the expression 'Roman Peace' was used when speaking of the good brought by the empire. They also spoke a good deal of the glory of victory. *Imperator*, the word from which we get our 'emperor', meant 'victorious general', and an emperor's reputation was badly damaged if his troops suffered serious defeats, whether or not he was personally in command.

Warfare played a central role in Rome's history. The Romans fought many wars, and thus conquered an empire that stretched from the Atlantic to the Euphrates, and from the Sahara desert to northern Britain. Its sheer extent remains impressive even today – no other power has ever controlled all the lands around the Mediterranean – and was even more remarkable in an age before modern communication and transport. More striking still was its longevity. Sicily was Rome's first province, and remained under Roman control for more than 800 years. Britain, one of the last acquisitions, was Roman for three and half centuries. An eastern empire that considered itself Roman survived even longer, and some regions there were 'Roman' for one and a half millennia. Other leaders and powers, most notably Alexander the Great and Genghis Khan, have expanded faster than the Romans, and a handful have controlled more territory – roughly a quarter of the globe in the case of Britain's own empire. Yet none have lasted anything like so long, and it is arguable whether or not any have had so great an impact on subsequent history.

The Romans were warlike and aggressive, but that scarcely requires saying for empires are not created or maintained without violence. Precision is impossible, but we can confidently state that over the centuries millions died in the course of the wars fought by Rome, millions more were enslaved, and still more would live under Roman rule whether they liked it or not. The Romans were imperialists – the word, just like 'empire', comes from the Latin *imperium*, although the Romans used it in a slightly different sense. Once again, to say this is merely stating the obvious. The Romans were highly successful, which in itself suggests that they were good at waging war and skilled in the politics of dominating others. Other empires have done much the same, although none have matched Rome's talent for absorbing others. When the empire finally collapsed in the western Mediterranean there was no trace of independence movements in any of the provinces, a stark contrast to the crumbling of the twentieth century's imperial powers after 1945. As the system decayed around them, the people in the provinces still wanted to be Roman. A world without Rome was very hard to imagine and does not seem to have held much appeal.

Rome's power lasted so long that memories of a time before Roman domination can only have been faint. Rebellions appear surprisingly rare, and nearly always occurred within a generation or two of conquest. When the empire was at its height, the greater part of the Roman army was stationed on its fringes in the frontier

zones – a second-century AD Greek orator compared the soldiers
to a protective wall surrounding the empire as if it were a single
city. Warfare continued, but it was waged mainly on these frontiers.
The provinces of the interior contained tiny garrisons, and many
areas rarely saw formed bodies of Roman soldiers. For periods of a
century or more, large swathes of the empire were entirely free of
warfare.

This at least is the traditional view, and is generally reflected in the
popular perception of Rome. Scholarly opinion changes far more
often, and any historian or archaeologist working on this period
would qualify much of this overview, and some would reject it altogether. For the moment, let us just say that the truth is a good deal
more complicated than this sweeping summary. Yet there can be no
doubt about the enduring power of Rome, or that its domination did
mean that large parts of the empire experienced no major military
activity, let alone open warfare for long periods of time.

It is important to remember just how rare this has been in
recorded history, most of all in the areas controlled by Rome. At no
other period since then has Western Europe, North Africa or the
Near East experienced a single century without major conflict, and
usually it has been a good deal more common than this. Those of
us living in the Western world in the last half-century or so all too
readily take peace for granted, assuming it to be the natural order –
we are too prosperous, too well educated, simply too advanced to
permit this ever to be shattered by war – and foreign affairs in general, let alone decisions about military commitments, play scarcely
any role in deciding the outcome of elections.[3]

In a sense, this may not be too far removed from the experience of
many living in the Roman Empire. If so, then this was at first almost
accidental. Rome did not conquer the greater part of the known world
to create a golden age of peace. Expansion came from the desire to
benefit, and Romans were quite open in talking of the wealth and
glory brought by empire. They also spoke a good deal about peace
as the most desirable condition. At the start of the first century AD,
the poet Ovid spoke of a monument to peace – specifically the peace

brought by the Emperor Augustus. He hoped that the goddess of Peace would let her 'gentle presence abide in the whole world' so that there would be 'neither foes nor food for triumphs, thou shalt be unto our chiefs a glory greater than war. May the soldier bear arms only to check the armed aggressor . . . ! May the world near and far dread the sons of Aeneas, and if there be land that feared not Rome, may it love Rome instead!'[4]

Ovid was one of the least martial of Roman poets, and yet even so his peace was the peace that came from Roman victory, where enemies were either defeated or persuaded to accept Roman dominance and 'love' Rome. It was not the peace between equals, each respecting the other. A little earlier, the poet Virgil told his countrymen, 'Remember, Roman, – for these are your arts – that you have to rule the nations by your power, to add good custom to peace, to spare the conquered and overcome the proud in war'.[5] The Latin verb *pacare* had the same root as *pax* and meant 'to pacify', and was often used to describe aggressive warfare against a foreign people. *Pax Romana* came from Roman victory and conquest. Wars were fought because they benefited Rome and – at least as Romans saw it – for the sake of their own security, and only then, with dominance achieved, was there some sense that there was a duty to govern the conquered well, to establish peace and security within the provinces. This did not alter the open desire to profit from their dominance, but complemented it. Peace promoted prosperity, which meant that the yield of tax and other revenue could be higher.

Rome seized control of the greater part of the three continents known to it, Europe, Africa and Asia. Virgil has Jupiter promise the Romans *imperium sine fine* – empire or power without end or limit. The conquered were given 'Roman Peace' whether they liked it or not, and the method was through the use or threat of military force, wielded ruthlessly and savagely – Tacitus' desolation called peace. The Romans were fully aware that others may not wish to be ruled by them, but that did not mean that they ever seriously doubted that it was the right thing to expand their power.

The Romans were warlike, aggressive imperialists, who exploited their conquests for their own benefit. These days empires are not widely admired, least of all by academics in the West. Britain's own imperial past is largely ignored (as indeed is history in general, apart from a few narrow topics and periods), or viewed with a bitterly hostile eye. Attempts in the USA to draw comparisons between their own situation and historical empires whether British, Roman or anyone else, tend to be controversial, reflecting very different views of the role that America ought to play in the world. A century or so ago most – though not all – people in the West had a vague sense that empires could be, and often were, good things. Nowadays the opposite is true. Moves to intervene overseas by the USA and its allies are readily criticised as imperialism, not just by the targets and their allies, but domestically.

The danger is that we have simply replaced one over-simplification with another. Dislike of empire tends to encourage scepticism over its achievements. Much recent scholarship has doubted the efficiency of the Roman state, whether as a republic or under the rule of the emperors. Archaeologists who used to talk enthusiastically of a process of Romanisation of the provinces have almost all rejected the term and the concept behind it, often with surprising passion. The influence and impact of Roman rule is questioned, and any sign of resistance – whether political or cultural – seen as more significant, and centuries of imperial rule viewed as aberrations. The Romans are depicted as brutal and exploitative rather than a civilising influence on the world, and as part of this wider scepticism the reality of any *Pax Romana* is questioned. Boasts of peace throughout the world become little more than propaganda to justify imperial rule, veiling endemic and frequent banditry, resistance and acts of oppression by the authorities. Many modern views of the Roman world are grim indeed. One characterised the history of the Roman Empire as simply 'robbery with violence'. Less extreme, but still critical:

> Roman claims that the provincials enjoyed unbroken peace were an exaggeration, and some Romans knew it. Quite apart from the routine violence that characterized life in all ancient societies, the

provinces also suffered revolts and civil conflicts of a more serious nature than emperors were prepared officially to admit. The provinces were pacified, but pacified repeatedly, rather than once for all, and they were not peaceful.[6]

Here something of the *Pax Romana* remains, but its extent is severely limited, although importantly the alleged 'routine violence' is not specifically Roman. Another approach is to admit that there was widespread peace over much of the empire, but to see it as coming at far too high a price for the provincial population: 'Roman peace – even if, for the vast majority of the population, this was the peace enjoyed by a domesticated animal, kept solely for what it could produce – was an enduring reality.'[7]

Yet the size and longevity of Rome's empire cannot be argued away, which means that such views assume either prolonged oppression or disturbances and large-scale bloodshed to be a feature of the stories of many or most provinces for much of the time, and make this long-term survival hard to explain. This interpretation implies that the Romans were even more skilled at domination than we would expect and, if true, would have a profound impact on our understanding of the period. Other scholars tentatively suggest that the long-term survival of the empire was the outcome of chance, of wider factors encouraging so much of the world to unite at this time around a common Mediterranean economic model. Yet so many centuries of success do not suggest mere coincidence, and still beg the question of why it was Rome and not some other state that dominated.

The signs of prosperity in large parts of the empire are obvious, which does not mean that this comfort and wealth was spread equally or at all fairly. It does mean that the provinces were not so heavily exploited as to ruin them and impoverish all of their inhabitants – which is not to say that some did not suffer. Nor is there clear evidence of warfare over large parts of the Roman world for long periods of time, and its presence has to be taken from hints, or simply the assumption that imperial propaganda must contain plenty of untruths. The claim that revolts happened is not easy to justify in the case of most provinces and periods. There is also the question of lower levels of violence and whether these were tolerated by Rome – or considered impossible to eradicate. It is common for scholars to assert that banditry was endemic in the empire, but the evidence is far from straightforward.

The period of Roman domination and empire represents a large chunk of the histories of the lands included within it, and it is clear that in many ways the experience of it was very different to the periods before and after the imposition of Roman rule. It is well worth looking again at the *Pax Romana*, and attempting to understand what it really meant and whether or not the Romans did preside over a peaceful and stable empire where war was rare and mainly banished to the fringes of the world. To answer this broad question we must look at how the empire was created and how it was run. Most importantly, in spite of all the problems of evidence overwhelmingly generated by the imperial power, we must consider the experience of the conquered peoples as much as that of the Romans.

I cannot hope to cover in detail all the ways in which life changed after the imposition of Roman power or direct rule, for the subject is vast and complex. Much of the evidence is archaeological, influenced by the amount and quality of excavations, surveys and other work done in a region. We have a lot more data for some provinces than others, and often it is concentrated in particular areas of those provinces and certain types of settlement, ritual or funerary practice. Analysing this evidence to produce a general picture of a province, and then comparing it with that of the periods before Roman rule in an attempt to discern changes, is not straightforward. In the western provinces it becomes much easier to date levels in an excavation after the arrival of Rome, which provides coinage and faster-changing patterns of ceramics and other goods. The pace of change in the pre-Roman Iron Age cannot be as readily measured as some developments in the Roman period. All data is subject to interpretation, and often opinions differ radically, often being overturned by fresh discoveries or new methods of analysis. I have tried to be fair, but have presented my own views on these matters. Others will see things differently.

This book presents an overview, and tries to give an idea of the range of different experiences, but cannot hope to be exhaustive. The works cited in the endnotes should allow the interested reader to discover more about the many topics touched upon only lightly here, for each will yield more references to additional studies. Many more books and articles could have been added to the notes, and as always I must acknowledge my debt to the labours of so many scholars. My aim is to present the most relevant material and ideas, and always to explain what we do not know as well as what we do know. When writing about the ancient world almost every statement could be qualified. I hope that the reader is shown enough of the evidence and the methods used to interpret it to make up his or her own mind on these issues.

The same is true of the broader issue of whether or not the Roman Empire was a good thing, as I do not feel that there is a simple answer to such a question. It is fruitless to ask what would have happened if the Roman Empire had not been created, but even so it is important to remind ourselves that Rome was far from the only aggressive, imperialistic state in the ancient world. We should no more idealise the provincials or the peoples outside the empire than we should the Romans. It is important to consider the frequency of warfare in each region before the Romans arrived to judge whether or not the situation improved or became worse. Empires are unfashionable, while much about Roman society is alien and unpleasant to modern eyes, but dislike for Rome must not translate into automatic sympathy with others, nor must it compel us to deny that the Romans achieved anything at all worthwhile. As misleading is the tendency to focus so heavily on Roman imperialism, Roman warfare or Roman Grand Strategy, so that all other participants are reduced to an entirely passive role. There were plenty of other peoples, states and leaders in this world with aims, ambitions and fears of their own.

The Romans were more successful than their rivals and created a vast empire which they maintained for a very long time. Its impact was felt in the provinces and also far beyond the frontiers. The question as to how far the empire enjoyed internal peace must always be weighed against its cost, and it is worth considering more generally just how life changed because of the empire. Thus any discussion of Roman Peace – whatever this truly meant – should be set in the context of Roman conquest, and of understanding how the empire worked. The administrative and military machinery of the Roman state limited what could be achieved, whatever the aspirations of its leaders. This is a book about peace and sometimes about defence, but it must also be a book about conquest, aggression, warfare, violence and exploitation, and so we should begin with the Romans as conquerors, rather than as imperial overlords.

PART ONE

REPUBLIC

THE RISE OF ROME

'But the Romans have subjected to their rule not portions, but nearly the whole of the world (and possess an empire which is not only immeasurably greater than any which preceded it, but need not fear rivalry in the future) . . . . For it was owing to their defeat of the Carthaginians in the Hannibalic War that the Romans, feeling that the chief and most essential step in their scheme of aggression had now been taken, were first emboldened to reach out their hands to grasp the rest and to cross with an army to Greece and the continent of Asia.' – *Polybius, 140s BC.*[1]

ORIGINS

Rome had an empire long before she had an emperor, but there was a time, well before that, when she was simply one Italian city among many – more specifically, one Latin community in the area known as Latium. The Latins were a linguistic group, not a united people, and in many ways their settlements had much in common with those of neighbours like the Etruscans or Greek colonies such as Capua. Rome began in the eighth century BC, roughly around 753 BC when later tradition held that the City was founded. The story of Romulus and Remus, twin sons of the war god Mars suckled by the she-wolf and raised by a shepherd, existed in many forms during antiquity, but little was known with certainty about the early years. No Roman began to write narrative history until around 200 BC. The Greeks began much earlier, but we should not forget that Herodotus did not write until after the defeat of Persia in 479 BC. The Greeks' knowledge of their own history in the eighth and seventh centuries BC was hazy indeed, and just as filled with legendary stories and the deeds of heroes. The Romans were not unusual in knowing little hard fact about their origins.

That is not to say that there were no records, for these were societies that from early on made some use of the written word. Laws were preserved, as were dedications of altars, temples and monuments to commemorate victories, and there was a rich oral tradition, with songs and stories told about the past, many of them preserved by aristocratic families and inevitably highly flattering to their ancestors. There is no good reason to doubt the basic outline of the later traditions about the City's early centuries, even if many of the incidents and individuals who figure in the stories were invented or distorted beyond recognition. It is safe to say that in the early centuries Rome was ruled by kings. The expulsion of the last king in 509 BC and the foundation of the Republic does seem to have been based on reliable records, even if the stories surrounding it included considerable romantic embellishment.[2]

Warfare is a constant theme in the traditions about monarchy and Republic alike. The scale was no doubt small, most of the enemies very close neighbours, and much of the time it was little more than raiding for cattle, captives and plunder. The Romans attacked and were attacked by nearby communities in this way, and only occasionally did the fighting escalate into major battles. The same enemies were fought year after year, which suggests that neither side was able to win a permanent victory over its rivals. Not all contact with others was martial, and there was also trade and peaceful exchange of skills and goods. In the first year of the Republic the Romans made a treaty with the great mercantile empire of Carthage in North Africa (its heartland in modern Tunisia), a long-forgotten copy of which, written in archaic Latin, survived in the state archives some 350 years later and was read by the Greek historian Polybius. It was mostly concerned with the rights and restrictions placed on Romans travelling in Carthaginian territory, but gives an indication of just how far afield merchants were going.[3]

Over time Rome grew in size and prosperity, its population increasing both naturally and from an unusual willingness and capacity to absorb others. Alongside warfare, the arrival of outsiders to join the community figures heavily in the later myths, whether it was Romulus gathering settlers from the vagrants and outcasts of Italy, the abduction of wives from the Sabines, or the arrival of the aristocratic Claudii with all their dependants under the Republic. Rome's power also grew, so that it became by far the largest and strongest of all the Latin cities. The 509/508 BC treaty with Carthage names five other Latin communities allied to Rome as well as 'any other city of the Latins who are subject to Rome'. These were not alliances between equals, but marked the rise of a dominant local power.[4]

Compulsion on the part of a stronger neighbour was one reason for the other cities to accept Roman supremacy, but so was the need for protection from very real threats. Late sixth- and fifth-century BC Italy saw widespread upheaval as groups like the Aequi, Volsci and Samnites, Oscan-speaking hill peoples from the Apennines, pushed out onto the more fertile coastal lands, while Gallic tribes drove into northern Italy. Many Latin, Etruscan and Greek cities were overrun by these invaders – Herodotus declared the defeat by one of these tribes of the great city of Tarentum (modern Taranto) in 473 BC as 'the worst the Greeks have ever suffered'.[5]

Rome survived and was able to protect its allies, but in such dangerous times warfare took on a harder edge, and as Roman power grew it could also prove more permanently decisive. In 396 BC the Romans sacked the Etruscan city of Veii and massacred most of its inhabitants, ending a rivalry that had been going on since Rome's earliest days. Veii stood on a strong natural position barely ten miles away from Rome, which is a reminder of the small scale of so much of this early warfare. The tradition that the siege took a decade may well be an invention meant to draw parallels with the epic siege of Troy, although it is possible that fighting did take place for a long time. It was during the course of this war that the Romans first began to pay their legionaries, suggesting that these soldiers were required to undertake continuous service away from their farms for long periods. Veii's territory was permanently added to the lands of the Roman people, the *ager Romanus*.[6]

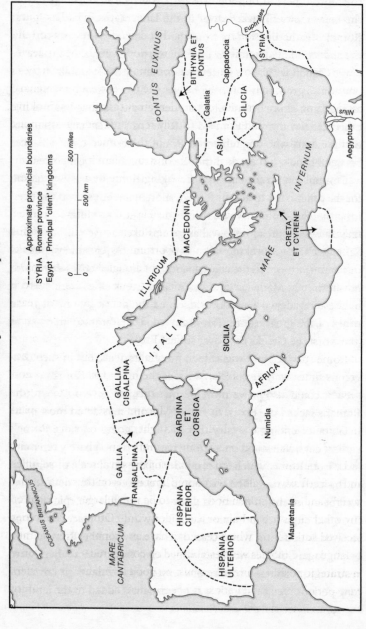

The Roman Republic and its empire, c. 60 BC

In 390 BC a band of Gallic warriors routed a Roman army with disdainful ease and sacked Rome itself. Later tradition tried to put a gloss on the humiliation by claiming that defenders held out on the Capitoline Hill, but admitted that the warriors were bribed to leave. It was a reminder of how dangerous conditions were in Italy in these centuries. Fortunately for the Romans, the Gauls were a mercenary band seizing an opportunity for plunder rather than invaders looking to settle. They left, and Rome gradually recovered, but the memory of these dark days long remained part of the Roman psyche. A visible sign of the trauma was the swift construction of expensive stone walls some seven miles in length, making Rome by far the biggest enclosed community in Italy.[7]

In the decades that followed, some Latin communities turned against Rome, either less convinced of Roman might or resentful of her dominance and sensing an opportunity while she was weak. Others maintained the alliance and fought alongside the Romans to defeat the rest of the Latins. In 340 BC a group of cities formed a league and rebelled against Rome, but they were beaten two years later and the attempt was never repeated. The next half-century saw warfare on an ever larger scale against Etruscan cities and Samnite and Gallic tribes, including an alliance of all three in the year 296 BC. The Romans suffered defeats, some of them serious, but in the end prevailed, their levy of citizen soldiers defeating other citizen soldiers and warriors alike. They learned from their enemies, copied tactics and equipment, and adapted to fight each enemy in turn.

The Roman Republic grew to be far more than the City of Rome and the lands around it. Roman citizenship was granted to loyal allies and to freed slaves – albeit with some limitations on the rights of the latter – and so the citizen body grew to be much larger than that of any other city-state in Italy or the wider world. Other communities received Latin status, which ceased to have any connection with race or language. Colonies were established on conquered territory, some in strategic positions and others just on good farmland. The settlers were both Romans and Latins, although often the entire community was given Latin status.[8]

Incorporation contributed more to the growth of the Republic than colonisation, significant though this was. Defeated enemies occasionally ceased to exist as political entities, but the vast majority became subordinate allies of Rome. More or less quickly they were granted Latin rights and even citizenship. Greek cities were jealous of their citizenship, even the smallest of them being determined to retain an independent identity. There were cases of Latin communities declining the offer of Roman citizenship – a decision respected by the Senate – but more often they willingly accepted. As a result the city-state of Rome grew to dwarf even the greatest of Greek cities. Athens at the height of its democracy and overseas empire grew less rather than more generous with its citizenship. As a result it boasted at most 60,000 male citizens, fewer than half of them with sufficient property to serve as hoplites, the armoured infantrymen who constituted the great strength of the army. An Athenian field force of 10,000 or so hoplites was a major enterprise.[9]

Writing in the first century AD, Pliny the Elder claimed that there were 152,573 Roman citizens in 392 BC, although the figure may include women and children. Some scholars are inclined to see this as too high, but more reliable are the numbers provided by the Greek historian Polybius for 225 BC. These are only for men registered to serve in the army, and, if no doubt rounded up and on the high side, at the very least they give an idea of scale. He states that there were 250,000 citizens eligible to serve as infantry and 23,000 as cavalry. Latins – there were at this date twenty-eight Latin colonies – provided 80,000 infantry and 5,000 horsemen. Adding in all other allies, the total numbers that could theoretically be called upon by the Roman Republic were a staggering 700,000 foot soldiers and 70,000 cavalry. The mobilisation of forces in the struggle with Hannibal, which began seven years later, makes it clear that Polybius did not exaggerate by much.[10]

THE REPUBLIC

Rome was larger than any other city-state, but its institutions were not profoundly different from many other communities in Italy and the Greek world. The same was true of the Latin colonies and allied cities, each of which ran its own internal affairs, electing magistrates and having its own laws. They were not permitted their own foreign policy, nor were links between the allies themselves encouraged. Instead each was an ally of Rome, and the Roman Republic was the centre of everything, not merely one strong element in a communal alliance. Even so, the allies did not pay taxes to Rome, nor did the Romans interfere in their day-to-day affairs, and their sole obligation was to provide contingents of soldiers when required. These men served in distinct units, but were under overall Roman command and subject to the regulations of the Roman army, which imposed harsh punishments on infractions of discipline and also paid them.

At least half of every Roman field army consisted of allied soldiers, and normally the proportion was higher – Polybius' figures show that the Latins and other allies made up nearly two-thirds of total manpower. Allies, and especially the Latins, shed their blood on behalf of the Republic, and also shared in the spoils of victory. Thus as Rome expanded the enemies of one generation helped as allies to win the wars fought by the next generation. Some became Roman, while all enjoyed the greater security that came from belonging to so great a military power. In essence, it was safer to be Rome's ally than its enemy.[11]

The Republic proved remarkably stable in comparison to other city-states, where political revolution was all too common. There were serious social tensions, but solutions were eventually found sufficient to satisfy most groups in society, expanding the elite from the original small circle of patrician families and limiting the power of magistrates. The system that emerged was based around preventing any one individual or group from securing permanent supreme power. All of political life was conducted at Rome itself, and a citizen had to be present to take part. This remained true as the citizen body expanded, and only those resident in or near Rome, or those with the wealth, time and inclination to travel there, could vote or stand for office.

Elected magistrates provided the state with its executive officers. The most important were the two consuls, who held power for just twelve months and gave their name to the year. The political year began in March – the month named after the war god Mars. Consuls were first and foremost war leaders, and they were elected by an Assembly of the Roman People structured according to categories of the early army. As time passed restrictions were created to prevent a man from standing for the consulship in consecutive years, and eventually a ten-year interval was set down in law, as was a minimum age of forty-two for candidates seeking it. Yet a relatively small number of aristocratic families supplied a disproportionately high number of consuls, both because of ties of obligation with many important voters, but also a tendency for the electorate to prefer familiar names. It was difficult – although never impossible – for a man from outside to reach the consulship, but even so competition for the magistracy was fierce. With only two posts a year, the consulship was a prize won by only a small minority of senators.[12]

Consuls did their best to win glory during their term of office, for this gave them personal prestige and status within the community and enhanced the reputation of their family with voters as well. Defeating the enemies of the Republic brought the greatest fame, ideally marked by the award of a triumph, when the victorious commander and his soldiers processed through the heart of Rome. The victor rode in a chariot, wearing the regalia of Jupiter Optimus Maximus (Jupiter Best and Greatest), his face painted terracotta-red like the clay statues of the god. At some point it became the tradition for a slave to stand behind him and whisper reminders that he was mortal. The day of the parade was soon over, but the fame of the deed remained, the laurel wreath displayed on the porch of the victor's house a constant reminder to visitors. Aristocratic families took every opportunity to advertise the successes of the current and earlier generations. Funerals were public events, and actors were hired to don the funeral masks and insignia of office of a man's ancestors, their deeds being recounted along with his to offer an implicit promise of what the generations to come would achieve if trusted by voters.[13]

The consuls possessed *imperium* or 'power' which included the right to command soldiers and to dispense justice, but this lapsed when their office expired. The citizens as a whole met in formal assemblies presided over by a consul or other magistrate to make declarations of war and peace, to pass laws and for elections. Unlike in Athens and other democracies, these Popular Assemblies simply voted yes or no on proposals put to them and were not permitted to debate issues or to propose votes of their own. Such discussion occurred in the Senate, the permanent council of some 300 members whose task it was to advise the consuls. Senators were men of mature years – one of their other names was the *patres* or 'fathers' – and wealth. They were not elected, but enrolled by the censors, the pair of magistrates who every five years carried out a census, listing every citizen and his property.

The Senate supervised all foreign affairs, as well as much domestic business. They received delegations from rulers, peoples or states when these travelled to Rome. (In the ancient world no state maintained permanent embassies with even the most important external powers.) The Senate decided what the main tasks of the consuls would be for the year, allocating to them *provinciae* or 'provinces'. At this stage the province was not a geographical entity but a sphere of responsibility, such as 'the war with the Samnites'. The Senate also decided what resources would be given to the consuls, announcing how many troops would serve for the year. Its decisions on all of these matters reflected the current influence of distinguished members and especially the consuls as much as a pragmatic assessment of the good of the Republic – something which was inevitably often a matter of opinion. It is a mistake to think of the Senate pursuing clear and consistent long-term policies, although there was obvious consensus on some broad aims, most notably guarding and expanding Roman power.

Legio or legion originally meant 'levy' and referred to the entire army raised from the Roman people. Over time, as the numbers of citizens grew, each consul was given his own legion and by the third century BC it was normal for them to command an army of two legions. The legion had become the most important unit of the army. It varied in size from at least 4,000 men to more than 5,000, reflecting senatorial opinion of the scale of the military problem. Each legion was also normally supported by a similarly sized *ala* or wing of allies, named because the two Roman legions would deploy in the centre of the line with one *ala* on either side.

Citizens were eligible for service with the legions on the basis of their property as registered in the census, since men were expected to provide their own equipment. The richest, able to afford a horse, acted as cavalry, while the strength of the army consisted of the equivalent of hoplites, armoured infantrymen fighting in close order. The young and the poor served as skirmishers. Military service was a duty to the Republic, and the pay issued by the state was modest, providing little more than subsistence level while a man was on campaign.

Legionaries were men of property – overwhelmingly farmers – who were felt to have a stake in the success of the Republic and who, when the army was disbanded, would return to their homes and normal lives. In the early centuries warfare was often little more than a brief seasonal interruption to the agricultural year, fought against similar enemies and most likely occurring when both sides could be spared from their farms. As Rome expanded, wars were fought further afield and on a larger scale, so that a man might find himself serving with the legions for much longer periods of time. At some point a law was passed stipulating that no citizen should be required to serve for more than sixteen years or sixteen individual campaigns if more than one was fought in a single year.

Romans – and their allies, who appear to have raised contingents in a similar manner – willingly accepted this obligation to their Republic. The levy worked because year after year men presented themselves to be selected by the officers tasked with raising new

legions. Romans of all classes appear to have identified strongly with
the state, and thus the Roman army was in a very real sense the
Roman people under arms, commanded by leaders it had elected.[14]

OVERSEAS

By the early third century BC the Republic controlled by far the
greater part of the Italian Peninsula south of the River Po. In 282 BC
the Greek city of Tarentum, made nervous by this, attacked a squadron of Roman ships, claiming that their presence was a violation
of treaty. Two years later they enlisted King Pyrrhus of Epirus to
fight on their behalf. Pyrrhus was a famous general, a man thought
exceptionally talented even in an era when Alexander the Great's
veteran generals were battling for power. He brought with him a
Macedonian-style army of high-quality cavalry, pike phalanxes and
war elephants, but although he beat the Romans in battle they refused to accept a peace imposed by the enemy. The war dragged
on, Pyrrhus' strength was slowly eroded – the expression a 'pyrrhic
victory' for a battle won at too high a cost to the victor is modern,
but appropriate – and in the end he gave up. All of Italy was now
Roman or allied, apart from the Gallic and Ligurian tribes in
the north.[15]

In 264 BC the Romans intervened in Sicily, sending an army outside
the Italian mainland for the first time. It was a provocative act, challenging the Carthaginians in what they considered to be their sphere
of influence, and soon led to the First Punic War. (Carthage was
a settlement originally founded by Phoenicians from what is now
Lebanon, hence the Latin name for them of *Poeni* and our Punic.)
The Carthaginians were a great maritime and trading people, but
their empire was based on conquest as well as trade. Their fleet was
famous and powerful, while the Romans had little experience or
knowledge of naval warfare. In spite of this the Romans constructed
hundreds of warships – the design of the first famously copied from
a Carthaginian ship which had run aground – and learned how to

defeat the enemy. Twenty-three years of war proved appallingly costly to both sides, but the Romans persevered and won.

Victory brought them their first province as we would understand the term, encompassing much of Sicily – the rest was made up of allied communities. A few years later the Romans cynically exploited Carthaginian weakness and seized Sardinia and Corsica as well. Resentment at their defeat and humiliation led the Carthaginians to expand their presence in the Iberian Peninsula. It was from his base there that Hannibal began his invasion of Italy in 218 BC, determined to restore what he felt was the proper balance of power. Within two years he had killed fully one-third of the Senate and over 100,000 Roman and allied soldiers. Some of Rome's allies defected, most stayed loyal, and the Romans refused to negotiate for peace, but kept raising new armies, learning all the time from their defeats. They contained Hannibal in Italy – he was not to leave until 203 BC – and prosecuted the war in other theatres, eventually landing in Africa and threatening Carthage itself. Hannibal was recalled to defend his homeland, only to suffer his first real defeat at Zama, forcing the Carthaginians to accept the peace imposed on them in 201 BC.[16]

Two new provinces were created in the Iberian Peninsula in the wake of this conflict – Nearer Spain in the east and Further Spain in the west – and over time these initially small regions grew larger. In the early decades of the second century BC a concerted effort broke the power of the Ligurian and Gallic tribes and extended Roman control up to the Alps. During the Second Punic War they had also found themselves at war with the kingdom of Macedonia. This was one of three great powers to emerge after the break-up of Alexander the Great's conquests, the others being the Ptolemaic kingdom based around Egypt and the Seleucid Empire with its heartland in Syria. There were also smaller kingdoms and leagues of city-states forming the wider Greek world. Rome attacked and defeated Philip V of Macedon in the Second Macedonian War (200–196 BC), and the Seleucid Antiochus III in the Syrian War (192–189 BC). By this time the Ptolemies were the weakest of the three, internally divided and under a young and ineffective king, but they had a long-standing alliance with Rome, having supplied the Republic with grain during the Punic Wars. As the Ptolemies wasted their strength in internal power struggles, over time it became clearer that the Romans were the dominant partner in this relationship, and only Roman backing prevented the kingdom from being carved up by the others.[17]

No new provinces came from these conflicts in the eastern Mediterranean, and after each success the Roman armies withdrew. Roman influence was maintained by alliance and the threat of renewed force. A sense of recovering Macedonian strength led the Romans to declare and win the Third Macedonian War against Philip V's son Perseus. He was deposed in 167 BC and the kingdom of Macedonia dissolved, but once again no province was created until after a final conflict when a pretender to the throne appeared in 149 BC. In the same year Roman suspicion of an economically strong, if militarily weak, Carthage caused them to provoke the Carthaginians into the Third Punic War. In 146 BC Carthage was eradicated as a state, the city physically destroyed and its population removed. In the same year Corinth in Greece suffered a severe, if less total destruction at the hands of the legions.

The provinces of Africa and Macedonia raised Rome's total to six – Corsica and Sardinia were treated as a single appointment. Slowly the idea of the province as a clearly defined territory emerged, but with the exception of Nearer and Further Spain none of the other provinces were physically adjacent. The Romans do not appear to have thought of their empire as a unit and instead each individual province was connected to Rome at the centre. At this stage there was virtually no settlement of any province by colonists. (Cisalpine Gaul, the area of Italy north of the River Po, was in some respects viewed as a province, but increasingly was treated much like the rest of the Peninsula and did see extensive colonization.) Apart from the provinces there were large areas where Roman influence was provided by allied rulers and states.[18]

Later in the second century BC the Romans added Asia – bequeathed by its last king to the Roman people and eventually accepted – and Transalpine Gaul (modern-day Provence) to the list of permanent provinces. This last addition hints at a growing sense of the strategic advantage of linking provinces together, since it provided a land bridge to Spain. Yet, as in the earlier period, annexation and direct rule did not automatically follow a successful Roman war, and areas such as Numidia in North Africa, defeated in 105 BC, were left in the hands of allied rulers.

The creation of this empire had profound consequences for Rome's political system, economy and society, but on the surface the Republic appeared to change remarkably little. Two consuls were inadequate for all the tasks that needed to be done, and so a greater role was given to the praetors, the college of magistrates junior to the consuls. Traditionally there was just one praetor, who remained in Rome and had largely judicial and administrative responsibilities. Around 242 BC a second praetor was created, and two more added to the college a few years later. This reflected not simply growing judicial activity, but also the need to provide governors for Sicily and Sardinia and Corsica. Another two praetors were introduced at the start of the second century BC so that there were sufficient magistrates to deal with the two Spanish provinces. There were few other visible changes, such as an increase in the number of quaestors, the most junior magistrates who came to have a largely financial role assisting provincial governors. Army service now often involved long years spent in more or less active garrison duty in one of the provinces. Yet no substantial bureaucracy was created to administer the empire, and in every region almost every aspect of administration was left to local leaders and communities.

Changes were happening in spite of this, and the imperial role created severe strains on the Republic, so that in the course of the first century BC it began to break down. In 91 BC a substantial number of Rome's Italian allies rebelled, resenting the limited rights many still possessed and the often arrogant behaviour of Roman magistrates. The war was fought on a large scale by armies as aggressive, disciplined, and well equipped as each other, and led to heavy losses on both sides. By 89 BC the Romans had won, as much by rapid grants of full citizenship as by force. Soon, all free inhabitants south of the Po were citizens. A year later a dispute between rival senators turned to civil war when a consul led his legions against Rome itself. Stability never really returned and civil wars followed one after another until the future emperor Augustus won the last one in 30 BC. Alongside the chaos and political violence, these years were also times of rapid conquest, as men like Pompey the Great and Julius Caesar carved out great swathes of new territory. Rome survived these decades of crisis, and the empire would grow stronger and more prosperous.

WAR

'. . . the young state, once liberty was won, waxed incredibly strong and great in a remarkably short time, such was the thirst for glory that had filled men's minds. To begin with, as soon as the young men could endure the hardships of war, they were taught a soldier's duties in camp under a vigorous discipline, and they took more pleasure in handsome arms and war horses than in harlots and revelry. . . . Their hardest struggle for glory was with one another; each man strives to be the first to strike down the foe, to scale a wall, to be seen while doing such a deed. This they consider riches, this fair fame and high nobility.' – *Sallust, middle of the first century* BC.[1]

MASSACRE

Late in 150 BC, several groups of Lusitanians came down from the hill country to make their peace with Rome in the person of the governor of Further Spain, Servius Sulpicius Galba. He was waiting with his army, the heart of it legionaries and Italian allies. Most of these soldiers were heavily equipped with long oval shields, mail armour and bronze helmets topped with either three tall feathers or a billowing horsehair crest. They carried the heavy throwing spear known as the *pilum*, and wielded a well-balanced cut-and-thrust sword which they knew as the *gladius hispaniensis* – the 'Spanish sword' – because they had copied the type used by Iberian warriors.

They were typical of the men who served the Republic out of duty, mainly farmers or the sons of farmers, and most were probably under thirty, for other than in emergencies the recruiters seem to have preferred to enlist the young. These men served out of a strong sense of duty to the state and because the wider community expected it of them. Many no doubt saw it as a chance for adventure away from the cycle of sowing and harvesting, and hoped to profit from the spoils of victory – their pay remained modest – before they returned home and became civilians again. Some may have come to the army with dreams of glory, of winning praise or one of the military decorations designed to encourage such spirit. Awards for valour were worn each festival day, so that brave former soldiers could be honoured by their fellow citizens.[2]

In many ways the Roman and Latin soldiers in the middle of the second century BC were much like plenty of other young men sent off to war in other ages and other countries. They were ordinary men by the standards of the times, and certainly had a lot in common with the citizens of most cities in the wider Mediterranean world. Citizenship brought legal and political rights and also obligations to the wider community. They served because they were citizens, and if they died it was as citizens and not soldiers that they would be commemorated. There were no permanent army bases or institutions, and even the legions were renumbered every year if the Senate decided to keep them in service. This meant that the two consuls always commanded the *First*, *Second*, *Third* and *Fourth* Legions. The Roman army is almost invisible archaeologically in this period, its soldiers merging back with the wider population at the end of each campaign.

A hint of professionalism came from a growing tendency for some men to seek prolonged service as centurions, the officers who commanded the basic administrative and tactical units of the legion, but even this was informal and we do not know how common it was. Most senior officers were like the men they led, citizens who interspersed spells of military service with normal civilian life. At the head of an army was the provincial governor, a magistrate elected by an Assembly of the Roman People. Either a consul or praetor, these were men successfully pursuing a career in public life. They were always wealthy and usually aristocrats, but eminence imposed even greater obligations on them – a man had to serve for ten years or as many campaigns in the army before he could offer himself as a candidate for even the most junior magistracy. Although a fellow citizen, the governor held *imperium* and along with his greater responsibilities had the opportunity to win far greater fame and wealth than ordinary legionaries.[3]

Great glory came to a magistrate who led an army of the Roman people to victory in war. There was also profit to be made from plunder and the sale of captives as slaves, and the prestige and wealth of a victor were great benefits to a man for the rest of his career, giving him an advantage over all the other senators jockeying for office in the fiercely competitive political culture of Rome. Since the tenure of each magistracy was brief, so was the window of opportunity for a man to make his name and fortune. Sometimes the Senate chose to extend a provincial command into a second year – in which case the man was given the title of proconsul or propraetor. A third year of command was almost unheard of in the second century BC. With ambitious new governors arriving so often, the system encouraged them to behave very aggressively.

In Lusitania in 150 BC the dreams of glory and rich plunder had turned sour both for the soldiers and Galba. The year before they had been badly mauled by these same Lusitanian tribesmen, or at least by men who looked much like them in their dark tunics and with long hair hanging down their backs – the custom was to plait it when preparing for battle. The Lusitanians were not a nation, but one of the three main groups of indigenous peoples in the Iberian Peninsula. The Iberians lived to the south, while the Celtiberians held central and much of northern Spain, their culture showing elements of Celtic and Iberian influences, but being clearly distinct from both. The Lusitanians were in the west, covering an area very roughly equivalent to modern Portugal. None of these peoples were politically united, and it is doubtful that any of them thought of themselves as Iberians, Celtiberians or Lusitanians. These were labels imposed by Greek, Phoenician, Carthaginian and Roman outsiders – in the last two cases by imperial powers expanding into the Peninsula. More important to each people were tribal groupings, and especially the close communities of each walled town or village.[4]

Galba was praetor in 151 BC, and received by lot command of Further Spain. There had been heavy fighting in both of the Spanish provinces since the middle of the decade and Galba was not the only governor to suffer defeat at the hands of the Celtiberians or Lusitanians. Roman citizens were well motivated and tended to prove excellent soldiers, if they were given time to train and were competently led. The longer a legion remained in service the better it became, so that during the latter stages of the Second Punic War and the early conflicts with the Macedonians and Seleucids they proved themselves as good as or better than the hardened professionals they faced. There had been far less fighting in the middle of the second century BC, and as the veteran generation faded away, officers and ordinary soldiers alike came to the army with far less experience and a complacent belief that they would win simply because they were Roman. Defeats became much more common, and wars were only won because of Rome's greater resources and persistence, and because the legions did learn from experience and improve.

Such setbacks shocked a Republic accustomed to victory. It is hard to see how Carthage presented any real military threat to Rome in 149 BC, but it is clear that many Romans were genuinely afraid of their old rival. When the inexperienced and overconfident Roman army and its commanders arrived in North Africa, the desperate enemy fought with determination and there was a string of reverses and failures which no doubt fed these fears. Polybius, who was in Rome during these years, reflected contemporary panic when he wrote of the struggle with the Celtiberians as the 'fiery war' because it raged almost unceasingly year after year. Rumours of this hard service against ferocious enemies reached Rome, and in 151 BC for once the sense of patriotism of its citizens wavered. Very few men appeared when the levy was called to raise an army to serve under the consul Lucullus in Nearer Spain. Only concerted encouragement and the very public volunteering of a popular young aristocrat eventually persuaded sufficient men to present themselves for the levy.[5]

These campaigns in both Spanish provinces were wars of raid and counter-raid, attacks on walled settlements and ambush. Battles were fought, but were often the result of sudden encounters and occurred in difficult terrain such as mountain passes. During these years marauding bands of Lusitanians ranged ever deeper into Further Spain, reaching the coast and at one point even crossing the Straits of Gibraltar into North Africa. Only rarely were the victims of their attacks Romans or Italians, for as yet there were relatively few of these in either province. Instead the targets were local communities allied to Rome. Galba had only a single legion and *ala* – together at most some 10,000–12,000 men and the normal force allocated by the Senate to a praetor. This was too small to defend so long and so open a frontier, and the problem only became harder when his strength was severely reduced by his defeat in 151 BC. The Romans could not hope to stop each raid as it came in, and the best they could do was try to catch the raiders as they withdrew, or launch reprisal attacks of their own against the Lusitanian settlements believed to be responsible. Every raid that succeeded – and still more every occasion on which the Romans caught the warriors but were defeated – encouraged more and larger bands to try their luck. We hear of the Lusitanians parading captured Roman army standards and other trophies around neighbouring communities and into Celtiberian territory to display their own power and encourage others to join them in fresh attacks.[6]

There were some lulls in the fighting, and for a while Roman reprisals prompted these same bands of Lusitanians to make peace with Galba's predecessor, but when he returned to Rome they broke the treaty and went back on the warpath. In 150 BC Galba attacked, having done his best to make up his losses from the previous year by raising local levies, men who quite reasonably saw the Lusitanians as enemies. Simultaneously Lucullus, whose command had also been extended so that he was now a proconsul, drove into Lusitanian territory from another direction, capturing one walled settlement after another. His resources were larger, for he led the standard consular army of two legions and two *alae*. The twin assault convinced the Lusitanians that it was better to seek peace, and so their envoys went to Galba, claiming that lands too barren to support their numbers had made them return to raiding to take what they needed from richer neighbours.

The Roman governor appeared sympathetic, declaring that 'poorness of soil and penury force you to do these things. But I will give my poor friends good land, and settle them in fertile country'. Galba was well thought of as an orator at Rome, although in this case he surely addressed the representatives via a translator. As far as we know he had never been to the Iberian Peninsula until he went out as governor of Further Spain, and few Roman governors had either the time or the inclination to learn local languages. Yet removing troublesome warriors and resettling them on better territory far from their homes was a technique that the Romans had used before and would use again, always with success. Taken away from their old territory and their old feuds, given the ability to support their families, and also no doubt aware that they were under the close observation of the authorities, raiders readily turned into peaceful farmers. Galba told the envoys to bring their people to an arranged spot so that they could surrender themselves to Rome's power under promise of resettlement.[7]

They were told to come in three groups, each presumably composed of specific communities, clans or the followers of particular leaders so that the division was natural and easy to arrange. We do not know the names of any of the groups or leaders. One source says that they numbered as many as 30,000 in total, the women in the colourful dresses and long cloaks favoured in the area, and children and perhaps some elderly as well as the warriors. There were probably more men of military age than in a normal population, for these were raiders reliant on their swords because they did not have enough good land or animals. With them came their horses and flocks and all the possessions they were able to carry, including their weapons. Each of the three groups went to the appointed place and camped there to wait for the Romans to arrive and assign them to their new lands.[8]

Galba came to the first group and ordered the tribesmen to hand over their weapons. This was a normal mark of surrender, but also a likely moment of tension – in 1890 the spark that ignited the battle (or massacre depending on your viewpoint) at Wounded Knee. Weapons – and especially expensive items such as swords – were highly prized and emotionally important as a means of protection for a man and his family. Yet the Lusitanians obeyed, and handed over at least some of their military equipment. Galba then ordered his soldiers to surround the Lusitanian encampment with a ditch. Perhaps this was justified as protection for the tribesmen and their families, now at least in theory weapon-less, but it would surely have made them nervous, adding to the tension of the situation.[9]

Then the Roman governor sent soldiers into the camp and they began to kill. After all the occupants were dead or captured, Galba moved on to the second and third groups and treated them in exactly the same way. This was a massacre, and one not carried out at a distance with modern firearms, but at close range. The Roman and Latin soldiers, and their local allies, did most of the killing face to face, cutting and thrusting with their swords – another source tells us that in battle it was normal for shields and the chests of cavalry horses to be drenched in blood. Livy described the wounds inflicted by legionaries using the Spanish sword, with 'bodies chopped to pieces . . ., arms torn away, shoulders and all, or heads separated from bodies, with the necks completely severed, or vitals laid open'. (Some of the grim pictures from the civil wars in Rwanda in the 1990s showing multiple machete wounds might best convey something of the horror of the scene.) If there was any fighting then it was one-sided, and Galba's men slaughtered at will. These were the survivors of last year's costly defeat at the hands of the Lusitanians, or local men from communities preyed upon by these very raiders, and so reluctance to obey the orders is neither hinted at by our sources nor likely. We do not know how many died, but the total was large enough to make this massacre infamous. Substantial numbers survived to be sold into slavery, and only a few Lusitanians managed to escape in the confusion.[10]

Galba's treachery was deliberate and premeditated, his orders to his soldiers clear. This was not some ghastly accident, where ill-judged or misunderstood words or actions ignited an already tense situation into an unplanned atrocity. Later the Roman governor claimed that he had acted in this way to pre-empt treachery on the part of the Lusitanians. His evidence was that they had performed a ritual where they sacrificed a man and a horse to the war god, something that it was their custom only to do before going on the warpath. Another source confirms this custom, and describes how they would take a war captive, swathe him in a cloak and then would stab him through it, watching how he fell and writhed to divine the future.

If Galba invented this story, then at least it suggests some attempt to understand the Lusitanians' customs. Perhaps he was mistaken – or even misinformed, since his allied soldiers may well have encouraged harsh treatment of the surrendering tribes for their own reasons. It is also possible that the sacrifice had occurred, although it may not have reflected the hopes or opinions of all of the tribesmen. In the loose political structure of the Lusitanians some leaders or groups may well have resented the decision to make peace with Rome, or simply have not trusted Galba and the Romans – with justification as it turned out.[11]

The news of Galba's actions provoked outrage at Rome, but not because of the massed slaughter and enslavement in itself. Such brutal methods were sometimes considered necessary in Rome's wars, and fitting punishment for enemies of the Roman people. Roman attitudes to atrocity in warfare were essentially pragmatic, and mercy and cruelty judged on their effectiveness in bringing a conflict to a successful conclusion. Galba's crime was to act in this way against an enemy who had already surrendered, wantonly breaking his own agreement with them. This was a breach of 'good faith' or *fides*, something on which the Romans prided themselves, choosing to believe that they dealt honestly and straightforwardly with others. In contrast they portrayed their old Carthaginian rivals as proverbially treacherous, just as the late-seventeenth- and eighteenth-century English maligned the Dutch with expressions such as 'Dutch courage'.

Once again there was an element of practicality to this. A

reputation for keeping agreements and treaties, for reliable support of allies and fair treatment of defeated enemies, helped to foster future negotiations with other peoples. There was also a religious dimension. The Republic's prosperity and success in warfare were held to rely on divine favour, confirmed in careful and regularly repeated ritual to placate the gods. Many of Rome's temples were built by victorious generals who claimed at a moment of crisis in battle to have vowed to honour a god or gods in this way. *Pietas* – a much stronger concept than the modern idea of piety, for it embraced reverence for parents and ancestors as well as gods – was one of the quintessential Roman virtues. Part of this special relationship with the divine powers was the belief that Romans behaved in a proper way, dealing fairly with others and only fighting just wars to defend themselves or their friends.[12]

Plenty of other imperial powers have had a similar belief in their own virtue. The massacre of the Lusitanians gives a far grimmer illustration of Roman expansion, but before we return to Galba's story it is worth looking at the wider picture, and seeking to understand what caused and drove the creation of the Roman Empire.

RICHES AND REPUTATION –
THE DRIVE TO EMPIRE

These are not new questions. Polybius began his *Universal History* around the middle of the second century BC – roughly contemporary with Galba's activities in Spain, although sadly his account of this has been lost – and for him one theme loomed larger than any other: 'For who is so worthless or indolent as not to wish to know by what means and under what system of polity the Romans in less than fifty-three years have succeeded in subjecting nearly the whole inhabited world to their sole government – a thing unique in history?'[13]

Polybius wrote his book in Rome, where he was one of many

hostages sent from Greece by the Achaean League of cities as surety of the good behaviour of their home communities. For a long time a guest in the household of a prominent Roman aristocratic family, the historian met many of the leading figures of the Republic and accompanied the famous Scipio Aemilianus when he captured and destroyed the great city of Carthage in 146 BC.[14]

How the Romans overcame the Carthaginians in the three Punic Wars features prominently in Polybius' work. He described the Roman military system in some detail, praising it for its order, discipline and also its encouragement of individual bravery. He gave even more importance to the Republic's political system, which he saw as a well-balanced mixed constitution combining elements of monarchy, aristocracy and democracy. Unlike most Greek city-states, which were prone to periodic revolution and over time would cycle through all of these systems, the Romans enjoyed stability and a truly unusual level of political and social unity. Roman strengths helped to explain the Republic's long-term success, but Polybius also looked at events elsewhere and in particular the rivalries of the kingdoms and states of the Hellenic world.

Modern scholars have accepted some of this view but, since it dealt with how rather than why, have for a long time looked elsewhere to explain Roman conquests. In the nineteenth and early twentieth centuries – an era when modern empires had colonised much of the globe – many were ready to take the Romans' own claims at face value. Faced with hostile neighbours, the Romans fought only to protect themselves, and so won conflict after conflict and acquired an empire almost accidentally. More recently the pendulum swung to the opposite extreme, a view that crystallised among English-speaking academics in the years following the Vietnam War, and especially among scholars who had become adults in the decades after the Second World War. Deep discomfort with warfare of any sort, let alone overseas adventures, pervades this scholarship, which portrayed Rome's political system, society and economy as driving the Republic to near-continuous aggressive warfare that was almost a biological necessity. Any talk of defence was a sham, and the

Romans were active and determined predators who attacked other peoples year after year.[15]

The studies of these years showed how central a role war-making played in the life of the Republic. Victory in war brought senators the greatest glory and wealth from plunder, and opportunities for command came only when a man reached the higher magistracies. Galba was one of six elected praetors in 151 BC, but there were only two consuls – in this case Lucius Licinius Lucullus and Aulus Postumius Albinus. Competition for this highest and most prestigious of posts was fierce, and simple arithmetic tells us that most praetors would not go on to hold the consulship. If a man was lucky enough to be given a provincial command as praetor in a province with an army – something no longer true of Sicily and sometimes Sardinia and Corsica – and if he faced a military threat – or at least something that could be presented as one – and if he was able to win a decisive victory, then it greatly increased his prospects of becoming consul. The consuls could expect to receive the most important commands of the year, but the larger scale of a war often made it difficult to win a complete victory before their twelve months of office had expired.[16]

Magistrates usually spent several months in Rome before travelling out to their province. In 153 BC the start of the political year was changed from 15 March to 1 January to allow them to reach a distant province and still be able to use the spring and summer months for campaigning. Extension of command as proconsul or propraetor was the exception rather than the rule, since each year brought a fresh crop of magistrates equally eager to win glory. With many governors in province for just a year, and scarcely any for more than two years, there was little time for a man to gain local experience and most were impatient for a quick success.[17]

In 264 BC an ambitious consul had helped to convince the Senate to intervene in Sicily, provoking the First Punic War. In 198 BC the consul fighting against the Macedonian King Philip V began negotiations to end the war because he feared that he would be replaced and so a rival would gain credit for completing the victory. For a while he was willing to offer the king generous terms until he discovered that both consuls of 197 BC were to march against the Gallic tribes in northern Italy and thus his own command was to be extended by the Senate. He immediately broke off negotiations, renewed the conflict and was fortunate enough to win the decisive battle, after which he was able to impose a harsher peace treaty on Philip V and take for himself the credit for having won the Second Macedonian War. When the Third Macedonian War broke out in 172 BC, one of the year's consuls was disappointed that the command in this war fell by lot to his colleague. Sent to Illyricum instead, he disdained the prospect of protecting a frontier against petty raids and instead began marching his army overland to Macedonia. A senatorial commission had to be sent to order him to return to his province.[18]

When Lucullus arrived in Nearer Spain in 151 BC he discovered that the war with the Arevaci, a Celtiberian people, had been concluded by his predecessor. Instead he attacked the Vaccaei, a tribal group allied to Rome. They were probably not wholly innocent victims, since they do seem to have raided other allied communities, but even so he had not been tasked with fighting them by the Senate. His methods were similar to those of Galba. Moving against the town of Cauca, he negotiated for the inhabitants to surrender on generous terms, but then broke his word and massacred many of them, selling the survivors into slavery. The next town surrendered and was granted terms which the governor kept, but the combination of cruelty and generosity failed to convince the third major community to submit when he approached it. Lucullus attacked and failed to take the town, so that his campaign ended in a sharp repulse.[19]

Other governors who went hunting for a triumph had rather more luck. In 189 BC the consul Cnaeus Manlius Vulso was given command in the Syrian War, but reached Asia Minor only to discover that his predecessor had already won it, defeating Antiochus the Great at Magnesia. Vulso led his army to the frontier with the Seleucids, trying and failing to provoke the king to break the peace treaty. Determined to win a major war, he instead launched an attack on the Galatians – three tribes who had migrated from Gaul in the third century BC and settled in central Asia Minor, routinely raiding their neighbours. In a swift and brutally efficient campaign he defeated and plundered them, and travelled home at the end of his year of office to claim a triumph. Opposition was strong, for he had not been authorised to fight this war, and a long debate in the Senate seemed to be going against him when the sun set and the meeting was closed – Rome's Senate could not legally meet in darkness. Overnight Vulso and his political allies called in favours wherever they could, and used the profits of his victory to buy new friends. At the next meeting the mood had changed, and Vulso was awarded a triumph which he celebrated in spectacular fashion.[20]

This was one of a succession of triumphs during the second century BC described as more lavish than all that had been held in the past. In every case these marked victories won in the wealthy eastern Mediterranean and set the mark ever higher for future triumphs. Competition became even more intense, as a man needed to win ever bigger and ever more profitable victories if he wanted to stand out from his peers.[21]

Eighty-five triumphs are recorded as having being celebrated between 200 and 91 BC. During that period, there were very few years when Roman soldiers were not actively campaigning somewhere, for not every provincial governor managed to win a triumph, some because they did not win the war and others because the scale of the conflict was too small. Early in the second century BC it was decreed that at least 5,000 enemy dead needed to have been counted after a battle for the victory to qualify for a triumph. On this calculation, the recorded triumphs would equate to at least 425,000 enemy corpses. The figure is rough, since some successes were much more bloody than this (while it is perfectly possible that in others the count was optimistic, since no one was likely to check too closely). The total casualties suffered by the enemy would be considerably greater if the losses inflicted in other operations not resulting in a triumph were added. Since Roman expansion did not begin in 200 BC or end in 91 BC, the grand total would be much, much higher – it was claimed that one million enemies died during Julius Caesar's Gallic campaigns alone. It may well be that more human beings were killed by Roman *gladius* swords than any other weapon before the modern era – the ubiquitous AK-47 has no doubt surpassed this grim record in the last half-century or so. In addition, any measure of the human suffering caused by Roman expansion would have to allow for the Romans' own casualties.[22]

Galba's slaughter and enslavement of the Lusitanians became notorious, but it is easy to find accounts of appalling Roman ferocity as a matter of routine in many campaigns. For instance, in 210 BC they stormed New Carthage (modern Cartagena) in Spain, and Polybius described how:

> When Scipio [the Roman commander] thought that a sufficient number of troops had entered he sent most of them, as is the Roman custom, against the inhabitants of the city, with orders to kill all they encountered, sparing none, and not to start pillaging until the signal was given. They do this, I think, to inspire terror, so that when towns are taken by the Romans one may often see not only the corpses of human beings, but dogs cut in half, and the dismembered limbs of other animals, and on this occasion such scenes were very many owing to the numbers of those in the place.[23]

Capturing a walled town by direct assault was a difficult and dangerous operation, and if the defenders rallied and continued to resist in the streets then it was perfectly possible for the attackers to be driven out even after they had got over the wall. Thus a deliberate policy aimed at terrifying inhabitants and garrison alike was a sensible if savage means of deterring this. Scipio does not appear to have wanted his men to hunt out the entire population from hiding places, but to kill those who were visible. The intention was to clear the streets and any open spaces where organised resistance could occur. This tactic might also have the advantage of making other strongholds less willing to risk defying the Romans in future.[24]

Rome's citizen soldiers were capable of appalling savagery. Generation after generation they were also willing to leave their homes for long periods of time. Six years at a stretch may have been typical for men sent to Spain in the second century BC, although it is possible that many served for longer than this. During this time a man lost most of the legal rights of citizenship, and was subject to corporal and capital punishment at the discretion of his officers, as well as the risk of death from disease or in battle against the enemy. To set against that he might also win the respect, even the admiration, of his comrades, and through them, that of the wider citizen community. More tangible rewards came from a share of the spoils of victory, which were supposed to be distributed in a well-established and organised system. Polybius' description of Roman soldiers slaughtering men and animals alike as they stormed New Carthage was intended to emphasise their discipline. The legionaries obeyed their orders to kill and terrify the inhabitants, rather than dispersing to loot, trusting that when the plunder was gathered they would receive their fair share.[25]

The scale of mobilisation of Roman citizens was unmatched until the conscription of Revolutionary and Napoleonic France surpassed even the efforts of Frederick the Great. Under the Roman Republic it lasted far longer and may well have represented a higher percentage of Rome's population, especially since it fell most on property owners. In the second century BC there were usually at least six legions in service every year, and sometimes as many as a dozen, with – in theory if rarely in practice – some 4,500–5,000 soldiers in each. During the struggle with Hannibal it had been common for as many as twenty to serve simultaneously. The reluctance of men to come forward when Lucullus raised troops in 151 BC was rare, and even in that case was soon overcome. While it is easy to understand the enthusiasm of the men who enlisted to fight Hannibal – this was an enemy on their doorstep who threatened the very life of the Republic – what is striking is the readiness with which Romans were willing to serve on ever more distant frontiers in tough campaigns that were fought for less obvious reasons.[26]

Many Romans benefited from successful war-making. Ordinary soldiers received a modest share of the plunder, and in some periods a proportion of them were granted land by the state at the end of their service, although this was not consistent enough to explain their willingness to serve. The senators who led the army to victory became rich, their wealth helping their careers and enhancing their own and their families' prestige, sometimes in the tangible form of monuments such as temples built from the spoils. Other wealthy men profited from contracts to supply the army, from undertaking the sale of plunder and war captives or from overseeing the collection of taxes in the provinces.

Slaves flooded into Italy throughout the second century BC and many were captives taken in war – Julius Caesar was believed to have enslaved one million people from 58–51 BC. Men made rich from the profits of expansion often invested in land in Italy, buying up large estates and purchasing slaves to provide the labour force to work the fields or look after herds and flocks. In the second half of the century many Romans began to worry that, as they sent their own young men abroad to fight for the Republic, their places and livelihoods were increasingly being usurped by foreign slaves. The truth was more complicated than this, but the influx of slaves did change the economy and society of Italy. It is doubtful that any war was fought simply to acquire captives, but they were certainly an attractive and lucrative by-product of expansion. Similarly the only real obligation on Rome's allies in Italy was to provide contingents of soldiers to serve alongside the legions, but there is no evidence for wars being initiated simply to preserve this relationship. However, in 157 BC Polybius explains the Senate's decision to send an army against the Dalmatians in part because 'they did not wish the Italians to become effeminate owing to the long peace, it being twelve years since the war with Perseus and the campaigns in Macedonia'.[27]

The Roman Republic celebrated military achievement as the greatest service of the state, and mobilised extremely large resources – especially of its own and allied manpower – to wage war virtually every year. No voices at Rome ever seem to have suggested that this was not entirely natural or a good thing. Even so, while some scholars began to stress Roman aggression as the overwhelming driving force behind the creation of the empire, others pointed out that these structural factors were far more complicated than this. The Republic was not a machine so geared to war that it simply sought out one opponent after another, did 'massive violence' to them and in the long run subjected all to Roman authority.[28]

There were long periods when fewer wars were fought. For instance there were thirty-nine triumphs celebrated in the thirty-three years from 200 to 167 BC, and then forty-six in the seventy-five years from 166 to 91 BC. Not every senior magistrate wanted or received a military province – Sicily was largely demilitarised after the Second Punic War and yet the post of governor remained prestigious. Even men sent to command armies in other provinces did not automatically use them. There is little trace of warfare in either Spanish province in the 170s and 160s BC. Triumph-hunting occurred, but was far from universal, while treachery and wanton massacre were exceptions rather than the rule. At times the Senate did intervene in the affairs of other states and send a magistrate and army to fight on the flimsiest of excuses. Sometime before 219 BC they made an alliance with the city of Saguntum in Spain which was at war with one of Hannibal's allies. Perhaps it was meant to curb the resurgence of Carthaginian power in Spain, but then and on other occasions the Romans were accused of making alliances simply to give them a pretext to fight a war, which would of course be just, since it was nominally waged to defend an ally.[29]

More often the Senate chose not to intervene in spite of repeated appeals for alliance and direct military aid. Sometimes this was a question of resources. Large though the citizen and allied manpower was, it was not infinite, nor could too high a proportion be called up for service for too long. Nor was there always a magistrate available to command. In 219 BC both consuls were sent across the Adriatic to Illyricum, which meant that no one was available to take an army to aid Saguntum when Hannibal besieged the city. Instead ambassadors were sent to demand that he stop. By the time the Romans were prepared to intervene militarily, Saguntum had been sacked and its population enslaved, and Hannibal was ready to launch his own attack on Italy.

Rome was not invariably aggressive, nor did it provoke every war it fought. One of the greatest weaknesses of most studies of Roman imperialism is that they tend to see it in isolation, as if everything depended on Roman behaviour and other states were little more than passive victims of imperialist aggression. We happen to know considerably more about Rome's history than that of almost any other state, and we also know that they carved out an empire that lasted for centuries. There is no doubt that the Republic was an aggressive imperial power, but as soon as we look more closely at contemporary states it becomes obvious that this was equally true of almost every other kingdom, state or people.[30]

Greek cities, including – in fact especially – democratic Athens went to war frequently and with every sign of enthusiasm, their citizens willingly volunteering for military service and honouring the war dead with great ceremony. Piracy was an altogether respectable pursuit for an Athenian nobleman in the sixth century BC and in later periods, every bit as honourable as peaceful trading. Greek killed Greek far more often than culturally different outsiders such as the Persians. Alexander the Great and his father Philip II fought long and hard to dominate Greece, and the son then embarked on one of the greatest programmes of conquest in history when he attacked Persia – ostensibly revenge for the Persian invasion of Greece a century and a half earlier, although that claim wore very thin by the time he reached India. Philosophers stopped just short of declaring war as normal between two states, but clearly thought that truly peaceful relations were unusual. It was common to declare a set number of years of peace as part of the treaty ending a war, and there was a good chance that one or the other party would break the agreement by resuming hostilities before this time had elapsed.[31]

Political systems made little difference to this frequent aggression, with democracies, oligarchies and monarchies all just as ready to attack others. The Successor kingdoms which emerged from

the wreck of Alexander the Great's empire were extremely bellicose, each ruler vying to prove himself the true heir to the great
conqueror. Pyrrhus readily accepted Tarentum's appeal to cross to
Italy and fight a war that had nothing to do with him in the hope
of winning power, wealth and glory. Nor was Carthage markedly
different, having carved out large territories in Africa, contested for
centuries with Greek cities to control Sicily, and later embarked on a
programme of conquest in Spain. For a while Pyrrhus was enlisted
to fight against the Carthaginians in Sicily, distracting him from the
struggle with Rome for a few years.

The slimmest of pretexts was sufficient to justify a war, and
the Romans were far from unique in making convenient alliances
to justify military intervention. Opinion in the wider Greek world
mattered, but only to a limited extent, and consistently successful
powers were unlikely to suffer much from offending it. There are
plenty of instances from Greek, Macedonian and Carthaginian
warfare of massacre, treachery and mass enslavement to match the
ferocity of Roman war-making. It is doubtful that the inhabitants
of Saguntum were subjected to gentler treatment by Hannibal's
soldiers than the people in New Carthage suffered at the hands of
Scipio's legionaries – or for that matter the Thebans when Alexander
the Great sacked their city in 335 BC. Warfare in the ancient world was
often extremely brutal.[32]

Greeks, and then the Romans, stereotyped 'barbarians' – at first
simply non-Greeks and including the Romans and other Italians –
as inherently savage and warlike. For all the entrenched prejudice
in their views, all the evidence suggests that warfare was extremely
common among the tribal peoples of the world. Fortifications
appear in many areas, and weapons figure heavily in the archaeological record, especially in Europe. Often these are clearly intended
for war rather than hunting – no one would choose a sword as
their main armament to go hunting for animals. Defended settlements and military equipment do not in themselves show that
conflict was frequent, but at the very least demonstrate that it was
important to display a capacity to employ military force. Yet there

is also direct evidence of large-scale violence in some parts of Iron Age Europe long before the Romans arrived. Julius Caesar claimed that the tribes of Gaul went to war with each other almost every year, and spoke of Germanic peoples maintaining strips of depopulated land around their territory to demonstrate their might and deter attacks.[33]

Much of this military activity was probably small-scale, raids rather than major invasions – a type of fighting fairly common in the Greek world as well, and in the form of piracy throughout the Mediterranean. That did not mean that it was any less traumatic for the victims, for the raiders might want cattle or other plunder or they might have come to kill. Head-hunting was common among many Iron Age peoples, with the severed head of an enemy often possessing a ritual significance greater than a mere trophy of victory. Posidonius, a Greek scholar who travelled widely in the early first century BC and visited the peoples of southern Gaul, wrote of heads displayed on buildings, and hosts proudly producing these grisly trophies to show to guests. At first he found this shocking, but gradually became accustomed to it. Archaeology confirms the display of heads and human body parts, especially in a ritual context, at a number of sites in Gaul. It is also clear that raids could be on a very large scale, and that major battles did occur, and that warfare sometimes led to widespread destruction and the displacement or even eradication of entire communities.[34]

The ancient world was a dangerous, warlike place. The most important contribution to the debate on Roman expansion has been to make clear that while Rome was extremely aggressive, so were almost all of its neighbours. (For those still determined to see the Romans as uniquely bellicose, the existence of such a state would surely in itself have been sufficient to militarise those around it, if only for self-defence.) This was an environment where survival depended on military strength. There is simply no evidence for any truly pacific state or people – and it is hard to see how any could have survived.

It is instructive that Polybius did not think to ask why the Romans expanded, as the answer was obvious. They were strong because of their political and military systems and so they conquered others. If others had been stronger, then the Romans would have been subjected to them. The domination of those around them by more powerful states was simply natural and required no explanation. Security for any state rested on its military strength, and especially others' perception of this. A people who seemed strong were far less likely to suffer attacks than those who appeared vulnerable to their neighbours.[35]

Rome was one of many aggressive, imperialistic states and kingdoms, unusual not because it was uniquely bellicose but because it proved so successful. Much of this rested on its capacity to absorb other peoples and tie them permanently to the Republic as loyal, if clearly subordinate, allies. The Romans overran Italy, and as they did so their citizen and allied manpower grew to outstrip that of any competitor. At first they did not apply the same approach to overseas provinces, although they did make considerable use of alliances of a different sort and let most communities continue to run their own affairs.

Military manpower allowed the Republic to field very large armies of patriotically committed citizen soldiers and permitted it to adopt an especially determined approach to warfare. The Romans proved capable of learning from mistakes and adapting the way they fought, but most striking was the refusal to accept that they had lost a conflict and the willingness to pour resources into the struggle until they prevailed. Pyrrhus' victories would have been enough to convince most other states to negotiate. The losses inflicted by Hannibal were far worse and could not have been sustained by any other kingdom of people. Yet in each conflict the Roman Republic endured and went on to win. These wars were initiated by the other side, even if in each case this could be interpreted as having been provoked by Rome's growing power, and the strategy of both Pyrrhus and Hannibal was an offensive to break Roman military might. There were plenty of other conflicts started by Rome's opponents, for the Republic was not the only predator in the world.[36]

FAITH AND RUTHLESSNESS

The Lusitanians treacherously slaughtered and enslaved by Galba were active raiders, doing what others in the region had done in the past and would do in the future. The first-century BC Greek historian Diodorus Siculus claimed that:

> One special custom is followed among the Iberians and especially among the Lusitanians: among those who are in the prime of life, those poorest in property, but outstanding in strength and courage, furnish themselves with weapons and resources, gather in the harsh mountain regions, and forming quite significant bands they overrun Iberia and collect wealth by plundering.[37]

Their victims were the communities living on better land, and the geographer Strabo explained that the efforts these made to defend themselves tended to escalate the violence, and over time left fields untended, as farmers were forced to turn raider or starve.[38]

The Lusitanian attacks were not primarily anti-Roman but the continuation of a long-established pattern of martial activity centred around raiding. The peoples of the Iberian Peninsula raided and fought each other long before the Romans – or for that matter the Carthaginians – arrived. This is abundantly clear from the frequency with which weaponry appears in the archaeological record – after all, it was the Romans who adopted the 'Spanish' sword. It is likely that the activities of the imperial powers of Carthage and Rome increased the intensity of indigenous warfare. In the past, mercenary service with the Carthaginians may also have removed many of the young warriors who would otherwise have turned to banditry, at least until this option was ended by Rome.[39]

Plundering attacks on allied communities are one of the most frequent explanations given in our sources for Roman campaigns, especially those fought on frontiers with tribal peoples in Spain, Gaul or Macedonia. As the experiences of Galba and Lucullus showed, the resulting operations were far from one-sided, with more than a few leading to serious Roman defeats. Those determined to see the Romans as invariably guilty too readily dismiss the sources as empty self-justification on the part of the conqueror. In some cases this may have been true – Lucullus' attack on the Vaccaei might or might not fall into this category. More often the raids surely did occur, whether motivated by sheer opportunism, poverty or long-standing grudges based on earlier conflict with other local peoples or the Romans.

Failure to deal with such attacks showed weakness and invited an escalation. If the Romans could not protect allied communities, then there was little reason for these to maintain the alliance and accept their subordination to Roman authority. In that sense continued Roman control depended on defending Rome's friends and their interests – we hear of one instance where a Roman commander attempted to return recaptured booty to its original Iberian owners, although we do not know whether or not this was normal. Therefore as the Republic's power grew and it acquired more provinces and more allies, almost inevitably the probability of further warfare increased.[40]

Galba's approach offered a short-term solution to one source of the problem. Perhaps he hoped that the terror it inspired would act as a deterrent in future, although since he was returning to Rome soon he may not have cared. By the time he was back in the City in 149 BC there were already moves to arrange the release from slavery of the surviving Lusitanians. The question was not whether it was right to enslave war captives, but instead the breach of *fides* to people who had surrendered themselves to Rome and been promised better treatment. Ultimately nothing came of the attempt, and as far as we know the Lusitanians spent the remainder of their lives as slaves.[41]

One of the most prominent supporters of the unsuccessful bid to free these slaves was the seventy-five-year-old Marcus Porcius Cato, a senior statesman and vocal champion of stern virtue. He was also one of the key figures in the attempt to prosecute Galba for his actions. The details are now obscure, and it is unclear whether or not this led to a trial or was a battle fought in the Senate and at informal public meetings. Cato had governed Nearer Spain as consul in 195 BC, so had seen frontier warfare for himself. This was also true of one of Galba's chief defenders, who had more recent experience having governed the same province in 153 BC. Later generations forgot the details of the arguments, and instead only remembered how Galba had played on the sentiments of his audience. He paraded his young sons and foster son and made a tearful speech commending them to the protection of the Roman people if he were to be condemned. Cato wrote that 'but for his employment of boys and blubbering, the accused would have got his deserts'.[42]

Galba went on to win the consulship in 144 BC and his reputation as an orator was greatly increased by his own escape from prosecution. It is worth remembering that he had suffered a serious defeat in 151 BC, reminding us that other factors as well as military victory determined the outcome of elections at Rome. Criticism of his undoubted treachery and cruelty shows that the Romans did believe that the representatives of the Republic should behave according to certain standards. His escape, on the other hand, demonstrates that such concern might well be trumped by political connections, skilful rhetoric or plain sentiment. On the whole Rome's elite were consistently reluctant to condemn one of their own. Even so, his attempt to be sent out again to Further Spain as consul failed due to strong opposition in the Senate.[43]

If Galba claimed that his brutality had been effective in ending the war, this was proved false within a few years as a survivor of the massacre proved himself an extremely capable and charismatic war leader. His name was Viriathus, and from 147 to 139 BC he raided into the Roman province, evading or defeating every army sent against him. As usual the victims of his attacks were Spanish communities, some of which were even persuaded to abandon alliance with Rome and seek his protection. In spite of the slaughter and enslavement of his kindred, Viriathus did not act out of simple hatred of Rome. His aim was the acceptance of his power by the Romans, something he achieved after letting a trapped Roman army go free in 140 BC. For a while the Lusitanian leader was acknowledged as a friend of the Roman people, before an ambitious new governor persuaded the Senate to let him renew the war. Unable to defeat him in battle, the Romans accepted an offer by some of his subordinates to murder Viriathus in return for a reward. These succeeded, but then found it difficult to claim the promised riches, even when they travelled to Rome. The war finally ended when some of the tribesmen surrendered and this time were peacefully resettled on better land.[44]

The death of Viriathus and the destruction of the Celtiberian stronghold of Numantia in 136 BC greatly reduced the frequency of warfare and raiding in both Spanish provinces, at least for a while. It did not altogether remove the problem and smaller-scale banditry or raiding continued, with the threat that this would increase in intensity if ever the Romans appeared weak. Strong garrisons were kept in both provinces for generations to come.[45]

FRIENDS AND RIVALS

'At the moment fear of a war in Gaul is the main topic of conversation [in Rome]; for "our brothers" the Aedui have just fought and lost a battle, and the Helvetii are without doubt armed for war and launching raids into our province.' – *Cicero, 15 March 60 BC.*[1]

'The friendship of the Roman people ought to be a distinction and a security to him, not a hindrance; and he had sought it with that hope.' – *Julius Caesar's version of the speech made by the Germanic leader Ariovistus, late summer 58 BC.*[2]

AMICI – THE FRIENDS OF THE ROMANS

In late summer 58 BC a Germanic king agreed to meet a Roman proconsul. The two men were in eastern Gaul, not far from the west bank of the River Rhine, and both were intruders to the region. Ariovistus, the German warlord, had arrived more than a decade earlier, called in to aid a Gallic tribe in a conflict with its neighbours, but had since come to dominate his allies and their enemies alike. The Roman was Caius Julius Caesar and he was a long way from his province of Transalpine Gaul. It was the first time that a Roman governor and his army had marched into this part of Gaul, and they had come in considerable force. He had 4,000 locally raised cavalry supplied by the Gallic tribes, other foreign auxiliaries and six Roman legions – since the enfranchisement of the Italian allies the old *alae* had vanished and now all Italians served as legionaries. It was a powerful force, buoyed by a victorious campaign fought earlier in the year. Ariovistus had also collected a large army of his own warriors, and they too were confident and accustomed to victory.[3]

The armies camped about a day's march apart, but they were not at war, nor had their peoples ever fought each other in the past. As recently as 59 BC the German leader had been formally recognised by the Senate as king and 'friend of the Roman people' – *amicus populi romani*. Caesar had presided as consul over the session and probably proposed the vote to favour Ariovistus in this way. Even so there was wariness on both sides and it had taken prolonged negotiation via messengers to hammer out the details of the meeting. It would take place on the solitary hill in an otherwise open plain an equal distance between their two camps. Only ten men would accompany each leader, and the rest of their escort was to consist only of horsemen. Ariovistus claimed that it would be too easy for a crowd of infantry-men to surround and capture him if they chose. Not everyone was inclined to trust Rome's much-vaunted *fides*, and the German had not become so successful a war leader by taking unnecessary risks.

Caesar agreed to these terms, fearing that otherwise Ariovistus would refuse to meet him at all. Unwilling to entrust his own safety to allied horsemen, he took some of their horses and gave them to men from one of his legions, the *Tenth*. The reliability of the legion-aries was more important than their inexperience when it came to fighting as cavalry, but then this was supposed to be a parley, not a fight. Caesar tells us that the soldiers joked that he was making them *equites* – the social class just below the Senate, named because origin-ally these wealthy men had provided the legions with their cavalry. By the first century BC equestrians served only as senior officers, and even the minimum property qualification for this status represented the equivalent of hundreds of years of pay for an ordinary soldier. For a while the *Tenth* took the nickname *equestris*, although few if any of its legionaries would ever rise so high.[4]

We know far more about this episode than most other incidents on the frontiers of Rome's empire because Caesar wrote an account of it in the first book of his *Commentaries on the Gallic War*. It is more than likely that this was published early in 57 BC, although some scholars argue that all seven books of the *Commentaries* were written together and released when his campaigns in Gaul were almost over at the end of the decade. Even if that was the case, this still represents a detailed narrative of what happened, written by one of the key participants and set down relatively soon after the events occurred. If Caesar was scarcely an independent reporter, concerned to be fair in everything he wrote, he was there, and so for once we are not dealing with fragmentary accounts set down a century or more later by authors who had never even visited the region. He wrote for an audience of contemporary Romans, none of whom were ever likely to question the fundamental rightness of the expansion of Rome's power. The *Commentaries* were intended to persuade Caesar's fellow citizens – especially those whose votes carried the greatest sway in elections – that the proconsul was a loyal, spectacularly talented and successful servant of the Republic. He could not invent or distort the truth too grossly, since plenty of his officers regularly wrote letters home and not all were too well disposed to their commander. The basic narrative is probably close to the truth, or at least the truth as the Romans saw it.[5]

Others, especially Ariovistus, would no doubt have told the story differently, but then there is nothing unusual in all our sources coming from the Roman or Greek side. Other accounts add very little that does not ultimately seem to derive at second or third hand from Caesar, and even these few fragments fit well with his version. Archaeology also broadly confirms the picture he paints of Gaul in this period. One of the most striking features is the large number of big walled towns or *oppida*, with signs of considerable industrial activity, making them economic as well as political centres. The impression, confirmed in Caesar and other written sources, is of developing states governed by elected magistrates and minting coins conforming to Roman weights and standards.[6]

Trade was conducted both locally and over long distances, especially between the *oppida*. There was also considerable contact with the Mediterranean world. Truly vast quantities of wine went north into Gaul from Italy. One scholar estimated that more than 40,000,000 wine amphorae passed up the Rhône and Saône rivers during the first century BC, and this is probably too low a figure. Goods also went the other way, especially metal ores, including the tin vital for making bronze, as well as large numbers of slaves. Tribal states and individual leaders grew rich by controlling the main waterways and levying tolls on goods passing along them. Such wealth readily turned into power. It allowed aristocrats to maintain large numbers of warriors in their household and, unless others could match this strength, gave them the chance to dominate politics within their tribes. If other noblemen were as powerful, then it strengthened the tribe's collective war-making capacity whenever they could be persuaded to work together.[7]

Inevitably the flourishing of trade increased competition between individuals and whole peoples. The Saône ran between the lands of the Sequani and the Aedui, both of whom profited and grew strong from traffic along the river, tying smaller neighbours to them as dependent allies. This led to conflict, which steadily escalated in scale as each tried to take sole control of the waterway. Both tribes were acknowledged 'friends' (*amici*) of the Roman people – as indeed were all the major states and leaders with territory near the province of Transalpine Gaul – but this shared status carried no obligation to be friends with each other. The conflict escalated in scale as allied tribes were drawn in, and over time the Aedui prevailed and this prompted some of the Sequani to seek help from outside. They enlisted the aid of Ariovistus, who brought his war band across the Rhine in return for the promise of land on which to settle. At the start there may not have been more than a few thousand warriors and their families, but over time more came to seek service and reward from this increasingly successful and famous war leader.[8]

The network of large *oppida* trading with each other had extended into the lands of the Germans, but in the generation before Caesar's arrival something had changed. The major towns among the German tribes were abandoned or shrank to far smaller and simpler communities, no longer producing high-quality goods or trading over any great distance. It is not clear why this happened, although a worsening cycle of internal power struggles within these communities offers a plausible explanation. Incursions from aggressive neighbours, whether raiding or migrating in search of better land, may also have played a role. Either of these scenarios – or a combination of both – would readily have thrown up warlords like Ariovistus looking for opportunities as mercenaries and eager to find a permanent home.[9]

His arrival shifted the balance of power back in favour of the Sequani, and eventually, around 61 BC, he inflicted a devastating defeat on the Aedui and their allies, killing many of their leading chieftains. Others began to perceive that the formerly strong Aedui were vulnerable, and in 60 BC they were attacked and defeated by the Helvetii, a people living in what is now Switzerland. This prompted the senior magistrate or *vergobret* of the Aedui to travel to Rome seeking aid. His name was Diviciacus and his tribe was Rome's oldest 'friend' in the region, and more than that were referred to as 'kinsmen' or 'brothers' – perhaps because of some imagined common descent from Trojan refugees. Since their rivals had gained the upper hand through securing foreign aid, the Aedui hoped to restore their fortunes by securing the help of an even more powerful outside force.[10]

They were *amici* of the Roman people, but 'friend' is perhaps not quite the most exact translation of *amicus*, and there were other Latin words with senses closer to our concept of natural friendship. *Amicitia* meant something more akin to associate or an informal ally and was a term commonly employed for alliances between senators. In such a relationship the connection was one of utility rather than deep emotional attachment, and the purpose was political benefit to both parties. Almost invariably one of the two was clearly superior in prestige, influence and wealth, and the term *amicus* was, strictly speaking, reserved for the less important man who sought association with him.[11]

The Romans saw their 'friendships' with outsiders in a similar way, naturally with Rome as the dominant partner, and it was a less clear relationship than a more formal alliance. *Amici* were expected to give support if it was requested, to respect Roman interests and in particular to keep peace with the Romans and not aid anyone who fought them. In return the Romans offered goodwill, occasional

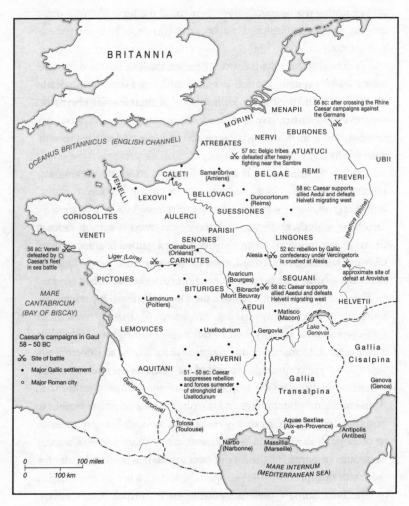

Caesar in Gaul

gifts, and more willingness to listen to embassies than they might to those sent by other leaders and states. Diviciacus met with lead-ing senators – the orator Cicero notes that he discussed the druidic religion with him, for the Gaul was an initiate in the priesthood, if probably not to the highest level (which required many years of study). The delegation from the Aedui had their case heard by the Senate, who expressed concern and gave some limited diplomatic aid. It looks as if the Roman proconsul of Transalpine Gaul in 60 BC met with Ariovistus, or at least communicated by envoys, which paved the way for his recognition as *rex et amicus* when Caesar was consul in the next year.[12]

In this way Ariovistus joined the Aedui and Sequani as 'friends', and the Romans could feel a degree of security for Transalpine Gaul. The threat of major war and upheaval on their borders appeared to have been averted, and with it the danger that this might spill across into the province. Ariovistus pledged to keep the peace with the Aedui and their allies, but the price of this was submission, marked by paying tribute and the handing over of hostages to him. Joined by more and more bands of warriors, the king – it is unclear whether he had always claimed this status or thought that he had won it through his victories – was stronger than any other leader. He demanded and was given more land from the Sequani and took hostages from his old allies as well as enemies to mark their acknowledgement of his greater power.[13]

Many Gauls resented the dominance of Ariovistus because he was a foreign invader, but his warriors had gained such a reputation for ferocity that none wanted to face them in battle. Some leaders were more frustrated because the king's presence made it harder for them to win supremacy in their own tribes, and a few of these began to search for some alternative outside force to match the German warlord. Diviciacus' younger brother Dumnorix looked to the Hel-vetii, in spite of their recent attacks on the Aedui, and married the daughter of one of their leading men. A secret plan was hatched to move a large part of the Helvetii and settle them on new lands they would seize from peoples to the west of the Aedui and Sequani.

Backed by their military might, Diviciacus would be able to control his own people, brushing aside rivals including his brother. Similar ambitions were encouraged in a nobleman of the Sequani. Together these newly installed leaders and the settled Helvetii would shift the balance of power in their favour and be well placed to dominate Gaul. Dumnorix's father-in-law fell from grace and died before the migration began, apparently taking his own life when he realised that rivals in the tribe were too strong for him. Even so the Helvetii persisted with the enterprise, although perhaps the objective was less focused.[14]

'ALL GAUL IS DIVIDED INTO THREE PARTS' – CAESAR'S INTERVENTION

Julius Caesar was particularly ambitious even by the standards of the Roman aristocracy. When passing through a tiny village he is supposed to have remarked that he would rather be first man in that community than second anywhere else, including Rome. Caesar spent borrowed money on a spectacular scale to buy popularity, and by the time he became consul his debts were huge. Apart from the usual aristocratic desire for glory, he needed the spoils of victory so that he could repay his creditors from the profits. An informal agreement with the two most influential men in the Republic, Pompey and Crassus, helped arrange for him to receive the combined provinces of Illyricum and Cisalpine Gaul for five years. This was awarded by a vote of the Popular Assembly rather than the Senate, so was not subject to annual revision. It would later be extended for another five years. It is likely that he planned to use Illyricum as his main base and to campaign in the Balkans, where the Dacian King Burebista was carving out a large empire for himself. Then the governor of Transalpine Gaul died in office, and the Senate decided to add this province to Caesar's command. No doubt his friends among the senators helped to secure this decision, but it is doubtful if anyone imagined that it would have such repercussions.[15]

In March 58 BC, news reached Caesar outside Rome that the Helvetii had begun to migrate and had requested permission to pass through part of Transalpine Gaul, pledging not to molest the provincials in any way. This does seem to have surprised him and the Romans in general. He hurried to the spot, delaying the migrants until he was able to shift his legions across the Alps to face them. Then he refused the Helvetii admission to the Roman province, forcing them to take a longer and more difficult route through the territory of the Sequani. Dumnorix helped to negotiate a deal to permit this, the Helvetii and Sequani exchanging hostages as a mark of goodwill.[16]

Elsewhere the migrants behaved less well. The Allobroges, a people forming part of Transalpine Gaul, as well as the Aedui and another tribe dependent on them, all sent envoys to Caesar complaining that the Helvetii were plundering their territory and taking captives as they passed. The proconsul needed a war, and protecting Rome's allies was an entirely proper reason to fight one. Caesar led his army out of his province and pursued the Helvetii, defeating them in a hard-fought battle not far from Bibracte, the principal *oppidum* of the Aedui. The migrants were forced to return to their homeland, apart from a sub-group whom he permitted to settle among the Aedui at the latter's request.[17]

Diviciacus and other Aeduan leaders who had appealed for Caesar's aid found themselves restored to prominence in the aftermath of this victory. Others were less pleased. Caesar claims that Dumnorix had worked to help the Helvetii defeat his army. In a private interview conducted with the aid of a trusted equestrian of Gallic descent from the Roman province, Caesar let Diviciacus persuade him not to punish his younger brother. This was another favour granted to an open ally of Rome, who pleaded on behalf of brotherly love, but also gave the more pragmatic reason that if Dumnorix was executed no one would believe that he had not asked Caesar to punish him in this way. The decision confirmed Diviciacus' influence with the newly arrived and powerful Romans, demonstrating the advantages to be gained by friendship with Rome and Caesar in particular. At the same time it weakened the younger brother's prestige, since he had needed to be protected. Covertly, Caesar also arranged for spies to watch Dumnorix in the future.[18]

Envoys came from many neighbouring tribes to congratulate Caesar on his success. After holding a council, the debates of which were held in secret, some chieftains came to him and appealed for aid against Ariovistus. Diviciacus was their spokesman, stating that he was the only one who had not given a family member as hostage to the Sequani and Ariovistus, or sworn an oath not to seek Roman help. Encouraged by Caesar, the other leaders supported him, making the same appeal with tears in their eyes. Some of the Sequani were there, but they remained silent out of fear of Ariovistus, who had a reputation for torturing hostages to death when angered.[19]

Caesar promised to help and claims that he believed it was possible to do this peacefully. He sent envoys to Ariovistus and for the first time requested a meeting at an arranged spot. The king refused, saying that it was too difficult for him to muster his army and move outside his own territory. Apart from that, if Caesar wanted to see him, then surely it was up to Caesar to travel to him. Ariovistus 'wondered what business Caesar and the whole Roman people might have in a part of Gaul he had conquered in war'. The proconsul replied with a reminder of the great favour done to him in 59 BC when the Senate had hailed him king and friend, and promised lasting gratitude and friendship if he now granted Rome's requests. These were for him to return the hostages to the Aedui, permit the Sequani to return the hostages they held, and refrain from aggression against the Aedui and their allies. The offer ended with a scarcely veiled threat, stating that it was his duty not to 'ignore the injuries suffered by the Aedui'.[20]

A warlord cannot be seen to give in to threats, for he relies on the fear his strength inspires in others. Ariovistus' messengers re-stated his claim to have won his dominance through victory. The Romans would not tolerate an outsider interfering in lands they had conquered, and so neither would he submit to the same thing. He would not return the hostages, but nor would he attack the Aedui as long as they kept their side of the treaty they had agreed after he defeated them. If they broke their word, then not even their special relationship with Rome would save them, for he and his warriors had never yet been defeated. Caesar's advance and interference in Gaul had already damaged his revenue, probably from disruption of the river trade.

A modern reader tends to be struck by the reasonable if blunt tone of Ariovistus' messages, where he asks for no more than the same licence the Romans took for themselves. At one point he talks of 'his province' as equivalent to Caesar's province. Contemporary Romans might well have understood the logic, but would never have accepted the sense. Instead they would have seen this as dangerous pride in a barbarian who did not realise his inferiority to Rome or the proper balance inherent in friendship with the Republic. Caesar is careful to emphasise the difference between the Gauls and Germans, the latter being less settled, culturally simpler and inherently more warlike, very numerous and eager for the more fertile lands of Gaul. The picture he paints is greatly exaggerated, sometimes altogether wrong, and often shown to be much more complicated even in his own narrative.

Exaggerating the distinction helped Caesar to justify his own actions. The nobility of the Gallic tribes were locked in an ongoing competition for supremacy, many aspiring to the permanent power of kings rather than the temporary influence of magistrates. Incursions by large numbers of warlike Germans threatened to make this already simmering instability boil over into chaos, unbalancing the networks of alliances and friendships surrounding and protecting the Roman frontier. More importantly, tribes on the move might chose to come through Gaul towards Italy itself. In the late second century BC, the Cimbri and Teutones, peoples of Germanic origin, had smashed a succession of Roman armies, invading Transalpine Gaul and then crossing the Alps into Italy before they were defeated. The fear they had caused – evoking folk memories of the Gallic sack of Rome in 390 BC – was still within living memory in Caesar's day.

In the *Commentaries* Caesar reminds his readers of this episode and makes it clear that he will do everything in his power to prevent a

repeat of it. From the beginning he sets down the Rhine as a boundary that no more Germans must be allowed to cross. He tells us that
his main reason for returning the Helvetii back to their homeland
was to prevent Germans from settling there and so establishing themselves right next to the Roman province. News that more bands of
warriors and their families were coming to join Ariovistus, and that
he was demanding that the Sequani provide land for them, prompted
the proconsul to march with his army towards the German king.
Ariovistus and his followers were not simply Germans, but Suebi, a
group of tribes renowned for their great numbers and their warlike
nature – in short, in Caesar's version they were more 'barbarian' even
than the other Germans. The character of the new arrivals was soon
revealed when they began raiding the Aedui in spite of the latter's
treaty with the king.[21]

Caesar pushed on, hurrying to reach the Sequani's main *oppidum*
at Vesontio (modern Besançon) as soon as he heard that Ariovistus
had mustered his army and was also heading there. Arriving first,
he paused to secure supplies for his army. In the next few days a
mood of despair spread among his officers and began to filter down
through the ranks, sparked by the tales told by Roman traders in the
town, who spoke of the immense size and ferocious fighting prowess of the Germans. Some also questioned whether the proconsul
should have led his army so far from Transalpine Gaul. As consul
Caesar himself had redrafted the law regulating the conduct of
provincial governors, repeating the existing ban on a governor from
fighting a war outside his province without explicit instructions from
the Senate. It is doubtful that his actions truly broke this rule, since
some discretion was granted to the man on the spot and his *Commentaries* present everything he did as not only in Rome's interest, but
in accordance with earlier decisions of the Senate. By a mixture of
bluff and shaming them – he claimed that he would march on with
just the *Tenth* if the other legions were too afraid to follow – Caesar
snapped his men out of their mood and the army left Vesontio to
confront Ariovistus.[22]

The proconsul claims that he still hoped to resolve matters through negotiation. Even so he took precautions, following a route recommended by Diviciacus that was longer, but passed through terrain less suited to ambush. A week later their scouts sighted Ariovistus' army some twenty-four Roman miles away. German messengers appeared informing him that the king was now ready to have the meeting Caesar had requested – in a sense, the Roman had come to him just as Ariovistus had demanded. Over the next five days they set down the terms for the parley, just as we saw at the start of the chapter. Caesar came with his newly mounted legionaries, and then rode forward to the mound with just a handful of companions. One was an interpreter, and the discussion was conducted in the Celtic language since Ariovistus was fluent after a dozen years in Gaul.[23]

Caesar began by reminding the king of the privilege bestowed when he was granted recognition and friendship by Rome. Yet the Aedui were older and very close friends of the Romans, and had always been the foremost tribe in Gaul. 'It was the habit of the Roman People to desire that their allies and friends should not only not lose status, but should gain in influence, dignity and honour.' He repeated his demand that hostages be returned, the Aedui be free from attack, and no more German warriors be permitted to cross the Rhine and swell the king's followers.

Ariovistus defended himself by saying that he had been invited into Gaul in the first place, had fought only when attacked and expected the defeated tribes to give him only what they had promised:

> The friendship of the Roman people ought to be an honour and a distinction to him, and not a penalty, and he had requested it with that hope. If because of the Roman people he was to be deprived of tribute and made to return the hostages, then he would recant his friendship with the Roman people as readily as he had sought it.

He brought warriors into Gaul purely to defend himself, not to wage wars of conquest. He was in Gaul before the Romans. 'Never before had an army of the Roman people come outside the borders of their province. . . . This was his province, just as that was ours.' The king declared himself 'not so much of a barbarian' not to know that for all the talk of the Aedui as brothers, they had not helped the Romans in recent wars nor had Rome assisted them against him and the Sequani. Caesar claimed to want peace, but it was hard to believe that he had not come to fight a war. Yet peace was possible if Caesar withdrew and left Ariovistus to enjoy the dominance he had won in Gaul, in which case he would be generous in reward and willingly fight campaigns on his behalf.

Caesar responded by asserting in fact that the Roman presence in the wider region was well established and Ariovistus was the newcomer. However, after a victory won over the Arverni and Ruteni, who lived near the western borders of Transalpine Gaul, the Senate had decided against occupation and granted the right for the peoples of Gaul to live in freedom under their own laws and leaders. At this point one of the proconsul's men told him that Ariovistus' horsemen were drifting forward and lobbing missiles at the legionaries of the *Tenth*. The talks broke up as each side rode to safety. Given the differences between the leaders, it seems unlikely that more discussions would have led to any compromise. When Ariovistus asked for new talks a couple of days later, Caesar did not want to risk going in person. He sent two trusted representatives – one of them the same man who had interpreted at the private meeting with Diviciacus – in his place. Ariovistus accused them of being spies and had them put in chains. Then he advanced to camp closer to Caesar's position and soon began to threaten his supply line.[24]

For a while the armies manoeuvred, fighting several small actions, until they clashed in a major battle. Caesar and his legions won, and ruthlessly pursued the enemy as they fled to the Rhine – the cavalry provided by his Gallic allies leading the chase and the slaughter. Ariovistus escaped across the river, but two of his wives and a daughter were killed and another daughter taken prisoner. His power was for ever broken, for a warlord cannot afford to be routed, and he seems to have died at some point in the next few years. The two imprisoned Roman envoys were released safe and sound, one claiming that German wise women had cast lots three times to see whether they should burn him alive, but that luckily each time the signs had told them to wait. This is one of the few anecdotes of barbarian savagery told by Caesar, and on the whole he avoids embellishing his narrative with descriptions of the strange appearance or behaviour of the tribes he encountered. For instance, he nowhere mentions the fondness of Suebian men for tying their long hair into a knot on the top or side of their head. He does claim that during the battle the warriors' wives watched the fighting from carts, calling out to their menfolk not to let them become slaves of the Romans, but this is a rare concession to colourful description of his enemies.[25]

ALLIES AND ENEMIES

Caesar had another victory – he ends the first book of the *Commentaries* stating simply that he had completed two great wars in a single season. It is hard to say whether he had always hoped to provoke Ariovistus to fight. If the German king had proved willing to accept the proconsul's demands and thus demonstrate his submission to the superiority of Rome, then this would in itself have been a major and honourable achievement. At its best, it would have been confirmed at a ceremony where Caesar sat on a platform surrounded by the standards and serried ranks of parading legionaries, making plain the majesty of Rome and Ariovistus' proper understanding of what it meant to be a friend of the Romans. There was glory in such a moment – if little in the way of loot – and following on from the earlier defeat of the Helvetii it would have added lustre to Caesar's reputation. We have to be careful not to assume that his victory over the Germans was inevitable. The fighting was close, and at this stage Caesar was still a fairly inexperienced commander and a stranger to most of his soldiers – hence the near-mutiny at Vesontio. When he arrived in Gaul, few if any would have guessed that he would prove to be so brilliant and successful as a general, let alone how far his armies would range. There is a fair chance that Caesar was still

contemplating shifting the focus of his operations away from Gaul
and back to the frontier in Illyricum.[26]

That did not happen, and the pattern of his first interventions in
Gaul was repeated time and again over the next few years. Over the
winter reports came to him that the Belgic tribes were exchanging
hostages and 'conspiring' against the Roman people. Most likely
the arrival of a Roman army so close to their territory – the legions
wintered among the Sequani – appeared to the Belgians as a direct
threat. It was certainly not something they could ignore, and the
leaders of one tribe decided to deal with the new situation in a different way. The Remi sent a deputation to Caesar and surrendered
themselves to the *fides* and might of the Roman people, offering hostages as surety as well as practical support such as grain to feed his
soldiers. They also provided him with information about the plans
and strengths of the other Belgic tribes.[27]

Caesar took care to treat the Remi well, force-marching troops to
protect one of their *oppida* when it was threatened by warriors from
the other tribes. Besieging the main town of another tribe, the Sues-
siones, he accepted their surrender readily when the Remi spoke up
on their behalf. Soon afterwards he similarly was generous in the
terms he gave to the Bellovaci, when Diviciacus of the Aedui es-
poused their cause. Leaders and peoples who welcomed Rome and
proved loyal and supportive did very well out of Caesar's presence.
A favour done on behalf of the Aedui or Remi placed the recipients
in their debt as well as that of Caesar and Rome. Simply having to
request it made clear their acceptance of Rome's superiority. In the
next few years the Aedui were restored to pre-eminence in central
Gaul, with many other peoples placed under obligation to them.
The Remi rose to be second only to the Aedui in matters of status.[28]

The presence of a Roman army, let alone its advance into a
region, could not be ignored, especially when it was strong and led
by so energetic and aggressive a governor as Caesar. Although only
a few other proconsuls ever enjoyed comparably long and large-
scale provincial commands, his behaviour was not fundamentally
different from that of other governors granted lesser resources and

shorter spells in office. The Romans were strong and might well prove willing to intervene and shatter the existing balance of power. Their friends – at least those who behaved in a suitably submissive way – might be able to harness this strength to their own advantage. In every province the Romans were met with leaders and communities who wanted their support. Through winning Caesar's trust, Diviciacus regained the prominence he had lost in competition with his brother and other leaders. The Aedui as a whole regained their prestige and influence over other tribes because they were seen as able to win favours from the Romans. Other tribes, such as the Remi, also did well, and so did individual noblemen. Caesar's favour was enough to raise some chieftains to be tribal leaders and kings.[29]

It is a mistake to view this process purely from the viewpoint of Roman expansion, and with the benefit of hindsight to see the creation of the empire as inevitable. In 58 BC few were likely to have guessed that Gaul would be ruled by Rome for the next 500 years. Roman intervention did not always translate into a permanent military presence instead of simply a system of alliances with independent peoples. Far more importantly, we must not assume that feelings towards Rome were foremost in the minds of leaders in Gaul or anywhere else. Noblemen were competing for rank and pre-eminence among their own peoples long before Caesar arrived. A wider aristocracy and the institutions of a state had in relatively recent memory supplanted the rule of kings, but the dream of achieving monarchy remained an attractive one for many. Tribes fought with tribes for dominance, to control valuable assets, or simply to protect themselves by intimidating potential aggressors. None of this was created by Rome, let alone by Caesar, although the growth of trade with the developed economies of the Mediterranean world may have escalated competition and war by increasing the prizes falling to the successful.

When Caesar chose to intervene against the Helvetii a new factor was introduced to this ongoing competition. Leaders and whole peoples had the choice between welcoming or resisting it. It was difficult for anyone to ignore the arrival of the legions, and attempts to stand apart risked an existing local rival harnessing Roman power for their own benefit, giving them a great advantage. On balance, well-established rivalries and old grudges counted for far more than attitudes to Rome. Exactly the same was true of the arrival of the Helvetii or Ariovistus and his Germans – better if possible to come to terms with them before competitors did.

Plenty of men did well from aligning themselves with Caesar and Rome. Those with existing connections such as Diviciacus and the Aedui in general were very well placed to achieve this – as indeed did the Sequani after the defeat of Ariovistus. The relationship between the Remi and Rome was new, since they lived too far from Transalpine Gaul for there to have been any earlier contact, but they nevertheless benefited on a grand scale. Apart from backing well-disposed leaders and having to provide soldiers – usually cavalry – and supplies on request, there was no interference in internal affairs.

Yet for all those who gained by friendship with the newly arrived Romans, there were others who lost out. Ariovistus' recent acknowledgement by Rome was trumped by the coincidence of the Aedui's older link and Caesar's current ambitions. Had the Helvetii not migrated and prompted the proconsul to respond, he might well have focused entirely on the Balkans and let the status quo in Gaul continue. Dumnorix had hoped to gain through support from the Helvetii once they established themselves. Instead they were defeated and he watched as his brother once again became ascendant in their tribe. Diviciacus may well have been dead by 54 BC, when his younger brother assured the ruling council of the Aedui that Caesar planned to install him as their king. In fact the proconsul continued to be suspicious of him and was determined that he should be one of the Gallic noblemen to accompany the Roman army when it crossed to Britain that summer. Dumnorix tried to avoid this, and then spread rumours that the Romans planned to kill these men once they were out of sight of the rest of Gaul. Meeting in secret with others, he wanted them to swear an oath to join together and act for Gaul, implying the expulsion of Caesar and his army. Several of the men informed on him to the proconsul to prove their own loyalty. Dumnorix slipped away from the camp, but was caught and killed when he resisted his pursuers. Caesar had given explicit orders allowing them to do this if he could not be brought back alive. The band of Aedui with him returned to the army and continued to serve alongside the legions.[30]

In spite of the circumstances of his death, Dumnorix appears only to have become a clear enemy of the Romans at a late stage, when he found that his ambitions were blocked by Caesar's distrust. A similar situation occurred a little earlier in 54 BC among the Treveri, a people famous for their excellent cavalry, who had sought alliance with the Romans three years before. Two chieftains were now competing for primacy over the tribe, and one of them, Cingetorix, decided to go to Caesar and pledge his loyalty. The other, his father-in-law Indutiomarus, began raising bands of warriors to fight and win control of the tribe through civil war. He only changed his mind when a steady stream of aristocrats going to Caesar made him doubt that he had sufficient support to win such a struggle. Finally he too went to the Roman camp, bringing as requested 200 hostages, including his son and other relatives, and pledging his loyalty. In meetings with the tribal nobility, Caesar persuaded them to back Cingetorix. It was a reward for loyalty, but also a pragmatic decision that it was better to have a reliable man – and one in his debt – leading the tribe.[31]

Indutiomarus resented the eminence of his rival, and the consequent diminishing of his own status and influence. He did not see the favour shown by the Romans to Cingetorix as the end of the game. Later in the same year the king appointed by Caesar to rule the Carnutes tribe was killed by ambitious noblemen after a two-year reign. The Senones tried to do the same thing to the king imposed on them by the proconsul, although in this case their king managed to escape to the Roman camp. Indutiomarus knew that it was unwise to act alone, since no single tribe stood a chance against Caesar's army, and apart from that he could not be sure of more than a fraction of his own people. He tried without success to persuade some of the German leaders from the far side of the Rhine to support him with their warriors. He did manage to convince two chieftains in a neighbouring Gallic tribe, the Eburones, to attack the force of one and a half Roman legions wintering in their territory. The annihilation through treachery of this garrison gave Indutiomarus enough popularity to expel Cingetorix and win leadership of the Treveri. The success proved brief, for when he attempted to attack another Roman fort he was specifically targeted and killed by a carefully prepared sally.[32]

Local rivalries, rather than hostility or affection for Caesar and Rome, seem to have been the driving force behind the power struggles within the tribes. Decisions were made on a pragmatic assessment of personal advantage and the prospects of success. As the legions approached, the Senones began to mobilise their forces, but realised that they were not ready so sent to Caesar offering to surrender. In a familiar pattern the Aedui spoke up for them and so the request was granted. The Remi spoke up for the Carnutes, similarly securing them peace in return for handing over hostages. War was waged on the Treveri, now led by a relative of Indutiomarus – presumably one not given over as a hostage. They were defeated, and he fled to take shelter among the Germans. Caesar reinstalled Cingetorix at the head of the tribe. The territory of the Eburones was devastated, and at the end of the year the proconsul ordered the execution of Acco, the principal leader of the coups among the Senones and Carnutes. He was beaten to death in a public display of Roman retribution.[33]

RESISTING ROME

By the winter of 53–52 BC, the mood of the Gallic aristocracy shifted. Men who had welcomed Caesar's arrival and done well from his support and protection now realised that this was to be no short intervention. The Romans appeared to be in Gaul to stay, and it seemed unlikely that they would withdraw back to Transalpine Gaul even when Caesar's term of command expired. Dumnorix had been killed for refusing to obey Caesar and Acco executed, demonstrating the Romans' willingness to dispose of even the most distinguished chieftains as it suited them. Neither man had been fighting against Rome when punishment was inflicted. In essence there was a realisation that Gaul had been conquered, similar to the change of heart when the Sequani understood that their ally Ariovistus had become their overlord. This was a blow to pride, especially since the Romans – like the German war leader – had again and again claimed to have intervened only to protect their allies. Even Caesar felt that it was natural for the Gauls, like all men, to fight for their freedom – not that this ever led him or his fellow citizens to question whether it was right for them to take it away.

At this late stage, hatred of the Roman invaders spread. The first organised meetings occurred secretly in the territory of the Carnutes. It is possible that there was a religious element, for it was among this people that the druidic cult traditionally assembled, and their authority in arbitrating disputes within and between tribes had been usurped by Caesar. Yet even now there remained an important element of pragmatism, just as there had been from the start. Caesar had prevented the Helvetii from shifting the balance of power in central Gaul, removed Ariovistus and stopped other Germanic groups from forcing their way across the Rhine. Leaders and tribes who had gained from Roman backing wondered whether this connection would continue to be so advantageous. It imposed limits on how much power an ambitious leader could achieve, especially outside his own people. From the beginning Gallic chieftains had matched Caesar in cynicism, using him just as much as he had used them. For many it now seemed that his usefulness to them was outweighed by the better prospects offered by his expulsion from the region.[34]

The main leader of the rising that followed was Vercingetorix of the Arverni. Caesar mentions that his father had been one of the most important chieftains in all Gaul, and claims that the son had staged a revolution within the tribe to make himself king. Another source says that the proconsul had shown him a good deal of favour and support. This was certainly true of Commius, another of the prominent commanders of the Gauls during this campaign. Caesar had employed him on a number of important tasks, and then further demonstrated his faith by making Commius king of the Atrebates and subjecting neighbouring tribes to his supervision.[35]

At first the Aedui stood apart from the war with the Romans, more concerned with a bitter dispute for the office of chief magistrate or *vergobret*. In spite of the ongoing campaign, the proconsul went in person to arbitrate, deciding in favour of one of the two candidates. His efforts to keep the Aedui firm in their alliance with Rome failed when the newly confirmed *vergobret* decided to join the rebellion. Caesar says that the new *vergobret* had received gifts from the Arverni which he shared with many young noblemen, speaking to them of their lost freedom. It may well have grated that the magistrate's appointment had needed to be confirmed by the proconsul – something which Caesar no doubt expected would win gratitude. Turning against the Romans would demonstrate that he was his own man. On top of that the majority of tribes had already joined the alliance against Rome and things did not appear to be going well for Caesar. If the legions were defeated then it was better to have joined the rising early enough to claim a share of the credit for the victory – being left as the most prominent ally of a defeated Rome was not an appealing prospect.[36]

The Aedui turned against Caesar in a series of impulsive acts amid a flood of false rumours. Almost immediately they challenged Vercingetorix for control of the campaign, trying to exploit the fact that they held many hostages on behalf of the proconsul and so were able to send these back to their homes. Even so, this attempt failed and they co-operated rather sullenly in the rest of the fighting. The Remi – recent friends and never spoken of as 'brothers' – stayed loyal to the Romans, as did their allies the Lingones. All of the other tribes joined the rising, but in spite of this Caesar's luck, skill and the stubborn determination of his legions ended the war in Roman victory.[37]

Vercingetorix surrendered and was held as a prisoner until he was executed in Caesar's delayed triumph in 46 BC. Commius fought on, survived two attempts to kill him – one when he had agreed to negotiate with the Romans. Eventually he escaped to Britain, declaring that he never wished to see the face of another Roman. Many tribes were severely punished by the enslavement of their captured warriors and the levying of heavy penalties. Caesar was lenient to the Arverni and the Aedui, releasing some 20,000 prisoners he had taken from them. New hostages were demanded and the proconsul spent the winter at Bibracte, but overall both tribes continued to enjoy a favoured status under Roman rule. In the short term legions were stationed in or near their territory to keep a close eye on them. Two years were spent in mopping-up operations and intensive diplomacy:

> Caesar had one main aim, keeping the tribes friendly, and giving them neither the opportunity nor cause for war. . . . And so, by dealing with the tribes honourably, by granting rich bounties to the chieftains, and by not imposing burdens, he made their state of subjection tolerable, and easily kept the peace in a Gaul weary after so many military defeats.[38]

Although there were revolts in Gaul in the decades after Caesar left, they were not on the same scale as the great rebellion in 53–52 BC, and it never again looked as if the Romans might be driven from the province. Some of this rested on the fear of Rome's military might, and also because conditions were made acceptable to the Gauls, and especially the aristocracy. There continued to be very little interference in the day-to-day affairs of the tribes. Only occasionally did the constraints on chieftains' ambitions provoke men to the desperate alternative of resorting to violence.[39]

Caesar overran Gaul in less than a decade. He spoke of 'pacifying' regions far from the borders of the Roman province, and treated as an act of hostility any welcome short of immediate surrender to his power. The speed of this conquest came from a combination of the peculiar political situation which gave a governor such a long command and the restless energy and skill of Caesar. Elsewhere in the empire things often happened more slowly, sometimes over several generations, but the processes themselves were similar. Regional and local politics were dynamic and saw ongoing competition, often vigorous and sometimes openly violent. When the Romans appeared on the scene they simply added a new element to this. In many cases it was not seen as the most important factor, and only hindsight makes us assume this.[40]

Leaders and communities in the wider world did their best to exploit Roman power for their own advantage. Sometimes they sought Roman help, like the Aedui against the Sequani, because their neighbours benefited from the support of some other external power. Equally, a Roman intervention on behalf of one group made others search for outside help to counter this. In most cases attitudes to Rome – or indeed the other powers – were far less important than the desire for short-term gain. Local ambition was the driving force, and this is something that would continue as a theme throughout the centuries to come.

Caesar exploited the rivalries within and between tribes, as did other governors in Gaul and throughout the empire. Rome did not always choose to intervene, and acknowledgement of friendship did not guarantee aid when requested. Cynicism and self-interest were common on both sides – something which should not surprise us. The leaders of the rising in Gaul hoped to be great and powerful men if they won. In most tribes there were others who managed to switch sides in time or who remained loyal. We hear of one Arvernian chief described as 'most friendly to the Roman people' who handed over a rebel leader to the Romans in 51 BC. Some tribes suffered badly – the archaeological record for the Belgic region suggests that this was devastated during Caesar's campaigns. Yet these were not wars of extermination. Most tribes were still there at the end of the wars, and many continued to prosper. Old friends of the Roman people flourished and new ones joined them.

TRADERS AND SETTLERS

'Poor men of humble birth sail across the seas to shores they have never seen before, where they find themselves among strangers, and cannot always have with them acquaintances to vouch for them. Yet such trust have they in the single fact of their citizenship, that they count on being safe, not only where they find our magistrates ... and not only among their own countrymen ... : no, wherever they find themselves, they are confident that this one fact will be their defence ... to cry "I am a Roman citizen" ...'
– *Cicero*, 70 BC.[1]

CIVIS ROMANUS SUM – ROMANS ABROAD

The campaigns in Gaul made Julius Caesar immensely wealthy and gave him glory on a grand scale. His victories were dazzling, skilfully advertised and resulted in the proclamation of unprecedented numbers of days of public thanksgiving at Rome. By the middle of the first century BC, the careers of men like Marius, Sulla, Pompey and Caesar were making it ever harder to achieve something more spectacular than the victories of the past. Yet the Romans were always especially excited by the news that their legions had marched into new territories and that previously unknown peoples and rulers had submitted to them. Caesar and *nostri* – 'our men', as he described his legionaries – had reached the far north-west coast of Gaul, twice bridged the Rhine to attack the homelands of the Germanic tribes and, most dramatic of all, in 55 and 54 BC landed on the mysterious island of Britain. It did not matter that the expeditions achieved little, that he narrowly avoided disaster, or that he left no garrison behind. Even men who did not care much for Caesar thrilled at the thought of a Roman army crossing the great ocean encircling the three known continents.[2]

Generals won fame by being the first to overrun a region, but in truth they were rarely the first Romans to reach an area, and almost always the trader preceded the soldier. Julius Caesar found merchants or *mercatores* in many of the *oppida* of Gaul, such as the men whose stories fed the panic in his army at Vesontio. One of the two envoys he sent to Ariovistus was a certain Marcus Mettius, chosen because in the past the man had received the hospitality of the German leader. While he may well have been involved in the diplomatic exchanges which led to the king's formal recognition by Rome in 59 BC, Mettius was almost certainly a trader doing business in the area, who had arrived months or probably years earlier.[3]

As we have seen, huge quantities of Italian wine were being sent north into Gaul, and the profits of this trade intensified rivalries in the tribal aristocracies and the great contest for power between the Aedui and Sequani. Roman merchants went at least some of the way with their goods, and it is hard to tell when and how often local middlemen took over. Caesar says that merchants went 'least often' to the lands of the Belgic tribes, and were banned from the territory of one of these peoples, the Nervii. The Germanic tribes on the other side of the Rhine were said to let traders come to them, but were keener to sell the spoils of their raiding than to buy anything. Caesar notes that they had no interest in the big draught horses bred in Gaul, in spite of their obvious superiority to their own small animals. We need to be a little cautious about some of this, for he expressly says that luxuries from the Mediterranean world corrupted a society, invoking a well-established tradition of the purity of simple cultures – a variation on the enduring image of the noble savage. In this case this was not for any sentimental reason. The Belgic and Germanic tribes were less effeminate and so far more dangerous enemies than other peoples in Gaul, which justified Caesar's interventions in these regions and his uncompromising attitude to them.[4]

Caesar does not specify the nationality of the traders who reached – or tried to reach – these tribes, although he does single out imported wine as a corrupting influence. Before his first expedition to Britain he sought information about the island from traders, who were the only people to go there without a very good cause. Merchants were summoned to his camp, but the Roman commander learned very little from them. It does look as if much of the trade with Britain was controlled by the Veneti, a tribe living in the area of modern Brittany, who sailed to trading ports like the one at Hengistbury Head in Dorset. They were famous sailors, but in 56 BC Caesar shattered the tribe, executing many of its leaders and capturing their fleet in a naval battle. Survivors were doubtless unwilling to volunteer information to their conquerors, and the merchants told Caesar only a little about the coastal areas of the south-east, nearest to Gaul. It is possible that some of these men were Roman and carried on small-scale trade with the peoples of that area. Whoever the men were, some of them told the Britons of his plans. Since this prompted several leaders to send envoys promising to provide hostages and submit to the *imperium* of the Roman people, Caesar may well have wanted the news to reach the island, hoping as usual to secure allies before he arrived there.[5]

It is probable that there were Romans doing business in the far north of Gaul, and a few crossing to Britain, even if the Veneti dominated trade across the Channel until their catastrophic defeat at the hands of Caesar. In the years that followed there was a clear shift in trade so that most goods from the Continent went to the south-east of Britain, and sites further to the west, such as the trading post at Hengistbury Head, went into rapid decline. Another consequence of Caesar's campaigns in Gaul was the opening-up of the trade routes to Britain to many more Roman merchants. The quantity of goods shipped there significantly increased, and it also looks as if this produced power struggles among local leaders and kingdoms very similar to those between the Aedui and Sequani.[6]

Caesar was an avid collector of objets d'art, and some said that he went to Britain in the belief that he would find a rich source of high-quality pearls. If the story is true, then it was merely an additional attraction to the glory of carrying Roman arms to such an exotic place, and his hope was disappointed. Cicero commented that the profits to be made from Britain were far less than expected – 'not a scrap of silver in the Island, nor hope of plunder except slaves, but I doubt we'll find any scribes or musicians amongst them' – and although he was talking mainly about the plunder from the expeditions it is likely that he was also thinking of longer-term prospects for trade had the island proved rich in anything worth having. In the second century BC the famous general Scipio Aemilianus – the man who destroyed Carthage and took Numantia – questioned merchants in Transalpine Gaul about the routes to Britain. They told him very little, which is probably once again a reflection of how far this traffic was monopolised by the tribes of Gaul's Atlantic coast. Thus some Roman governors showed an interest in trade with lands beyond the provinces, but there is no evidence that this was ever a primary concern in decisions to expand into new territory. Rome does not seem to have fought wars to open up new markets to Roman businessmen, even if this was usually a consequence of the Republic's expansion.[7]

It was as individuals in the hope of profit and not as representatives of state interests that some Romans travelled far outside the provinces of the Republic. Around the middle of the second century BC rich and readily accessible gold deposits were discovered by the Taurisci, a people living in Noricum – the region centred around the modern Tyrol in Austria. Large numbers of Italians, presumably including many Romans, flocked to the area to work alongside the locals. As far as we can tell they did not bring expertise, only an enthusiastic willingness to work in an effort to become rich, making them more like the 'Forty-niners' than technical supervisors. Polybius says that in just two months the price of gold in Italy plummeted by a third as the market was flooded. This prompted the Taurisci to expel the Italians and work the deposits on their own – whether to control the sheer quantities being extracted or simply to keep the profit to themselves is unclear.[8]

The expulsion was not seen as a hostile act, and there are signs that plenty of Romans and Italians continued to go to Noricum to do business. Diplomatic relations were good. In 113 BC the king of

Noricum was clearly an ally, enjoying ties of hospitality with Rome, prompting a governor to lead a Roman army to aid him against the migrating Cimbri – unsuccessfully as it turned out. The tombstone of a man with the curious name of Pompaius Senator was found in the East Tyrol and has been dated to around 100 BC. The probability is that he was there on business.

Excavations revealed an entire Roman trading settlement outside the Norican hilltop town at the Magdalensberg. Established early in the first century BC, this covered an area some 330 feet by 179 (114 by 55 metres), with shops and houses around a central courtyard. The first buildings were of timber, but later they were rebuilt in stone with cellars for storing merchandise. By the second half of the first century some had plastered walls decorated with good-quality wall paintings showing images of gods, goddesses and figures from myth. The Magdalensberg was probably the seat of the king of Noricum, and the Romans brought in wine and oil in amphorae, functional items such as tools and pots, as well as decorated lamps and expensive black pottery from Etruria. In return the Romans traded for local produce, most of all iron, which was mined and smelted in great quantities there. This trading post gives an indication of the sort of communities set up beyond the provinces, for the area did not come under Roman rule until the end of the century.[9]

There were Roman traders dotted around the world, some as individuals and others congregating in communities, but it is impossible to gauge their numbers. What is certain is that they were never the only merchants at work, for there were always local men, and rarely would the Romans have been the only foreigners. Long-distance trade did not begin with the Romans, but had developed during the Bronze Age and in a few cases even earlier. Massilia (modern Marseilles) was founded by Greeks from Asia Minor in the sixth century BC and soon developed extensive trade links with the tribes on its borders. Although far more successful than most, this was simply one colony among many in a long process that saw Greek settlement all around the shores of the Mediterranean and Black Sea. Some of the colonies were small and primarily farming communities, but most engaged in trade to a greater or lesser extent.[10]

The Phoenicians were the great sailors of the ancient world, and early in the last millennium BC their ships often visited Spain – the Tarshish of the Old Testament – and even went to south-west Britain for tin, which was highly prized because it permitted the making of bronze. Phoenician colonies were established in Spain and North Africa, one of the latter being Carthage, founded perhaps in the eighth century BC. Over time the city outgrew its origins and became an empire and coloniser in its own right. In 509 BC the new Roman Republic signed a treaty with Carthage, which included clauses restricting the Romans and their allies from trading – or raiding, since the two were often linked – beyond Cap Bon in North Africa. Any ships blown off-course beyond this promontory were forbidden to buy anything save what was needed 'for the repair of his ship or for sacrifice, and must depart within five days'. Roman merchants were permitted to go to other areas, but were only to conduct business in the presence of a local official.[11]

Later treaties restricted the Romans and their allies from other specific territories, clearly assuming that otherwise merchants would try their luck there. Some markets and sources of material were jealously guarded, and for a long time only the Carthaginians knew how to reach the north-west coast of Spain, a region rich in mineral resources. On one occasion a ship from the Punic colony of Gades (modern Cadiz) was followed by Roman vessels eager to discover the route. The Carthaginian captain lured them onto a shoal by deliberately running his own ship aground. Escaping on a piece of wreckage, he was rewarded by his city with money equivalent to his losses on the voyage. It looks as if the sailors of Gades kept the secret for some time after they became part of the Roman province, and it was only in the early first century BC that a governor secured all merchants access to the mines in the north-west.[12]

For all the restrictions the treaties placed upon Roman traders, in areas such as Sicily these traded on the same footing as their Carthaginian counterparts. Until the First Punic War, relations were good between the two city-states. A community of Carthaginian merchants was well established at Rome itself, and although most left when war broke out, others returned at the end of each conflict. It is possible that some Romans were established in Carthage and any of the other communities where they were permitted. Numbers may well have been small, and for a long time the sheer scale of Punic trading dwarfed the operations of Roman and Italian merchants. Carthaginian trade was based on the highly organised cultivation of well-irrigated estates in North Africa. The agriculture of Roman Italy was less sophisticated and produced a far smaller surplus for export. Yet Rome continued to grow, so that its population outstripped that of any other state. As time went on, there were simply more and more Romans looking to make money overseas. As the Republic acquired provinces, such men found fresh markets.[13]

MARKETS AND EXCHANGE

Amphorae break, but the fragments are virtually indestructible, and both easy to recognise and very visible in the archaeological record. An ancient shipwreck is more likely to be found if the vessel had a hold full of such large pottery containers. This makes it much easier to find evidence for the traffic in any products carried in amphorae – hence the ease with which we can confirm the shipment of so much Roman wine into Gaul in the first century BC. Other goods – whether slaves, livestock or animal products, clothing and material, minerals or anything else worth transporting – are by their nature almost invisible archaeologically. Literary mentions of such things tend to be vague and of little use in judging the scale of this activity. Thus it is clear that so much Italian wine went into Gaul, but far less clear what went back the other way.

It was said that Gallic leaders were willing to exchange a slave for an amphora of fine wine, although some scholars prefer to see this as the Romans misunderstanding the social obligation on a host to surpass in value any gift presented by a guest. If the estimate of at least 40,000,000 amphorae going into Gaul is remotely correct, then sheer numbers make it impossible that more than a tiny fraction were exchanged in this way, exploiting the cultural obligation of hospitality. We should also remember that Dumnorix of the Aedui based his position on controlling tolls levied on cargo going up the River Rhône. Both the quantity and the profits going to intermediaries indicate commercial transactions rather than exchange of gifts. Most tribes in Gaul – and those in southern Britain – minted coins matching first Greek and then later Roman standards of silver and bronze, so some of this wine may well have changed hands for money as well as goods the merchants wanted to take back with them.[14]

We simply cannot trace much of the trading activity or the commodities sent in either direction, still less understand the scale of such activity. Ornate tableware from the Mediterranean, whether ceramic or more often in silver or other precious metals, is similarly prominent archaeologically in Iron Age Europe, for in the main it was only the rich and powerful who enjoyed items from so far afield. Such things may turn up as grave goods or ritual deposits and are spectacular, but it is harder to say how they reached these places. Some came to tribal rulers as diplomatic gifts. In 169 BC envoys came over the Alps to Rome from a Gallic king or chieftain – Livy, who tells us the story, notes that a century and a half later there was no longer any record of the man's tribe. His name was Balanos, and he offered to help Rome in their current war with Macedonia. A grateful Senate sent in return gifts of 'a golden torque two pounds in weight, a golden bowl weighing four pounds, a horse with decorated tack and a cavalryman's weapons'. We do not know whether Balanos did subsequently aid the Romans' war effort.[15]

Prestigious gifts were a routine part of diplomatic exchanges. In some cases objects presented by Roman envoys may well later have been given by the recipient to cement alliances with other leaders and other tribes, and so travelled further and further away. Others might change hands through warfare as valuable spoils, and indeed in some cases first left the Mediterranean world as loot from raiding. Similar gifts could equally have come from merchants eager to win favour from local rulers in an area where they hoped to operate. Some may even have travelled as goods for trade rather than gifts, but in each of these cases the discovery of the artefacts themselves in an Iron Age context is unlikely to make clear how they arrived.

Diplomatic gifts explain the presence of some precious objects from the Greco-Roman world in lands far from Rome's provinces, but do not alter a picture of large-scale long-distance trade continuing and growing in the last centuries BC. This is reinforced by the frequent and usually incidental mention of Roman and Italian merchants in many areas. In 229 BC ship owners complained to the Senate about the predatory attacks of pirates loyal to the Illyrian Queen Teuta. The merchants were primarily from southern Italy, whose Greek communities had long-established commercial and cultural links with the wider Greek world. This was not the first time they had complained of this ongoing piracy, but matters came to a head when a number of ships were plundered as they lay at anchor in a city stormed by the Illyrians. Some of the traders were killed and others taken prisoner. In 70 BC the orator Cicero claimed that on many occasions 'our ancestors . . . fought great wars . . . because Roman citizens were said to be insulted, her merchant sailors imprisoned, her traders robbed'. No clear examples apart from the Illyrian war appear in our sources, and even this was a little more complicated. Yet in the same speech he also claims that outside the empire, a poor man who raised the cry 'I am a Roman citizen!' (*civis Romanus sum*) would not be harmed even by barbarians. So great was the fear of Rome's power.[16]

In 146 BC the Romans razed Carthage to the ground. A small African province was created and directly administered, but most of the territory to the west was given to an enlarged kingdom of Numidia. Within a generation we hear of substantial Italian trading communities permanently resident in at least two Numidian cities, Cirta and Vaga. Similar groups tend to be more visible in the Greek world, which had a much stronger tradition of setting up inscriptions. A monument found in a small town on Sicily's northern coast was erected in 193 BC to honour the provincial governor by men describing themselves as *Italicei*. Italians appear in many other Greek cities. Around 174 BC the Seleucid King Antiochus IV Epiphanes paid to complete the construction of the Temple of Olympian Zeus – or Olympieion – in Athens. This sort of gesture to shared Hellenic culture was common for the Successor kings who ruled fragments of Alexander the Great's conquests. Yet in this case the contract to do the work was given to a Roman, a certain Cossutius, who was subsequently honoured by the Athenians and so presumably did the job satisfactorily.[17]

Probably the largest concentration of Romans and Italians was on Delos, placed under Athenian jurisdiction and declared a free port by Rome in 166 BC in the aftermath of the Third Macedonian War. In spite of its small size, the island was well placed and had long acted as a major entrepôt for goods going east and west. The Romans were relative latecomers to the communities of foreign merchants established at Delos, but their numbers grew rapidly. Among other things they constructed a complex known as the Agora of the Italians, where a rectangle of double-storied porticoes surrounded an extremely large open and unpaved courtyard.

In the years after it was made a tariff-free port, Delos became the greatest centre of the slave trade in the eastern Mediterranean. The numbers of human beings trafficked through the little island were enormous, even if Strabo's claim that it could process no fewer than 10,000 people in a single day is an exaggeration. Most of the Romans who went to Delos came for the slave trade, although the identification of the Agora of the Italians as a slave market is uncertain, largely because we do not yet know what such a building should look like. Other trades were conducted there as well, and we hear of Romans dealing in olive oil, but it was the buying and selling of human beings that dominated, continuing even after a failed rebellion by slaves in the port in 130 BC.

The profits of overseas expansion allowed Rome's rich to invest in grand rural estates which required a steady supply of servile manpower as a labour force, a demand that could not always be met by war captives. At the same time Rome's expansion destroyed or crippled the great powers of the Hellenistic world, making it harder for them to maintain navies capable of controlling piracy. Rhodes had played an important role in this, but it lost out commercially to the free port of Delos and was less able to fund an effective fleet after 166 BC. Piracy flourished in the eastern Mediterranean, and the pirates took captives whom they sold as slaves, many of them passing through Delos. If the Romans were aware of this then they were not inclined to do anything about it.[18]

There is no sign that being Roman or Italian gave the traders at Delos any advantage over men from other nations. They were more directly connected to the big market for slaves in Italy, but otherwise did business on the same terms as everyone else. Over time, there as elsewhere it became more and more common for men from Italy to be referred to as Romans rather than Italians. In part this reflected the growing numbers of citizens, but until the aftermath of the Social War most Italians continued to lack the franchise. To outsiders it was probably easy to lump all of them together with the City that controlled Italy, ruled several provinces, and had become the most formidable power in the entire Mediterranean world. For similar reasons, non-citizen Italians may have chosen to present themselves as Romans and felt it advantageous in business. Roman dress was distinctive, from the style of shoe to the shape of the tunic and most of all the toga, instead of the various types of cloak favoured in Greece. Even when men settled in communities and took part in local festivals, joining with Greeks and other foreigners to fund dedications in the temples or to thank local officials, most still dressed in these immediately recognisable fashions, setting themselves apart. At whatever distance, they proclaimed themselves as belonging to the great power, both out of pride and in the hope that they would be treated with more respect and care as a result. After the Social War virtually all Italians were Romans in the legal sense, as were the freed slaves they often employed in their businesses.[19]

Whenever a region was turned into a province, the number of Romans active in the area increased dramatically. Apart from the traders already in Gaul, many more followed Julius Caesar's legions, with merchants, investors and money lenders operating on a small or very large scale. Some sold directly to the soldiers – we hear of the men caught at their stalls outside the walls of a winter camp by one surprise attack – while others were there to buy up the spoils of warfare, such as plunder and captives, and still more because they sensed new opportunities opening up. There were clearly far more Romans doing business in Gaul by the end of Caesar's spell as governor. In the great revolt of 53–52 BC these men became targets of the rebels and there were several massacres of Roman civilians. Opportunity was mixed with risks, especially in newly won territory or beyond the provinces.[20]

In spite of the long tradition of establishing citizen and Latin colonies in Italy, the Romans were slow to do this in conquered territory overseas. Even so, communities with less prestigious legal rights were set up. Scipio Africanus settled a large number of convalescent soldiers at Italica (modern Santiponce) after he had driven the Carthaginians from Spain in the Second Punic War. It is hard to know how many soldiers took their discharge – or indeed deserted – to settle in a province where they had served. This probably became more common the longer a man spent there and by the end of the second century BC, when most legionaries were recruited from among the poorest rather than from men of property with farms and families drawing them home. In 171 BC representatives from a group of some 4,000 people claiming to be offspring of Roman soldiers and local women came from Spain to petition the Senate for a settlement of their own. Citizens were not permitted to marry non-citizens, which made their children both illegitimate and foreign, but the Senate was sympathetic. They were settled at Carteia (near Algeciras in the far south), and the community was granted Latin rights – something not otherwise done outside Italy under the Republic.[21]

The first overseas colony for citizens was founded at Carthage in 122 BC, but soon lost its formal status when the man who had introduced the law to create it was killed in a bout of political violence.

However, some settlers had already gone out and been allocated farms, and these families remained even though the community was no longer a colony. In 118 BC Narbo (modern Narbonne) was founded in Transalpine Gaul just three years after the creation of that province. The first settlers were former soldiers, and this was also true of the community set up at Aquae Sextiae (Aix-en-Provence) a few years earlier. In each case the original population was soon swollen by others who visited or chose to live in the area.[22]

In 69 BC the orator Cicero claimed that Transalpine '. . . Gaul is packed with traders, crammed with Roman citizens. No Gaul ever does business independently of a citizen of Rome; not a coin changes hands in Gaul without the transaction being recorded in the books of Roman citizens.' He lists several groups active in the area as well as the colonists – businessmen/bankers (*negotiatores*), tax-collecting companies (*publicani*), farmers (*aratores*) and ranchers (*pecuari*). Although Cicero exaggerated the ubiquity of Roman businessmen in the province, it is clear from other sources that there were a lot of them. Some Romans preceded the arrival of the legions, sometimes by decades or even longer periods. Many more followed the army, hoping to profit through business of many sorts and on a wide range of scales.[23]

ROMAN AND NATIVE

Gallic rebels slaughtered Roman traders and businessmen in 53–52 BC. The civilians were vulnerable, had wealth and possessions worth stealing and were symbols of the Roman conquest. In one case some were enslaved instead of killed, and we do not know whether this was to protect their lives or meant to humiliate them. Cicero claims that Narbo was besieged in the 70s BC, which suggests that even a generation or more after the creation of a province there was sometimes a risk to Romans in the area. One of the purposes of colonies and the informal settlements of citizens in the provinces was to act as garrisons, much as earlier ones had done during the conquest of Italy. More than once we hear of forces being raised from Roman citizens working in a province.[24]

Even traders operating outside the provinces occasionally took on a military significance. In 112 BC a struggle between rival members of the Numidian royal family erupted into civil war. Jugurtha chased his half-brother Adherbal into the city of Cirta and besieged him there, but found it difficult to capture the place because of the resistance of the community of traders – a 'multitude of toga-wearers', as they were called by the historian Sallust. For more than four months the city repulsed all attempts to take it, until the Italians persuaded Adherbal to surrender and trust to the fair arbitration and power of Rome. Sallust says that they were confident of good treatment for themselves because they were Romans. Jugurtha showed no such restraint, torturing his half-brother to death and executing everyone who had fought against him, Italians and Romans included. It took considerable agitation on the part of a popular politician at Rome to force the Senate to act and send an army against Jugurtha. Even so the war proved a long one, and a few years later another community of traders was slaughtered in the town of Vaga.[25]

The largest and most infamous massacre of Roman civilians took place in Asia in 88 BC at the orders of King Mithridates VI of Pontus. An ambitious, capable and ruthless man, Mithridates was one of the last great Successor monarchs in the Hellenistic world and was eager to enlarge his realm. This, combined with the unusually provocative and corrupt behaviour of a Roman governor of Asia and his senior subordinate, swiftly led to war. The Romans were unprepared, reliant mainly on local allies, and were quickly beaten, allowing Mithridates' armies to advance into Asia. The Senate decided to send one of the year's consuls and several legions to deal with the king, but then rivalry for the command led to Rome's first civil war and those same legions marched on Rome itself. For the moment the Romans seemed very weak, while Mithridates was strong.

The king then sent a secret message to all the civic leaders and local governors or satraps throughout Asia, instructing that on a given day:

They should set upon all the Romans and Italians in their towns, and upon their wives and children and their freedmen of Italian birth, kill them and throw their bodies out unburied, and share their goods with King Mithridates. He threatened to punish any who should bury the dead or conceal the living, and proclaimed rewards to informers and to those who should kill persons in hiding. To slaves who killed or betrayed their masters he offered freedom, to debtors . . . the remission of half their debt.[26]

It was claimed that 80,000 died in the ensuing bloodbath. At Ephesus some of the Romans sought sanctuary in the great Temple of Artemis, only to be dragged away from statues of the goddess and slaughtered. At Pergamum their attackers were only a little more squeamish, shooting down with arrows those who clasped the images of Aesculapius, the god of healing, rather than touching them. At Adramyttium fugitives ran out into the sea only to be pursued and killed, the children with them being drowned. In another city it was claimed that the infants were slaughtered first, then the mothers and finally the men. The people of Tralles hired a foreign thug and his band to do the killing for them, who had no scruples about chopping off hands if any of the victims tried to cling to a statue of a god in the hope of sanctuary.

Some Romans changed their distinctive costume and dressed as Greeks in an effort to escape the slaughter – perhaps especially Italians only recently granted the franchise. Few were successful. A former senator named Publius Rutilius Rufus, exiled after being condemned for corruption and extorting money from the provincials while serving in the Asian province, did the same thing and survived. His conviction was considered a great injustice, proved by the fact that he went into exile in the very province where he was supposed to have committed his crimes and was welcomed by the provincials. This goodwill no doubt helped his survival. On the island of Cos, Romans took refuge in another temple to the god of healing and this time were protected by the locals.[27]

No doubt stories grew in the telling, as did the alleged scale of the massacre. Cicero, the source closest in time to the event, does not give a number for the dead, and modern scholars usually assume that it is grossly exaggerated. The same is true of the 20,000 said to have died in Greece and islands including Delos when Mithridates invaded a little later. Whatever the true figure, the total of deaths was clearly considerable, on a far bigger scale that any other massacre of Roman civilians. It is testament to the substantial number of people living and working outside Italy, especially in the provinces. Some would also see it as clear evidence that Rome in general, and these Roman businessmen in particular, were widely loathed by the provincial population, who readily turned on them at the first opportunity.[28]

As we have seen, Romans dressed distinctively, and in some places formed large communities. Such groups did not always hold themselves apart from locals and other foreigners, as joint dedications make clear, but they could also be high-handed. Cicero tells a story of a senator named Caius Verres, who was serving as a *legatus* (or governor's senior representative) in Asia in 79 BC, almost a decade after the massacre. The Roman became obsessed with the unmarried daughter of a local notable, in spite of never having seen the girl, and tried to use force to have her brought to him. His host resisted, and was soon supported by a crowd of townsfolk who drove Verres and his followers out, killing a lictor and injuring several of his attendants. The next day they gathered to lynch the *legatus*, until Romans resident in the place managed to persuade their neighbours to disperse. Up to this point their conduct was reasonable, but later some of them took part in a trumped-up prosecution of the father for assaulting a representative of Rome. The man and his son were found guilty and both executed.[29]

Such gross miscarriages of justice were rare – and as we shall see, Verres was subsequently brought before a Roman court for many more abuses committed while he governed Sicily. A more common cause of ill-feeling was the activity of the *publicani*, the private companies who secured the rights to collect taxes in the provinces, and of the *negotiatores*, the bankers/moneylenders, both sometimes inclined to go to extreme lengths to extract payment from individuals and communities. We shall look at them in more detail in the next chapter, when we consider the Romans' system of administering the provinces, but even other Romans often saw them as greedy.[30]

Yet it is not quite so simple. In 88 BC Mithridates' troops overran Asia Minor, which had become a province of Rome almost half a century earlier in 133 BC. The massacre of the Romans was not the spontaneous reaction of an oppressed population now free to act because of the arrival of liberators. At Ephesus statues of Romans were thrown down, but there was no killing until the order came from the king. There and elsewhere the slaughter was carried out only after specific instructions to the leaders of communities. Some of these were newly installed tyrants or factions supported by the king and eager to justify his trust in them. The rest were faced with a stark choice of obedience or punishment. In the past they had been occupied by the Romans and now they were occupied by the army of Pontus, and in neither case did any one community have a realistic chance of resisting the might of the conqueror in the long run. Rome appeared on the verge of collapse as several years of fighting with the Italian allies was followed by civil war. The legions might never return, for Mithridates was powerful and he could no more be ignored by the peoples of Asia Minor than Ariovistus and Caesar's arrival could be ignored by the tribes of Gaul. It was surely better to obey and turn against a distinct and clearly visible community of foreigners than to face the anger of the openly ruthless invader. The chance to share in the profits of this mass murder were an added attraction.

Mithridates had in the past and would again in the future negotiate with and make peace with Rome. His orders for the pogrom in Asia Minor were not out of sheer loathing for Romans or a desire to eradicate the Roman Republic. He allegedly ordered the gruesome execution of a senator captured in the early stages of the fighting – the man was killed by having molten gold poured down his throat – but this was to highlight the man's greed and corruption, which had done much to start the war. Another distinguished Roman prisoner was humiliated by being led publicly as a captive. The massacre throughout Asia was a cynical but logical act. It brought a haul of plunder to help fund the war, but more importantly committed the communities to Mithridates' cause, for they were bound to fear terrible retribution if the Romans did return. We should also remember how long a band of Roman traders had helped the city of Cirta to resist a siege. Especially if they were aided by locals, some of these Romans might have held out against him. Capturing towns by siege was time-consuming and usually costly in lives and money. Killing the Romans removed this risk.[31]

We do not know how far the wider population joined in the slaughter. It is possible that plenty of people resented the Romans or had old scores to settle and were willing to take part, but equally possible that the killing was mainly done by the partisans of the newly installed leaders or men commanded by civic leaders. Most people may simply have stood by, glad that they were not the targets of this appalling violence and too frightened to intervene. Perhaps few were inclined to take risks to protect Roman neighbours or refugees who had come to their community. When Mithridates was beaten, the returning Romans punished some communities, mainly by imposing heavy levies on them. It did not take long for traders and businessmen to return. The locals may have resented them, but it did not stop them borrowing money or doing business with them. There was no repeat of the bloodbath of 88 BC.

News of the massacre in Asia caused widespread anger at Rome. Yet war had already been declared against Mithridates, and once the initial phase of the civil war had run its course, a consul took his army east to deal with the king of Pontus, first expelling him from Greece and then beating him in Asia. The slaughter of so many Romans did not provoke the war, nor did it prevent the Roman general from agreeing peace terms with Mithridates – admittedly encouraged by his desire to return to Italy, where his Roman enemies had gathered once again. In 229 BC the complaints of traders had convinced the Senate to send ambassadors to Queen Teuta in Illyria, and it was the murder of one of these representatives which had led to the declaration of war. The massacre of Italians at Cirta by Jugurtha similarly outraged many Romans, but did not in itself cause an army to be sent against him. Just as wars were not fought to gain access to trade routes, there is no evidence that the killing of Roman civilians by a foreign leader or community in itself would provoke the Senate to action. In the provinces, things were very different, and it is to the administration of these that we must now turn.[32]

'HOW MUCH DID YOU MAKE?'
– GOVERNMENT

'The Senate's judgement that a province has been held and preserved
by its governor's mild and upright administration rather than by the
swords of an army or the favour of the gods is a far greater distinction than a triumph.' – *Cato to Cicero, April 50 BC.*[1]

PROCONSULS

On the last day of July 51 BC the proconsul Marcus Tullius Cicero
reached the city of Laodicea, having crossed the boundary from Asia
and entered his own province of Cilicia. He had left Rome in May
and made his way to the port of Brundisium (modern Brindisi), the
main route to the east. Cicero was in no great hurry, tarrying at his
own and friends' villas along the way. There were more delays when
he fell ill, and later as he waited for one of his senior subordinates to
arrive, so that it was early June before he set sail. The fifty-five-year-
old proconsul paused to visit Athens for twelve days, and did not
land at Ephesus on the coast of Asia until 22 July, where he rested
for four days. From then on he travelled overland, following the old
trunk road that led in time to Tarsus and eventually the great city of
Antioch in Syria.[2]

The governorship of a province was a prize that went only to men
doing well in the Republic's fiercely competitive public life. By this
time magistrates spent their year of office in Rome, and only then
were given a command. The most important went to the former
consuls, with the title and *imperium* of a proconsul. Former praetors
sometimes received this title, but were allocated the less important
provinces. Any command was an honourable distinction. In some

there was the opportunity to win military glory, while all offered the chance of profit, most of all for the unscrupulous. By the middle of the first century BC bribery was rife in elections, the candidates trying to outspend each other and purchase the support of voters, trusting to a provincial command to restore their finances.[3]

Provincial commands were coveted by many ambitious – and plenty of desperate – senators, but not by all. Cicero held the con-sulship in 63 BC, winning the magistracy as soon as he had reached the minimum age. This was a point of pride for an aristocrat, but a truly remarkable distinction for a 'new man' like Cicero, the first in his family to become consul. During his twelve months of office he defeated a coup launched by a group of senators and their asso-ciates, but then chose not to follow his consulship with a provincial command. He had done the same after his praetorship, and the only overseas service of his entire career before 51 BC was as quaestor in Sicily in 74 BC. The Cilician command only came about because a new law stipulated a five-year interval between holding a senior magistracy and going out to a province – a measure aimed mainly at curbing electoral bribery. Introduced in 52 BC, this inevitably meant a shortage of governors for the next few years, and so any former consuls and praetors who had not held a command in the past were obvious candidates to undertake these duties.[4]

Cicero was not keen – '"putting panniers on a draft ox", not the right sort of job for me', he wrote of one of his first tasks when he reached Cilicia – but he was obliged to go. His command was to begin when he reached the province and to last for a year. How-ever, the Senate had the option not to appoint a successor at the end of this period and instead to extend his command. Fear that this would happen plagued Cicero, who wrote letter after letter urging his friends to do everything possible to prevent this, and lobbied the incoming consuls and other magistrates in the same cause. To his great relief, his term was not extended, for his attitude to the post did not mellow over time.[5] 'The City, my dear Rufus,' he wrote in June 50 BC to a young friend, 'cling to the City and live in its limelight. Serving abroad, as I have known since my youth, is obscure and sordid for those whose efforts can win fame in Rome.'[6]

The greatest orator of his day – and that was the common opin-ion and not simply his own – Cicero's political rise rested heavily on the speeches he made in the Senate, at public meetings, and most of all in the law courts. By Roman standards he had very little military experience, at most a couple of years in his late teens. Yet he was far from unique. The governor appointed to Syria at the same time as Cicero was one Marcus Calpurnius Bibulus, colleague of Julius Caesar as consul in 59 BC. He had not taken a province after that magistracy, nor had he held one after his praetorship in 62 BC. This was largely a matter of choice, for he was a man of modest abilities and not someone whose oratory or skill as a political operator could only shine in Rome.

It is worth remembering that even a man who won praetorship and consulship and followed each with a provincial command still spent the bulk of his career in Rome. A senator was not free to travel as he willed, and required formal permission from the Senate to leave Italy, something only given in exceptional circumstances. Ambitious young men like Cicero and Caesar went to the Greek east to train in oratory, but once they were enrolled as senators, something that automatically followed the quaestorship, they could only go to the provinces in an official capacity, as governors, on the staff of another governor, as senior officers, or as part of a senatorial delegation – usually sent as boards of three on some diplomatic service.

There were a few senators who chose long service with the le-gions, such as Marcus Petreius, 'the military man [homo militaris] who had served with considerable distinction for more than thirty years as tribune, prefect, legate and as a praetorian governor', but these were rare enough to invite comment. When the forty-one-year-old Julius Caesar arrived in Gaul, he had spent at most nine years away from Italy and quite possibly less. Apart from a handful of unusual individuals, for most senators provincial service was an interruption of their normal life and career. Many welcomed the opportunity, and nearly all were glad of the honour and especially the profits of overseas service. The poet Catullus claimed that the first question he was asked on returning from a spell on the staff of the governor of Bithynia was 'How much did you make?'[7]

Yet for all the appeal of a province, every senator knew that the experience for good or ill would be a brief one before a return to public life back in Rome. One-year commands were fairly common, and it was exceptionally rare to spend more than three years as a governor. It was unusual and purely coincidental if a man returned as governor to the same province in which he had served as quaestor. The Romans did not feel any great need for specialists in this or any other aspect of public life, and the vast majority of governors had never before visited a province until they arrived as its governor. Nor did most of them pay much attention to what went on in their empire. Cicero later joked about his surprise when he came back from a term as quaestor in Sicily. Some people had not even noticed that he had been away, and another thought that he had been to Africa and not Sicily. It reinforced his sense that only what happened in Rome really mattered.[8]

The Senate gave each governor instructions (*mandata*) sketching his responsibilities and perhaps drawing attention to particular concerns – in Cicero's case he was to ensure the security of King Ariobarzanes, whose Cappadocian kingdom bordered on his province. However, no example survives and so it is hard to know how full these instructions were. In 59 BC Julius Caesar had introduced the latest in a succession of laws regulating governors' conduct, repeating a ban on their leaving or taking troops beyond the boundaries of their provinces without permission. It also regulated the expenses a governor and his staff could claim to support themselves as they went about their duties, and insisted on detailed account-keeping of all their activities. Neither instructions nor legislation covered the numerous day-to-day decisions, large and small, required of a governor. Communications were simply too slow for the Senate to direct them, and both their will and the law could be ignored by the man on the spot if he believed – or at least could argue – that this was in the best interests of the Republic. Thus Caesar claimed that all his interventions further and further away from Transalpine Gaul were entirely justified by the situation. Governors could not be recalled prematurely once given a command, and could not be regulated closely, so that it was only on their return to Rome that their actions might be challenged.

Each governor issued an edict before or on arrival in the province. Cicero followed the normal practice of drawing heavily on those of previous governors. In particular, much of the text and the overall template came from the edict of Quintus Murcius Scaevola, who as consul had governed Asia in an exemplary manner in 95–94 BC, so that the Senate formally recommended that others copy his edict. This included a formal statement that disputes between provincials would be resolved according to their own laws. Another clause stated that as governor he would not enforce the terms of contracts that did not deserve in good faith to be followed. Cicero adhered to this ruling in practice, and noted that the proconsul in Syria had announced the same approach, although he chose to word it slightly differently. This tendency to copy earlier edicts helped to give some continuity to Roman administration in each province, but it was not compulsory and an incoming pro-magistrate could make drastic changes, albeit with the risk that this might be used against him should he ever be brought to trial.[9]

For the duration of his command, there was no higher authority within his province than the governor. This also meant that there were many issues for them to decide and much to do, dealing with small local problems, and for Cicero these were pale imitations of the serious matters debated and decided at Rome. Hence his foot-dragging progress to Cilicia, a journey that could easily have been done in half the time. Yet it should also be said that the state did little to arrange for appointed governors to reach their commands. Only very rarely would they be carried in a navy ship, and instead they took passage on merchant vessels going in the right direction. Nor was there any official postal service to permit the governor and Senate to communicate while he was away, and instead any correspondence went by private means.

Cicero was not alone in taking longer than was necessary to reach

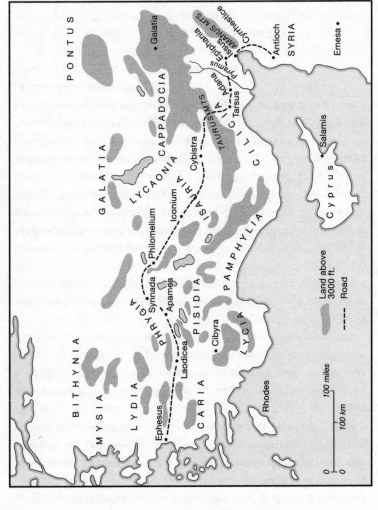

Cicero's province of Cilicia

his province. Yet we should be glad that the reluctant proconsul was forced away from the limelight of Rome, for his letters written over the next twelve months provide us with by far our most detailed picture of the activities of a Roman governor under the Republic.

CILICIA

Cicero's province was prestigious, as befitted one allocated to a former consul, and was garrisoned by two legions. As well as Cilicia itself (equivalent to much of southern Turkey today), several regions of the province of Asia were added to his command, as was Cyprus, annexed by Rome in 58 BC. Two important allied kingdoms, Galatia and Cappadocia, bordered on the province and the proconsul was also expected to ensure their stability and security. Apart from protecting Ariobarzanes, there was the hovering threat of a major attack by the Parthians. In 53 BC a Roman invasion of Parthia had met with disaster at the Battle of Carrhae, and since then there had been several Parthian raids into the province of Syria. A larger-scale attack might easily reach Cilicia as well, and this possibility fed Cicero's fear that he would be called on to serve there for longer than a year.[10]

It is a mistake to imagine a Roman governor processing in great state guarded by serried ranks of soldiers and attended by a large and sophisticated staff of bureaucrats. The Senate might allow a governor to raise a fresh draft of soldiers or even entire legions to take to his province, but only when this was felt to be necessary. Cicero is unlikely to have had a single soldier with him as he travelled to Cilicia, apart from a handful of senior officers. A governor's staff was known as his cohort. The term was borrowed from the army, but whereas a cohort of legionaries had a paper strength of 480 men, a proconsul rarely had a tenth of that number to aid him.

The Republic provided each governor with a quaestor, the most junior of the magistracies for which the minimum age was thirty, and unlike the praetors and consuls these went to the provinces in their year of office. Twenty quaestors were elected each year and allocated by lot to their duties, which were predominantly financial, but could stretch to a range of other tasks including military command. Pompey the Great and Julius Caesar chose their quaestors, but this was exceptional and a reflection of their overwhelming influence. Cicero did not know the quaestor allocated to him at all well. The Senate allowed governors a set number of senior subordinates or legates (*legati*) – Cicero had four, two of them ex-praetors. One was his younger brother Quintus, who had governed Asia and later served as legate with Pompey during the war against the pirates and with Caesar in Gaul. All were senators, and in this case all boasted better military credentials than their commander, but ability was not necessarily the main factor in their choice, for these were relatives, friends or friends of friends. The word for legate was the same as the one for ambassador, and these men were considered representatives of the governor, their *imperium* delegated from his.

Quaestors were young men at an early stage in their careers, while the legates were chosen by the governor and might or might not be experienced. Only a few of the junior officials were remotely professional in the modern sense and even these were often selected by the governor. There was the *accensus*, who was something like a chief clerk in charge of the day-to-day running of the governor's office. Usually this man was a freedman, often of the governor, although in Cicero's case he took a former slave of one of his friends. A good *accensus* needed a talent for administration, but had to be kept on a tight rein. More than a decade earlier Cicero had warned Quintus to make sure that the freedman did not abuse his access to the governor and the governor's official seal. There was also a scribe (*scriba*), in this case probably a freedman of Cicero's, and he often worked with the quaestor to keep financial records. Added to these the state provided lictors – twelve for a proconsul – who acted as guards, attendants and doormen. On official occasions they carried the *fasces*, a bundle of rods surrounding an axe, and at the governor's command could inflict corporal or capital punishment. There were also messengers (*viatores*), heralds (*praecones*) and priests (*haruspices*) to perform sacrifices – perhaps two or three of each.[11]

All in all, a governor's cohort was not so very different from the staff of a magistrate in Rome and reflected the household of an aristocrat. This was reinforced by the personal freedmen and slaves, including in this case Cicero's long-time secretary Tiro, cooks and other functionaries. Another group were the 'tent-companions' (*contubernales*) or family members and friends. Cicero had his son and nephew with him, in part for the adventure, but also to gain experience. Young aristocrats learned about public life by following older members of the family as they went about the daily business of being a senator, whether in Rome or in the provinces.

Even with these additions a governor's cohort remained small. Sometimes he would add a few men seconded from the garrison of his province. The duties of the *praefectus fabrum* – the title does not have an ideal translation, but prefect in charge of logistics gives a rough idea – included the supply of the army, but this man was often given wider responsibilities by governors. Yet the legions of this era could not provide large numbers of administrators, and as proconsul Cicero simply did not have the resources to carry out the day-to-day administration of all the communities within his province, nor was he expected to do this. The Roman way was to let each city or other grouping – tribes were common in some regions, especially in the west – govern itself. The governor was there to protect the province against internal and external threats, to oversee administration and taxation from a distance, and to act as the supreme judicial authority.

A governor held supreme military and civil power in his province, but the balance of importance between the two varied from region to region and over time. By the middle of the first century BC Asia, Sicily and Africa rarely had a legionary garrison. There might still be forces raised from local allies, and small-scale problems with banditry, piracy on- and offshore, or other threats to peace. In Sicily in the 70s BC slave rebellions had occurred within living memory, so that at harvest time one of the governor's jobs was to tour the province and look for any signs of a fresh outbreak. Rebellion by the free provincial population does not appear as a realistic threat by this time. In contrast, in Gaul Caesar spent spring, summer and early autumn campaigning with the army. Even so, in all but one case where rebellion prevented this, each winter he returned to his province, and usually went south of the Alps to Cisalpine Gaul to hold assizes.[12]

The bureaucratic machine simply did not exist for a governor to settle down in one place for a year or more and direct the province from there, and so all governors toured the area under their control. Provinces were divided into a number of assizes (*conventus*) where he would stop, hold court and be open to appeals. This meant that a governor spent much of his time on the move, even when he was not engaged in military operations. Since the praetorship could not be held until the age of thirty-nine, even the most junior governor was at least forty, and many were older. Levels of health and fitness inevitably varied. Men like Pompey and Caesar kept themselves in training, but others are unlikely to have been so disciplined. We hear of one praetorian governor in Spain who was captured by the enemy and killed because the tribesmen holding him could not believe that someone so old and fat held any importance as a prisoner.[13]

When he was with the army a governor rode on horseback or sometimes even marched alongside the column. Travelling with just his staff, he was unlikely to do this except over short distances. A chariot offered an alternative, but that meant standing up, and so again was unsuitable for long journeys and, if used at all, chariots were probably kept for entering a city in some style. Most of the time a governor travelled in a four-wheeled enclosed carriage (*raeda*) drawn by mules or the local equivalent. This permitted a degree of comfort, shelter from the elements, and the chance to rest or work. Caesar was renowned for dictating to a secretary on journeys, composing letters and literary works alike. Even so in bad weather, and wherever the roads were in a poor state, long days spent in such a vehicle no doubt reinforced the appeals of life back in Rome for a man like Cicero. At night a governor and his staff might pitch camp – Caesar's law granted them an allowance for tents – or if they had reached a town or city, accept the hospitality of an important local man.[14]

Cicero arrived in Cilicia with the summer's campaigning season already well under way, but only then began to receive up-to-date news about the military situation and the threat posed by the Parthians. Even this was incomplete. He had arranged to meet his predecessor, the outgoing proconsul Appius Claudius Pulcher, changing his own route to make this possible. This was a courtesy rather than a requirement, and would have had the advantage of giving him up-to-date information. In the event Appius did not show up, having changed his mind without bothering to inform his successor. At first Cicero had trouble finding out where the garrison of the province was. Before he arrived he had heard of discontent among the soldiers, for their pay was heavily in arrears and there may also have been other problems. On arrival he discovered that five cohorts, half of one of the legions, had marched off and were camped on their own, without any officers. It seemed that Appius still had another three cohorts – and the ones closest to their proper strength – as an escort, leaving not much more than half of the army in the main camp.[15]

Although he held some brief assizes on his way to the army, Cicero had clearly set the rest of the summer aside for military operations. The errant units were gathered up, and the ease with which the five mutinous cohorts returned to the fold suggests that part of their grudge was with Appius or one of his senior subordinates rather than anything deeper. Cicero advanced with his reunited army to the borders with Syria, ready to support Bibulus in the event of a Parthian invasion. He also felt that it was good to stiffen the resolve of the allied kings of Cappadocia and Galatia – and indeed to send a message of Roman confidence and strength to the monarch of Armenia, whose realm lay beyond them.[16]

In September a few raids by the Parthians were repulsed, and reports made clear that there was no likelihood of a major invasion in the immediate future. Cicero decided to lead a punitive expedition against the peoples who lived in the rugged hill country around Mount Amanus, which lay along the border between Cilicia and Syria. Having pretended to move away, the Romans force-marched back and attacked, surprising the locals and burning several of their settlements. Cicero then besieged the walled hilltop village of Pindenissum, which surrendered after fifty-seven days. This yielded plunder that he gave to the troops, and captives to be sold as slaves. Better yet, this display of Roman force, and the Romans' willingness to attack even such a minor mountain stronghold, convinced a neighbouring community to send envoys to him seeking peace with Rome.

Cicero had no illusions about the obscurity of his enemy – '"Who on earth are these Pindenissitae of yours?"' he wrote, imagining his friend's question. '"I never heard the name." That's not my fault. I cannot turn Cilicia into Aetolia or Macedonia.' For all his joking, his soldiers had hailed him as *imperator*, and this was the first step in winning a triumph, something which he came to crave. Soon letters would go to influential senators urging them to support the vote to grant him a public thanksgiving, which was the next stage in the process. It seems unlikely that he had inflicted 5,000 casualties on the enemy, even if prisoners are included, which is a reminder that we should not assume every Roman victory really involved bloodshed on this scale.[17]

The peoples of the Amanus mountains were 'perpetual' enemies and given to raiding and robbery. Earlier on, Cicero had explained that communications were often poor in Cilicia because of the activities of bandits. Bibulus soon followed his example and launched his own expedition against that of Mount Amanus, which lay within his province of Syria. If the Parthians had appeared in greater force, then no doubt neither proconsul would have turned his attentions to the villages in this area. That does not mean that the hostility of the Pindenissitae and their neighbours was imaginary. Banditry was, and would continue to be, a real problem in this area, not helped because it lay between the two Roman provinces. The tribes in the Alps were also well known to extort money from travellers and even Roman armies moving through the high passes, something that would not end until their suppression at the end of the century.[18]

It is too simple to see Cicero as simply indulging in triumph-hunting – desperate though his desire to win the honour would prove. Once again we should remember that the chief victims of banditry were the more settled provincial communities. As yet no governor had dealt permanently with the problem, but that was a question of resources and competing priorities as much as lack of Roman interest in the matter. Cicero had demonstrated Roman power, showing that the Romans were willing to besiege and capture a mountaintop stronghold, even if this took them many weeks. It showed the inhabitants of the area that they were vulnerable to retribution, and so made them more likely to submit to Roman demands in future. Unfortunately, Bibulus' expedition ended in a minor disaster, with an entire cohort of legionaries wiped out by the locals, so that the façade of Rome's strength was swiftly cracked. Afterwards one of his legates won a minor victory, but the region was far from permanently under Rome's control.[19]

It was now winter, which meant that there was no real prospect of a Parthian invasion before the late spring or early summer, when there would be sufficient grass for grazing. Quintus took the legions into winter camp, and on 5 January 50 BC Cicero set out to travel back westwards along the main road. He stopped at some of the cities along the way, and dealt with some business, but by 11 February he was at Laodicea. Here he held grand assizes, setting aside two weeks for the business of each of the six assize regions. The proconsul did not go to Cyprus and, since the laws of that island forbade cases being heard anywhere else, he sent a representative to hold an assize there in his place.[20]

MAKING MONEY

As governor Cicero's authority was supreme, and many decisions were entirely up to him. Inevitably this meant that there were plenty of individuals and communities wishing to gain his favour and secure a particular outcome. Most governors and their staffs expected to be entertained lavishly whenever they stopped in a community.

This was considered no more than the appropriate honours due to officials of Rome, but it was also an opportunity for the hosts to make a connection with the governor and those close to him. Thus it could work to their advantage, even if provincials had no choice about offering this hospitality and could be compelled if reluctant. In spite of the regulations of the Julian Law, there was little they could do to resist demands imposed on them, or at least on their pockets. As we have seen, in 79 BC a householder and his neighbours resisted by force the attempted rape of his daughter by the legate Verres, although in the long run the man and his son were condemned and executed on trumped-up charges. Later, as governor of Sicily from 73–71 BC, Verres was accused of multiple thefts of artworks – or their forced sale at absurdly low prices – from the houses of his hosts. The power of a governor meant that it was unwise to refuse him anything. Individuals were unlikely to take the risk, and even communities had little chance of success.[21]

If there was a Roman garrison in the province, then the governor was also fully entitled to demand that these be billeted on the provincials. Such guests were less distinguished, less influential and usually even less welcome, not least because the costs of feeding and accommodating them were considerable. A visit for months on end by thousands of legionaries in a city, bored, all too often unpaid and not always well led or disciplined – and yet still Romans very conscious of belonging to the City that ruled the world – did little for the peace and calm of a community. Yet there were usually ways of avoiding this disruptive burden. Cicero claims that every city was surprised when he did not ask them for money to be excused from this:

> Before my time, this time of year was devoted to profit. The wealthier cities used to pay a lot of money to avoid having soldiers quartered on them for the winter – Cyprus used to pay nearly 200 Attic talents; an island that under my administration I can say speaking only the truth, has not been asked for anything. They are all stunned, because I will accept no honours save for verbal ones. I will not accept statues, nor shrines, nor statues of me in a four-horsed chariot.[22]

Cicero was unusually scrupulous, and tried to restrict his staff to taking no more than the law allowed them when they travelled as his representatives. He was not wholly successful in this, but it is fair to say that by and large he and his cohort behaved about as well as could be expected – a burden to the provincials, but a much lesser one than most governors. Privately, Cicero felt that his predecessor Appius Claudius Pulcher had behaved like a 'wild beast', and so he 'tried not to re-open the wounds inflicted [on the province], but they are obvious and cannot be hidden'. The payment to avoid having troops quartered on them – and it is worth noting that there was no good military or logistical reason to send them to Cyprus in particular – was just one of Appius' demands. Like many Roman governors, he seems to have taken payments to ensure favourable judgements. Trials were especially susceptible to this, not simply with the verdict, but decisions over where they would take place, the appointment of judges and advice to them. The victors in such cases were likely to have to pay for their success, regardless of the rights and wrongs of the case.[23]

A governor was concerned with disputes between communities, and might be encouraged to take an interest in internal matters, but his prime focus was with cases involving Roman citizens. As we have seen, the large numbers of traders and businessmen already active in a region rapidly grew once it became a province. Some were men of wealth, at times ostentatious and even vulgar in its display. Cicero was more amused than impressed when he encountered Publius Vedius, 'a dubious character, but with ties to Pompey'. The proconsul met him on the road, with a large entourage and two chariots, one with a baboon as passenger, as well as a horse-drawn *raeda* carriage and a litter. Litters carried by slaves were popular and had a particular association in the Roman mind with the wealth of the east, but were not considered quite proper. Vedius was probably an equestrian, but even more important than this was his connection with Pompey the Great, not only Rome's most famous general and perhaps the wealthiest man in the Senate, but also thought likely to come to the east soon to wage war on the Parthians. Thus for all his view of the man, the proconsul treated him with respect and passed the time of day. Vedius was also important enough to be fit material for gossip, and Cicero gleefully passed on a story he heard sometime later. When some of the man's baggage was mistakenly opened, it was discovered to contain little portrait busts of five married aristocratic ladies.[24]

Many Romans lacked Vedius' connections, but as a group the *publicani* were numerous and dangerous to ignore. The Roman Republic lacked the resources to carry out many tasks and from its earliest days had looked to private citizens to undertake them, whether in small matters such as providing sacrificial animals for the state cults, or far larger things such as building work, and supplying the armies. Normally several individuals would take on these public contracts, and although the Romans never developed anything equivalent to modern corporate law, the associations did develop a group identity and owned property. Reliance on private suppliers of services was common in the Greek world but, as Roman power grew, the sheer number and scale of contracts dwarfed earlier practices. Polybius claimed that 'almost everybody' at Rome was involved in some shape or form in this. Senators were excluded from public contracts, and he was clearly talking in the main about wealthier citizens, and most of all equestrians.[25]

On the whole the system functioned with reasonable efficiency. There was a case during the Second Punic War when two out of nineteen *publicani* contracted to supply the legions fighting in Spain were caught out in a major fraud, claiming compensation for non-existent cargoes when their decrepit ships were lost at sea. Few nations have been entirely free of profiteers in time of war, and it is notable that the other seventeen did a good job. After the defeat of the Carthaginians, Spain opened up new opportunities for the *publicani*, such as the extensive silver mines near New Carthage. The state did not have the machinery to exploit these, and so let contracts for working them. *Publicani* bid at Rome for the rights to mine, buying them for a set sum which permitted the state to know what its revenue would be. Polybius, who had visited the area, claimed that the treasury received 25,000 denarii a day from this source. Clearly the contractors needed to produce more than this to make a profit, and seem to have done so on a considerable scale. Yet the Republic was not always willing to open such opportunities to them. When Macedonia became a province, the royal mines were closed because the Senate did not want to open them to the *publicani*.[26]

It was as tax collectors that the *publicani* became infamous and widely loathed – hence the despised publicans of the King James Bible, even though these were local agents of the companies rather than *publicani* in the strict sense of the word. In Asia and the other eastern provinces, contracts to collect the main taxes were farmed out to them, as indeed were many other levies and duties there and in the rest of the empire. Rights to collect them were auctioned off in Rome by the censors, usually going to the highest bidders, just as contracts for services went to the lowest. A decade before Cicero went to Cilicia the *publicani* who had bought the rights to collect taxes in Asia asked for a rebate, for the province was not in a good enough condition to allow them to turn a profit, and there was a danger that they would make a loss. He and many others thought the demand was scandalous, but were unwilling to oppose it openly. Others did so, and it took several years before the companies got their way.[27]

The sums involved in the major public contracts were massive – many times the one million sesterces which by the end of the first century BC became the minimum property qualification for membership of the Senate – and their wealth gave the *publicani* considerable influence. In most cases the Republic had no real alternative other than to employ them if it was to receive revenue from the provinces. Success in politics required a man to spend lavishly, but much of a senator's wealth was tied up in the rural estates that were the proper source of income for an aristocrat. Many borrowed to fund their careers, often enough from men who had interests in the companies of *publicani*, so that when they arrived as governors in a province they had to be careful in their relationship with them. As Cicero wrote to Quintus when his brother governed Asia:

And yet to all your good intentions and diligence there is the serious problem of the *publicani*; if we oppose them, we will alienate from ourselves and the Republic an order that has deserved well of us and the state . . . and if we give in to them in everything, we shall allow the ruin of those whose safety and indeed interests we ought to protect.

Balancing the needs of the influential *publicani* and saving the provincials from penury demanded a 'divine' virtue – something his older brother claimed Quintus possessed. In Cilicia Cicero tried to do the same thing, only permitting the companies to take what they were due, but at the same time insisting that the provincials paid promptly. He claims that this satisfied both sides, which was surely true.[28]

A weak governor let the *publicani* squeeze the provincials too tightly, raising more than was the legal due, perhaps forcing communities to borrow at extortionate rates to have the ready cash to pay them. An unscrupulous governor could do even worse, combining with the tax collectors and using his authority and the force at his command for their mutual profit. Verres collaborated with the *publicani* collecting the tithe on the grain harvest in much of Sicily, and had the latter destroy many of their records for what they were doing. A few governors resisted the companies, but when Scaevola and his legate Rutilius Rufus did so in Asia, it provoked the latter's prosecution and exile. For all that he surely did not deserve this fate, it is perfectly possible that Rufus had taken gifts from grateful cities and so was technically guilty, even if the majority of other provincial governors took as much or more and were never condemned. According to Livy, as early as the second century BC the opinion was voiced in the Senate that 'wherever there was a *publicanus*, there is either no effective law or no freedom for the provincials'.[29]

The *publicani* were influential because so many of the men taking these contracts were equestrians, and from the late second century BC the wider equestrian order played more of a role in politics and especially in political trials. They were simply too important for most senators to risk offending. In Cicero's day this influence was enhanced because some powerful aristocrats came to have an interest in the tax-collecting companies, even if as senators they could not directly take on such contracts. Crassus, nicknamed *dives* or 'the rich', championed the cause of the *publicani* wanting a rebate after buying the rights to collect taxes in Asia at too high a price.[30]

Senators were restricted by law from involvement in large-scale trade, for instance by being forbidden from owning a large merchant ship, but, as with the bar on bidding for public contracts, ways were found around this rule. There were many Romans active in the provinces, and all could try to win favour and support from the governor. There was no assurance that this would work, and in exceptional cases a man like Verres might even rob, imprison or execute them. Such acts flouted the laws protecting citizens, but if a governor chose to ignore them then there was no one to stop him. Verres later claimed that the men were rebels who had fought for the losing side in Rome's recent civil war.[31]

Few governors took the risk of abusing fellow citizens to this extent, but their response to appeals depended a great deal on their assessment of the individual and most of all his connections and supporters. Cicero wrote many letters recommending acquaintances to other governors and received plenty on behalf of men active in Cilicia, and such letters are the commonest form of literature to survive from the Roman world. A man would only be in his province for a few years at most, but the favours traded there might help him throughout his career. In 51–50 BC Cicero sent several letters to Minucius Thermus, governor of Asia:

> May I therefore request you in virtue of the very close connection between us and our many equal and mutual good offices to exert your benevolent influence on Marcus Anneius' behalf . . .

> I have long been on very familiar terms with Lucius Genucilius Curvus, a very worthy gentlemen who never forgets a service. I thoroughly recommend him to you . . . I hope you will accommodate him in all respects so far as your conscience and dignity will allow . . . for he will never ask you anything unbecoming to your character . . .

Cluvius of Puteoli . . . is convinced that unless he settles some business which he has in your province during your period of office
through my recommendations, he may as well give it up as lost . . .[32]

Sometimes existing associates appealed directly on their own behalf.
Cicero had asked his young friend Caelius Rufus to write to him
with the political news of Rome. Part-way through the year, Caelius
was elected aedile, a magistrate whose responsibilities included
staging games at Rome. If these pleased the crowds, then their votes
helped a man win the higher magistracies, but inevitably spectacular
games were expensive. Caelius asked Cicero to send him panthers to
be displayed and hunted in the arena. This was normal and in fact
Caelius' colleague in the office, a man with no claim on Cicero as far
as we know, also wrote on the off-chance of being given animals for
his own games. In both cases the proconsul refused, although with
Caelius he added humour to the refusal, claiming that the panthers
were the only persecuted inhabitants in his entire province and so
had fled abroad.[33]

Some recommendations were on behalf of provincials, but the
majority were for Romans. A man named Scaptius came to Cicero
for assistance in collecting money owed by the city of Salamis on
Cyprus. He had a letter from Marcus Junius Brutus – later famous
as one of the murderers of Julius Caesar, but at this time seen as a
man to watch in the next generation of senators and senior magistrates. Atticus, a friend from Cicero's youth who chose to remain an
equestrian and not enter politics, but still managed to know practically everyone of importance, was especially keen for the orator to
place Brutus in his debt. Scaptius asked for the army rank of prefect.
Appius had granted this to him, along with command of a couple
of troops of cavalry – perhaps fifty or sixty men. With these he had
blockaded the city council of Salamis inside their chamber, refusing
to let any of them out until five had starved to death. Yet even this
brutality did not secure the money owed.

Cicero had made clear that he would not give army posts to anyone
with business interests in Cilicia, although he was willing to grant the

empty title to businessmen elsewhere. Scaptius' request was refused and the cavalry were withdrawn from Cyprus, but Cicero promised to arbitrate in the matter. His edict stated that he would honour no loan contract requiring payment at more than the legal rate of 12 per cent compound interest. Scaptius was asking for 48 per cent – the difference was 106 to 200 talents – and this was a sum the Salaminians were incapable of paying. (An Attic talent weighted some 25.86 kg or just under 57 lbs and was valued at 24,000 sesterces or 6,000 denarii in Roman currency.) Yet as the negotiations progressed he revealed that it was not in fact his money, but that it was Brutus' and Scaptius was merely his local agent. He also cited two senatorial decrees passed to allow the loan in the first place at the higher rate in spite of the law, measures clearly secured by Brutus and his friends. Cicero considered this outrageous and in no way invalidating the law or his decree, and felt that 12 per cent compound interest offered a handsome enough profit. He refused to oblige Brutus in spite of repeated demands, privately stating that, if he knew the truth of Scaptius' activities, then his esteem for the up-and-coming man was much reduced. Yet in the end the longer-term importance of friendships at Rome trumped Cicero's sense of right and wrong. He did not force Scaptius to accept payment at 12 per cent, and instead granted his request to let the matter lie. Brutus would try to get the 48 per cent with the aid of the next proconsul.[34]

Julius Caesar once said of Brutus that 'whatever he wants, he wants badly' and nowhere is that more clear than in this episode – a shock to anyone familiar only with Shakespeare's 'noblest Roman of them all'. His letters to Cicero were rude, in spite of the latter's high rank and greater age. Brutus was also owed money by King Ariobarzanes of Cappadocia and King Deiotaurus of Galatia. In this case the rate was no more than the legal maximum of 12 per cent, but the latter was too impoverished to pay anything and the former was even more heavily in debt to Pompey and was incapable of paying either creditor back in full.[35]

Especially with the lurking Parthian threat, it was important not to weaken the loyalty or strength of the allied kingdoms any further.

Soon after arriving in Cilicia Cicero had prevented an attempt to dethrone Ariobarzanes by exiling a powerful high priest before civil war broke out. The king was grateful to the proconsul, but it would make no sense to weaken his rule by dunning him too severely for money, since this might provoke more unrest in the kingdom. Cicero managed to get some money paid to Brutus' agents, although only a fraction of the loan. Pompey fared less well in proportion to the sum involved, but was content with a part of the interest, and Ariobarzanes was not ruined. Brutus' thanks was gruff, and it is hard to know whether he was simply too arrogant to accept that anyone else should be paid before his own claims were satisfied, or was so short of disposable funds that he was desperate for money. Loans to provincials could yield very high interest, but this came at considerable risk. Like Ariobarzanes they might well have a lot of other creditors and there were competing demands for assistance from the Roman governor. Moneylending in the provinces brought some people fabulous profits, but there were surely others who lost out or were even ruined when they were unable to make the debtors pay.[36]

As always, the better-connected had far more chance of getting what they wanted. It took an exceptional governor to ignore the pressures of pleasing other senators, especially men of status and influence. Cicero was deeply offended by Appius' failure to meet him when he entered the province. Not only was this rude, he then discovered that his predecessor was still holding assizes, no doubt doing favours for friends and lining his pockets for one more month. This was wholly illegal, since only one man at a time could hold *imperium* in a province, but no one could stop him. For all his private comments about Appius' appalling extortion, Cicero was scrupulously polite in his letters to him, not saying anything about this and pretending that the talk of Appius still holding court could only be malicious gossip. His predecessor's replies were offensive, complaining when Cicero reversed any of his decisions and when he stopped the communities from spending more money on sending delegations to Rome to praise Appius' government of the province. This was something most governors expected, regardless of how well or badly they had treated the provincials, but it was an expensive burden on the cities. Cicero joked that Appius was like a doctor whose treatment was killing a patient and yet resented another physician coming along with a cure, but he continued to be scrupulously courteous in his letters to him and made no mention of his depredations in his despatches.[37]

Cicero would have to sit in the Senate alongside Appius and the other former consuls when he returned to Rome, and do business with Pompey, Brutus and all the others who had urged him to aid their friends. He did not go as far as openly to help any of them to extort more money than they were due from the provincials, nor did he compel the latter to pay more than they could afford. At one point he notes that when he looked into the cities' finances he found widespread embezzlement by local magistrates. The matter was dealt with quietly, the men returning the stolen money and nothing more being said – raising the suspicion that the sums he discovered were merely the tip of the iceberg. However, this did do a good deal to restore the cities' finances and so make it easier for them to afford to pay taxes and debts. For the moment the *publicani* and the creditors were satisfied – if with little grace in the case of Brutus.[38]

For all his disgust at Brutus' greed and Scaptius' brutality in trying to collect his money, Cicero did not make the scandal public, just as he did not openly talk of Appius' abuses. Similarly, he said nothing publicly about the defeat suffered by Bibulus' men near Mount Amanus, even though the latter was in due course granted a triumph for his campaign. This award was helped by the influence of Bibulus' father-in-law, Cato the Younger. The latter had refused to vote for a thanksgiving to celebrate Cicero's successful campaign in spite of a friendly request. Cato's blunt explanation that he felt the proconsul's just administration was more admirable than mere military success rang hollow given his subsequent backing of his relative. This was politics, a world of traded favours, old obligations, compromise and deals done in the hope of future advantage, and in that sense it would be familiar to the men and women in public life in many countries throughout history. Good administration of Cilicia was just one, and not the most important, of Cicero's priorities, but his own reputation acted as a stronger check against giving in altogether to pressure from others.[39]

By Roman standards Cicero governed his province well. Helped by his experienced legates, he acted promptly to offer support to Syria against the threat of Parthian invasion. He was fortunate that a major attack did not come, for he was well aware that his army was small, the two legions under-strength and not in a high state of training or of good morale. Local allies, with the notable exception of the kingdom of Galatia, were too poor to muster any significant force. He also felt that they were unlikely to fight with spirit on behalf of Rome, given the conduct of governors like Appius and the constant demands from the *publicani* and Roman moneylenders. A detachment of Cicero's army won a skirmish with Parthian raiders, and the concentration of his forces on the border presented a bold front, even if there were other reasons why the Parthians chose only to raid and not to invade – something they would only do in 41 BC. The campaign near Mount Amanus was a useful operation against communities prone to prey on more settled areas of the province. It was a display of force intended to intimidate and led to the burning of several villages, the full destruction of one walled town and the enslavement of its population and the surrender of others.

Cicero launched the expedition because he had an army at his disposal and nothing else to do with it. Had the Parthians arrived, then the campaign would not have been fought. Other governors may not have chosen to risk dangerous operations in the mountains, but most probably would have done the same thing as Cicero. It did not represent a concerted effort to suppress the peoples of the region and bring permanent peace and security to the province, and instead was a sporadic effort in that direction. Peace in the province and security for allies and provincial communities was an admirable aim and a properly just cause to wage war, which of course also brought the prospect of glory and plunder. Personal advantage combined with benefits for the Republic in a way that the Romans would have seen as entirely honourable and worthwhile. Cicero was able

Julius Caesar: Caius Julius Caesar was one of the greatest conquerors in the history of Rome, overrunning Gaul between 58–51 BC, and leading raids across the Rhine and to Britain. A million are said to have died during these campaigns and as many more were enslaved. His success provoked rivals in the Roman Senate, leading to the civil war and his rule as dictator. (W&N Archive)

Pax: This coin minted by the short-lived emperor Galba in AD 68 carries the slogan *Pax Augusta* on the reverse. Maintaining peace through Roman strength and success was one of the central jobs of the emperor. In Galba's case it was brief, and his murder precipitated a civil war lasting for over a year. (Guy de la Bédoyère)

Arles: Trade long preceded the arrival of the Roman legions in most areas. This relief from Arles depicts a barge trading on the River Rhône, carrying goods in barrels and amphorae. Vast quantities of wine from Italy went north into Gaul long before it became a Roman province.

Puteoli flour mill: By the end of the first century BC the population of the city of Rome had swollen to around one million people. The *Pax Romana* allowed wheat and other staples to be brought from all around the empire, but especially Sicily, Egypt and North Africa, to feed the population. These flour mills in the bustling port of Puteoli were part of the system developed to transport and prepare this food supply.

Trajan's Column, Germanic chieftains: Throughout Roman history, diplomacy always accompanied military force, and many leaders and peoples readily allied with Rome. In this scene from Trajan's Column we see a group of ambassadors from various barbarian tribes waiting to see the emperor. Several of these chieftains have their long hair tied into a knot on the side of their head, a style associated with the Germanic Suebi.

Trajan's Column, Decebalus: While some leaders welcomed the Romans, others refused to submit. King Decebalus created a powerful empire based around the kingdom of Dacia, raided into the Roman empire and forced Domitian to grant him generous peace terms. Attacked by Trajan, he chose to commit suicide rather than be taken alive, a moment depicted on Trajan's Column.

Trajan's Column, Romans looting: Aggressive warfare could be profitable and the Romans openly boasted of the plunder gained from victory over foreign enemies. This scene from Trajan's Column shows a Roman legionary loading looted metal vessels on to a pack mule. Gold from his Dacian victory paid for Trajan's lavish and extensive forum complex in the heart of Rome.

Cologne reconstructed coach:
In all periods, a Roman governor spent a lot of his time on the move, holding assizes in the main communities of their province. Although they travelled by river or sea when this was possible, most journeys were overland, using a carriage like this reconstruction in the Roman archaeology museum at Cologne. It was well designed, and Roman craftsmen would have had little to learn from carriage-makers in the eighteenth century.

Kalkreise reconstructed rampart:
In AD 9, the recently created province in Germany erupted into rebellion. In a carefully prepared plot, the rebel leader Arminius led the provincial legate and three legions into a trap. This reconstruction in the archaeological park at Kalkreise shows the rampart his followers built to channel the Roman column and destroy it. This was the most successful rebellion ever mounted against Roman rule.

Masada: Herod the Great built a number of luxurious fortified palaces, including this one at Masada beside the Dead Sea. Seized early on in the Jewish rebellion against Nero, a band of dissidents held out here for three years after the fall of Jerusalem. In spite of its immense natural strength, the Romans besieged and took the fortress. Famously, the defenders killed their families and then committed suicide rather than surrender.

Above **Xanten reconstructed city walls:** Some cities in the Roman provinces did not bother to construct fortifications. Others did, but, like this reconstruction at Xanten, they were intended more to look impressive than in anticipation of any attack. In this case the towers barely project in front of the curtain wall. Walls were a mark of status, and in conditions of the *Pax Romana* any attack was seen as unlikely.

Bath samian bowl with gladiators: This bowl of red samian ware from Bath is decorated with a pair of gladiators duelling. Gladiatorial games were popular throughout the empire, whether staged in purpose-built amphitheatres or other permanent or temporary venues. In some cases it proved necessary to legislate restricting the amount communities were allowed to spend on these entertainments as rival cities tried to outdo each other.

Villa: The Romans were always eager to win over local aristocracies, encouraging them to adopt Roman ways and to serve the empire. Especially in the western provinces, the coming of Rome introduced new styles of building to a region, such as the luxurious country villa as centrepiece to an estate. This reconstruction at Wroxeter gives an idea of a moderately large villa. (© Martyn Richardson/Alamy Stock Photo)

Caesarea Pontius Pilate inscription: This stone, later reused in the construction of a theatre at Caesarea, bears the only inscription naming Pontius Pilate, surely the most famous of all Roman governors. Somewhat clumsily executed, suggesting a man unwilling to spend too much, it records the construction of a Tiberieum – presumably a building honouring the emperor Tiberius. In the Gospels, Pilate is pressed into executing Jesus because it was claimed that the 'King of the Jews' was a rival to the emperor.

Bath Sulis Minerva: The Romans rarely suppressed local religions and more often encouraged them, incorporating them into the pantheon of Rome's gods and goddesses. This gilded statue head from Bath depicts Sulis Minerva, the combination of an old Celtic and a Roman goddess who presided over the hot springs and bath complex at Aquae Sulis.

Scythopolis: The city of Scythopolis was the only one of the Decapolis or 'Ten Towns' situated west of the River Jordan. Although overtly Greek, it had a substantial Jewish minority. In AD 66 these fought alongside other townsfolk to repel an attack by Jewish rebels. However, soon afterwards they were massacred by some of their Gentile neighbours.

Cologne tombstone of Athenian flute-player: Under Roman rule goods and also people moved further and more freely than ever before. This memorial stone from Cologne in Lower Germany was set up in honour of the sixteen-year-old flute-player Ruphus by his father, a native of Alexandria and a citizen of Athens.

Iron Age round house: Round houses were characteristically British and had a long history before the Romans arrived. Throughout the Roman occupation, many people continued to live in farming communities based around several of these houses as well as animal pens. Even so, such sites show that goods from the empire were far more readily available than in the past, and it is hard to portray such settlements as a sign of people rejecting the Roman world. (© DJC/Alamy Stock Photo)

British victory: Commodus was the son of the much-admired Marcus Aurelius, but unlike his father he spent little time on the frontiers with the army, preferring life in Rome and displaying his prowess in the Colosseum. This coin celebrates a victory won in Britain by the provincial legate. Victories won by the provincial armies were attributed to the emperor, but so were defeats. (Guy de la Bédoyère)

to secure Ariobarzanes on his throne without direct use of military force, refusing the king's request for a few cohorts of legionaries to back him up. This occurred while the Parthian threat still loomed and the proconsul did not want to weaken his main army, so was a deliberate balancing of resources to the threats faced.[40]

The military side of Cicero's role was discharged competently and successfully, and he was able to leave his province at the end of his twelve months before any fresh onslaught from the Parthians developed. The harvest in 51 BC was poor in the regions of Asia attached to Cilicia, raising the risk of famine, especially for the poorer inhabitants of the cities. Cicero used 'his authority and powers of persuasion' to ensure that any provincial or Roman businessman hoarding stocks of grain made sufficient available to the communities. He was proud that he did not need to bully or begin legal action to achieve this. Administratively the proconsul stuck to the terms of his edict, was fair and consistent in his judgements and made himself readily available, even if by holding the main assize at Laodicea he forced those from other regions to travel to him. It looks as if he went through the cases faster than he had anticipated and did not need to use all the days set aside for them. Cicero compromised his own standards to an extent, most notably by not resolving the situation of the Salaminians. He may also have taken gifts he considered acceptable and some of the other perks of his position, for it is likely that he profited from his term as proconsul, if only from a share in the sale of prisoners.[41]

Cicero was in Cilicia for just twelve months, before heading home and leaving his inexperienced quaestor in charge, waiting for a new proconsul to arrive. Cicero was not keen on doing this, but had no one more senior or trustworthy who was able and willing to take on the job. All in all, the inhabitants of his province had done better under his administration than under some of his predecessors, particularly Appius Claudius Pulcher. He had cost the provincials less than most governors, proved fair in his judgements and had maintained reasonable security, allowing them to get on with their lives. Banditry was still a problem and would remain so, and the inhabitants of the

Amanus range were no more than contained for the moment. The provincials had been spared a major war with Parthia, and whatever their feelings towards the Romans and their eastern neighbours they will not have wanted campaigning armies fighting through their lands. For the moment rule by Rome was a fact of life, and they well knew that it could be far less pleasant than Cicero had made it.[42]

PROVINCIALS AND KINGS

'At the time I am dealing with, Comanus and his brother arrived on an embassy from the younger Ptomely and Menyllus of Alabanda from the elder one. They all entered the [Senate] house together, where they had a long and acrimonious dispute with each other; but when both Torquatus and Merula confirmed the statements of the younger brother and warmly supported him, the Senate decreed that Menyllus must leave Rome in five days, that their alliance with the older Ptolemy was at an end, and that legates should be sent to the younger brother to inform him of their decision.' – *Polybius, 140s BC.*[1]

'AT LEAST THEY THINK THEY HAVE SELF-GOVERNMENT'

In Cicero's day there were more provinces and more Roman governors than in the second century BC, and the proconsuls and propraetors undertook a wider range of activities beyond their purely military role. Even so, their involvement in the everyday administration of their provinces was limited, while as in the past the dominance or hegemony of Rome was a distant presence, doing little to change life in a region. This was especially true of the eastern Mediterranean, where a succession of major military interventions did not result in a permanent presence until Macedonia was given a governor and a garrison in 146 BC. Usually this was a former praetor in command of a single legion which, supported by Latin and Italian allies, would not have numbered more than 10,000 men. When the province of Asia was established its garrison was as small or smaller. There were no other Roman soldiers anywhere in the Greek world except on the rare occasions when a major war erupted.[2]

The small size of Rome's permanent military commitment to the eastern Mediterranean makes it abundantly clear that these were not armies of occupation. In the past, the kings of Macedonia had fought frequent campaigns on their northern frontier in response to raiding from the Thracian and other tribes living beyond them. Rome dissolved the kingdom after the defeat of Perseus, but the four regional administrations or *merides* they created in its stead lacked the ability and probably the resources to perform this defensive role effectively. In 149 BC a pretender to the Macedonian throne invaded at the head of an army of tribesmen, beating the local forces and then defeating and killing a Roman praetor sent against him. This Fourth Macedonian War spilled over into fighting in Greece and came at a time when Roman attention was focused on the final confrontation with Carthage.

It seems that the decision to send a governor and legion to Macedonia was intended to prevent a repeat of this crisis. Communications were improved by the construction of the *Via Egnatia*, which eventually stretched from the Adriatic to the Aegean coast. This was an asset should armies ever need to pass through the region for major campaigns further east, but it is more likely that its primary purpose was to allow the provincial garrison to move and be supplied in all seasons. Although the evidence is poor for the next half-century, it does look as if there were frequent campaigns against tribes like the Scordisci, and there were several Roman defeats as well as victories. Even at the end of the second century BC when Italy faced the menace of the migrating Cimbri and Teutones, the military presence in Macedonia was maintained in spite of a desperate need for soldiers elsewhere. For several years consuls were sent to the province – another indication of the importance placed on maintaining military dominance on the frontier. The Senate obviously considered this to be highly important, and not simply an opportunity for governors to go hunting for triumphs.[3]

The governors of Macedonia were kept busy with military matters, and in a law passed around 102 BC it was necessary to stipulate that they should spend sixty days on justice and administration in the area of the Chersonese lately added to their responsibilities. They had neither the time nor the authority to visit Greece to the south, and communities there were left to run their own affairs. There is no good evidence for the alleged Roman preference for installing oligarchs in the city-states and removing democracies. Nor was there routine, frequent or even periodic interference in the internal and external politics of the cities of Greece initiated by the Romans. Rome was concerned by any serious threat to its *imperium* in the sense of its power and dominance, but that did not mean an automatic and aggressive response to any slight inflicted on its representatives.[4]

In 87 BC a cohort of Roman soldiers was billeted in the city of Chaeronea for the winter months. The officer in command made sexual advances on a local youth named Damon, resorting to threats after gifts and persuasion had failed. Repelled and frightened, Damon and a group of sixteen friends drank heavily, smeared their faces black with soot and attacked the Roman at dawn while he was sacrificing in the market place. The officer and several soldiers were cut down and the killers fled into the countryside. In their absence they were condemned to death by the city council, but the youths returned that night and murdered several of the leading magistrates before vanishing again. For a while Damon and his friends lived as bandits. A Roman legate passed through the city to collect the remaining soldiers there and add them to his army. He investigated the matter and judged that the officials had acted properly. However, a little later Damon was granted an amnesty and returned to hold the prestigious post of gymnasiarch – in charge of the city's gymnasium, that quintessential symbol of Hellenic fitness, competition and culture. In spite of this honour, he was murdered while in the bath. A neighbouring city then went to the governor of Macedonia, claiming that the leaders of Chaeronea had been involved in the original killings. As advocate they hired a Roman, no doubt hoping that this would count in their favour, but, after the legate was contacted by letter and confirmed his original judgement, the charge was dismissed.[5]

Both the legate and the governor of Macedonia were satisfied that the city authorities had dealt with the matter justly and were willing to leave it there. In part this no doubt reflected the dishonourable behaviour of the murdered officer. Homosexuality between Roman soldiers was punishable by death, while love affairs with civilian boys or youths were not widely admired even though they were not illegal. Yet it is striking that the killing of an army officer did not prompt a knee-jerk desire for revenge. The Romans may have been unaware that Damon was pardoned and honoured by his city, for there is no evidence that they took any trouble to find out what happened to him or to ensure that the local authorities hunted him down. They simply do not appear concerned about how the matter was resolved, or at all angry at his escaping formal punishment and receiving a prestigious post. Chaeronea was an ally, had behaved properly in its initial response, and was fully entitled to enforce its own laws as it saw fit. The case was raised by another Greek city, Orchomenus, a long-time rival of Chaeronea hoping to damage their neighbour and win Roman favour.[6]

It would be quite possible to write a history of the cities of Greece – and indeed the kingdoms and city-states in Asia and further afield – in the second and early first centuries BC in which Rome played a minor, for much of the time even irrelevant, part. Long-standing rivalries like that between Chaeronea and Orchomenus continued to be played out, as did the internal politics of each community. Sometimes both were violent – as in the case of Damon and his slaughter of civic leaders, subsequent rehabilitation and murder. Between communities and kingdoms full-scale wars continued to be waged just as they had been in the past. This was an area that had rarely known long stretches of peace, and had only briefly been united by force under Alexander the Great. Since his death the major Successor kingdoms had vied for power, attacking each other at the slightest hint of weakness, and making and breaking alliances as convenience dictated. None was ever able to gain permanent advantage, and gradually their power was eroded by these conflicts and contests for supremacy among their royal families. Smaller kingdoms flourished as their power declined, Pergamum, Bithynia and Pontus in Asia being the most successful.[7]

Rome eventually deposed King Perseus and dismantled Macedonia. The Seleucid Antiochus III was defeated in 189 BC, but this was far from a fatal blow to his power and the kingdom soon recovered much of its strength. The treaty imposed by Rome barred him from maintaining certain military assets such as warships and war elephants, but there was no concerted effort to keep an eye on the king or his heirs. In 163 BC a Roman embassy touring the east to confirm existing alliances discovered that the Seleucids had plenty of both banned items, and ordered the ships burned and the animals hamstrung. A year later the former consul leading this embassy was murdered in the gymnasium at Laodicea by a local angered at this humiliation. No reprisals were taken by Rome, even when the murderer travelled to Italy and offered himself up for justice. This was at a time when the Republic had no other major military commitments. The killing was not seen as a blow against Rome's *imperium*, and was the action of an individual not sanctioned by the new claimant to the throne. It is possible that the ambassador was felt to have behaved too harshly. Every few decades a party led by a senior senator went to the Hellenic world to visit allies and renew the bonds with Rome. In each case they confirmed existing relationships and were not expected to make drastic changes, but did gather information about the places they visited.[8]

Disinterest characterised Roman attitudes to most events in the Hellenic world after the major conflicts fought in the first few decades of the second century BC. The kingdoms and cities of the region were almost all allies – or if not were keen to gain this status. As in Gaul, the Romans were rarely inclined to take sides in struggles between allies and friends, unless these had a direct impact on Rome's power and interests – something especially rare before the acquisition of Asia as a province. Rome was distant and did not follow events closely, but her overwhelming military might was a factor to be considered by Hellenic leaders and communities. Just like the chieftains in Gaul and elsewhere, the possibility of enlisting Roman support was an attractive one for these men. At the very least, they needed to make sure that rivals did not gain this advantage and use it against them, so that it was better to act first and secure Rome's goodwill. For Greek leaders the Romans were simply one more player to add to the many great and small powers competing on the international stage. The basic rules of the game had not changed.

Roman embassies to the east were rare, but the traffic of ambassadors going in the other direction was constant. The presence of a proconsul and garrison in Macedonia also meant that a steady stream of envoys went to him seeking Roman friendship or support however vague. A common appeal was for arbitration in a dispute with another community. Such requests had been routinely made to the Hellenistic kingdoms or to the bigger cities and leagues, and some communities continued to go to them instead of Rome. It was an opportunity to show respect to a powerful state and to renew or create a bond of friendship. Normally a third party was asked to provide judges to decide the case, thus giving all parties involved a chance to cement good relations with yet another community. Once again, this was 'business as usual' in the Greek world and the Romans were enlisted as simply another Hellenic power. They did not act in response to all appeals, invariably passed the task of deciding the matter on to a third party, and showed no real interest in the outcome, let alone in making sure that the decision was enforced. No doubt the community who first appealed hoped that the respect shown to Rome would aid their cause, and the appeal usually began with a reminder of past friendship and loyalty.[9]

In most cases we hear of an appeal to Rome because the case was recorded in an inscription set up by a city to commemorate the decision – something unlikely unless the Romans were moved to act. Even so, their involvement was minimal. The Second Macedonian War was declared in 200 BC in response to appeals for aid against Philip V from Athens and several other states, but he was already considered an enemy of Rome because of his alliance with Hannibal in Rome's darkest hour. Military intervention was extremely rare and only occurred when it was perceived to be in Rome's interests. In 169 BC the Seleucids invaded Ptolemaic Egypt. The Senate delayed making a decision for some months, and so it was not until the next year that an embassy went to Egypt. Its head, Caius Popillius Laenas, buoyed by news of the recent decisive victory over the Macedonian King Perseus, acted with supreme self-confidence. When he met King Antiochus IV he refused to shake hands and bluntly demanded that the Seleucid king withdraw his army. Antiochus asked for time to confer with his advisers, but Laenas used his stick to draw a circle in the dust surrounding the king and demanded an answer before he stepped out of the ring. The Seleucid king backed down and withdrew to his own realm.[10]

This was Roman diplomacy at its most brutal, with a senator making a foreign king and his army cave in to his demands even though he was backed by only the distant threat of military force. The incident became famous as 'the day of Eleusis', a great source of pride to Romans, but that should not hide the basic truth that such behaviour was very rare. The Republic showed great reluctance for military adventures in the east simply to support allies in the area. One reason was the heavy military demands of the frontiers in northern Italy and then southern Gaul, and in Spain. Rome was glad to acquire allies in the east as elsewhere, but there were plenty of occasions when they refused offers of assistance from Greek communities because they did not wish to place themselves under future obligation. Hellenic leaders knew that they could not rely on Roman backing for their own security, and so continued to pursue their ambitions as before. Rome rarely acted, and even when it did choose to intervene often did not insist on having its way. Shrewd leaders also knew that Rome's displeasure could well be turned around in time, and so they invaded their neighbours or overthrew family members to seize power. There was a good chance that the Senate would accept a *fait accompli*.[11]

DEALING WITH ROME

The Roman Senate was preoccupied with the annual cycle of politics, with domestic matters, competition between its members, and waging war or dealing with major threats to the interests of the Republic. It lacked the time, knowledge and administrative machinery to observe closely and involve itself in the complex and ever-changing affairs of the many states and kingdoms in the wider world. Alliances varied in the degree of friendship they created, but rarely required direct military support when the ally was attacked – especially if the attacker was also an ally. Harnessing Rome's reputation, influence, let alone any degree of direct action, took considerable effort. The governor of Macedonia might be persuaded to make a decision setting up a means of arbitration in a dispute, but did not have the authority to form an alliance, although he could recommend this to the Senate. At the very least, he would return to Rome at the end of his term of office and so honours paid to him might help to recruit a sympathetic ear in the Senate.

The most effective way of gaining Roman favour was to go to Rome itself, but there was no guarantee that a legation would be granted an audience by the Senate. Most embassies who gained this honour were heard in February, and only a matter of immediate and deep concern to the Republic was likely to be given a hearing at other times of the year. Plenty of delegations wanted an audience and time was limited, so for most there was a wait of months or even years. Sensible ambassadors went to senators' houses first thing in the morning when they received friends, clients and petitioners in the reception room or *atrium*. The presence of representatives of foreign kings or communities added to the reputation of the host, and so if he wished this to continue he would hopefully do something on their behalf. Yet there were 300 or so senators – 600 after the expansion of the Senate during Sulla's dictatorship – and only a small proportion had enough prestige to stand a good chance of raising something at a meeting.[12]

A prior connection was an asset, for if a senator or his ancestors had helped in the past then there was an obligation on them to act again, which would in turn reinforce their prestige as patron of a foreign community. The conqueror of a region was expected to become the patron of the peoples there, as was each successive governor, so as new provinces were acquired then more communities established such a link. It was also worth cultivating any Roman of note who passed through a city. Many young aristocrats went to the Hellenic world to study oratory before their formal careers began, including Cicero and Julius Caesar who both spent time on Rhodes. Others passed through Greece on their way to commands in Asia and later Cilicia. Athens had a distinct advantage from its pre-eminence as the centre of the Greek culture, which came to obsess the Roman elite during the course of the second century BC. As Horace later put it, 'captive Greece captured the fierce conqueror'.[13]

A lot of senators on official journeys paused to visit Athens and were received with great ceremony, inspecting a parade of the *ephebes*, the young male citizens undergoing a period of military training. It was common to be initiated into the sacred rites of the Eleusinian Mysteries. Cicero tells us that Lucius Licinius Crassus, a quaestor returning from a posting to Asia but later famous as an orator, arrived two days late for the ceremony and requested the Athenians to stage the whole thing again so that he could take part. They refused, and Crassus sulkily cut short his visit. Not every senator needed to be accommodated in all his demands, especially by a city as famous as Athens. Ptolemaic Egypt developed something close to a formal tour of its sights for visiting Romans, including a trip to the Nile and the opportunity to see the sacred crocodiles being fed. Roman visitors were pampered and entertained, but not free to do whatever they liked. When one accidentally killed a cat – an animal considered sacred by ancient tradition – he was lynched by a mob of Alexandrian citizens. Merely being Roman did not make visitors immune from local taboos.[14]

The prestige of the community or leader who sent an embassy to Rome increased the chance of catching the attention of senators and eventually winning a hearing in the Senate. Almost as important was the choice of ambassadors. Skill at oratory was essential, and anything marking them out as worthy of respect was an asset. Athens once sent the heads of all its philosophical schools as part of an embassy. Past success was another recommendation, since it showed

that a man knew how to work the system to advantage. Some ora-
tors made multiple visits to Rome. An inscription records no fewer
than five successful trips to Rome made by the orator Menippus of
Colophon in Asia on behalf of his home city in the late second century BC, stating that he 'maintained the force of laws regarding every
kind of charge even in cases involving the Romans'. In one case a
citizen of Colophon was charged with killing a Roman and had been
summoned to Rome by the orders of Roman magistrates. Menippus
successfully reasserted a senatorial judgement stating that even cases
of this sort must be dealt with at Colophon by the city's own laws.[15]

On the whole the Romans respected precedent and tried to be
consistent in their decisions, which still meant that sometimes they
needed to be reminded of past judgements because they lacked the
bureaucratic support to have such information always at their finger-
tips. As well as their knowledge and connections, many ambassadors
made gifts to prominent men in the hope of gaining their goodwill
or even active support. Cicero mentions that Cleopatra promised to
give him several books during one of her visits to Rome, presents
'that had to do with learning and not derogatory to my dignity' –
and was bitter when they never appeared. He considered a present
of this sort as entirely honourable and appropriate. At other times
gifts of money or artworks were given, sometimes on a considerable scale. On one occasion the Senate formally barred a group of
ambassadors from borrowing any more cash at Rome because they
were simply handing it out to buy senatorial support. Jugurtha spent
freely to win backing for killing his brothers and seizing sole power,
and is supposed to have claimed that Rome was 'a city up for sale,
and doomed to speedy destruction if it ever found a buyer'.[16]

The Numidian king was one of many monarchs to travel to
Rome to present their case in person. Such royal visitors were the
most prestigious petitioners of all, but that did not in itself ensure
either that they would be received or that they would get what they
wanted. Jugurtha arrived without his royal regalia, wearing clothes
intended to excite pity. Roman senators felt themselves more than
equals to any king and expected the monarchs to act accordingly, so

that pomp and ceremony were unlikely to create a good impression. In 167–166 BC Prusias II of Bythinia exploited this sentiment in a way that the historian Polybius found contemptible. When Roman ambassadors came to his own court he shaved his head and donned the cap, toga and Roman-style shoes worn at Rome by a slave receiving his freedom, and claimed, 'In me you see your freedman who wishes to endear himself and imitate all things Roman.' When he travelled to Rome and was granted an audience in the Senate he prostrated himself on the floor of the chamber and hailed the senators as 'saviour gods'. For Polybius this made it 'impossible for anyone after him to surpass him in unmanliness, womanishness, and servility', but he did receive a favourable response, while a rival prince who came to Rome a little later was not even given an audience.[17]

In Egypt the Ptolemies spent much of their time and efforts in vicious power struggles waged within the family. The brothers Ptolemy VI and Ptolemy VIII plotted against and fought each other for decades, both seeking Roman support and travelling to Rome in the hope of securing it. After his brother and sister had sent envoys who dressed and acted as the humblest of suppliants, Ptolemy VI adopted a very different if equally extreme approach in his desire not to seem over-proud or to demand anything from the Senate. Expelled from his kingdom, he travelled to Italy as a private citizen and then took up residence in one of the least fashionable areas of Rome, sharing lodgings with a Greek artist or writer – our sources are unclear on this last point. He did not approach the Senate in any way, but waited for his condition to gain their attention. Once this was done, he was brought to the Senate, Rome's governing body apologising for their failure to act sooner, giving him money and insisting that he resume dressing and living in a more fitting style. The ploy was successful up to a point, but even so real backing was limited to instructions that envoys already going to the east were to add Alexandria to their itinerary. A century later, Cleopatra's father Ptolemy XII was driven from Egypt. It took bribery on an immense scale to win him the backing of powerful senators, even more to secure a senatorial decree in his favour, and then more bribes and a delay of several years before the proconsul of Syria marched his legions into Egypt and restored the king to power.[18]

Roman attitudes began to change as Rome acquired more provinces and the power struggles of neighbouring kingdoms and states came to pose more direct threats to her interests – hence Cicero's instructions to intervene on behalf of Ariobarzanes in Cappadocia. Yet in the main, the initiative remained with the allies to seek Roman aid, so that they still needed to win backing from the governor and send or go to Rome itself to influence the Senate. The same was true of communities in the provinces, where the presence of a governor inevitably meant that a Roman was involved in more decisions and that there were more opportunities to seek his arbitration or support. As we have seen, there were severe limits to how much any governor could actually do, and much was still left in the hands of the local communities.

Roman provinces were not disarmed, and cities and other groups were expected to undertake military action to deal with banditry and piracy and take some care to their own defence. Cities in Sicily, Greece, Asia and Cilicia constructed, maintained and manned warships as part of their treaty obligations with Rome. The young Julius Caesar was captured and ransomed by pirates while in the east studying. Once released, he cajoled allied cities into providing him with a squadron of their ships and led these to capture the band. Only then did he approach the governor of Asia, who presumably was busy with many other concerns. Our sources do not suggest that he persuaded a Roman officer in charge of these warships to act. Here, as often elsewhere, the command was entrusted to local men. In 74 BC, during a second spell of study, Caesar on his own initiative led local forces to drive off a raiding party sent into Asia by Mithridates of Pontus.[19]

Allies were expected to raise land forces as well. Sicily had suffered two serious slave rebellions in the last decades of the second century BC and local troops were deployed in both as well as regularly being mustered in case of future outbreaks. This was not an exclusively Roman problem – Athens put down at least one servile revolt around the same time. Rome had always relied on allied soldiers to supplement the legions, and sometimes these formed the bulk or all of the troops available. The opening stages of the first conflict with Mithridates were fought almost entirely by local allies led by a governor and his legate. Many provincial communities retained some military capacity, often backed by traditional institutions for raising and equipping soldiers, and electing or appointing officers to lead them. Local aristocrats were able to win glory fighting on behalf of their home city even when fighting as allies of Rome. Excavations at a house in Segesta in Sicily dating to the late second century BC revealed a room decorated with carvings of eight warship rams, a traditional symbol of victory at sea. The only difference with the past was that within the province they were no longer free to wage war against their neighbours and instead had to employ legal means to settle differences. Allied kingdoms bordering provinces felt no such restraint, as the frequent palace coups and civil wars testified.[20]

Although a governor was supreme in his province, it was possible to appeal over his head to the Senate, but this was difficult and often impractical if he was only in the province for a year. One of Verres' victims in Sicily did manage to secure a hearing at Rome, but the senators agreed to let the governor's father deal with the matter by quietly persuading his son to change his decision. Verres ignored this, trying the man in his absence, then tampering with the official record. The Senate did nothing more about the matter. In most cases complaints were not raised until after a governor had returned to Rome. In 140 BC a delegation of provincials accused Decimus Junius Silanus, a former praetor and governor of Macedonia, of wrongfully taking money. When the Senate heard the complaint, it granted a request by Silanus' father to investigate the matter privately. The stern conclusion of the father was that his son had failed to live up to the standards of their proud ancestry. Silanus hanged himself.[21]

The only significant restraint on a governor was his fear of attack on his return. Until then, when he laid down his *imperium*, even direct instructions from the Senate could be ignored while he remained in his province. This meant that justice was at best retrospective. In 171 BC representatives from towns in Spain came to Rome to complain of the conduct of several men sent out to govern the province, begging that the senators would 'not permit them, its allies, to be more wretchedly despoiled and harassed than its enemies'. Discovering that large sums of money had been extorted from the provincials, a special tribunal was set up, the delegates naming four prominent senators to act as their advocates – non-citizens could not play any part in legal judgements or other formal procedures at Rome other than as witnesses. One former governor was acquitted and two went into voluntary exile before a verdict was reached. There was a rumour that the advocates were unwilling to make charges against some others who were 'noble and influential', and the presiding praetor brought proceedings to a close by leaving Rome to govern one of the Spanish provinces. However, a request from the delegates was granted and a law passed which banned governors in Spain from setting the value of grain levied as a 5 per cent tax to Rome, from forcing communities to sell this to them at this price, or from stationing officers in their towns to collect money.[22]

It was not until 149 BC that that a permanent court was established to deal with crimes of extortion in the provinces – the *quaestio de rebus repetundis*. This still required a charge to be brought by a Roman against the former governor on his return home – there was no Roman equivalent to 'the crown against . . .' or 'the state against . . .'. A praetor presided, and the jurors were senators, while the advocates also came from the senatorial class, even if some prosecutors were young aristocrats not yet enrolled in the Senate. This was trial by a man's peers, who were often sympathetic or simply more concerned with trading political favours than establishing the truth. In 122 BC the jury was changed so that it was drawn from the equestrian order, and this issue became a political battleground until 70 BC, when composition was settled at one third senators, one third equestrians and one third *tribuni aerarii* (a poorly documented group with a slightly lower census qualification than the *equites*). In spite of the notorious conviction of Rutilius Rufus mentioned earlier, it is hard to tell whether the bias of the court changed markedly with each reform. Some equestrians were *publicani* or had ties to them, but that does not mean that the latter effectively controlled the court. Details are not available for many cases, but our sources mention forty-six prosecutions which occurred in this court in the years between 149 and 50 BC. These break down into twenty-two acquittals, twenty convictions and four where the outcome is unclear. The picture is likely to be distorted because the sources are poor for some decades and were always more inclined to mention convictions.[23]

On the whole the system favoured the former governor. Prosecution was less honourable than defence, since the aristocracy frowned on ending another man's career, so this was usually the preserve of the young. More experienced and prestigious senators tended to defend, and loyalty to a friend or political ally was seen as admirable even when he was patently guilty. Plenty of governors who had abused their power avoided even being charged in the first place, their own record, family name and connections ensuring that no one wanted to risk earning their enmity. In some cases this fear extended to communities in the province and it was common to ensure that they sent embassies praising the governor soon after he left – hence Appius Claudius Pulcher's annoyance when Cicero prevented it. At the very least, this could be cited as evidence that any subsequent charges were invented.

Verres' tenure in Sicily from 73–71 BC was marked by profiteering, extortion and abuse of power on a spectacular scale. Cicero claimed that the governor joked that his first year was devoted to making himself rich, the second to gathering money to hire the best advocates and the third to raising the cash to bribe judge and jury at his inevitable trial. New-found wealth, as well as artworks and other valuable presents, helped a man to buy friends to add to his existing connections. Rome's political system, where the judge of the court changed every year, and many days were not available for trials because of festivals or other public business, was also subject to manipulation. Verres and his supporters first tried to put up an unknown as a tame prosecutor, but at a public hearing Cicero beat this challenger to the right to undertake the case. They then tried to limit the time he had to gather witnesses and evidence, and to delay the trial until the following year, when an associate would preside over the *repetundis* court. Cicero outmanoeuvred them each time, and then broke with convention by delivering a short, blistering speech to start the prosecution instead of the normal lengthy oration. Some defence was made by the leading orator of the day, but the long succession of witnesses and testimony soon convinced Verres to admit defeat. He went into exile at Massilia, taking much of his plunder with him. Almost thirty years later Mark Antony found it worth his while to execute the former governor so that he could confiscate his wealth and art collection.[24]

Cicero handled the prosecution with great skill – and made sure that everyone was aware of it, publishing an extremely long five-part follow-up speech which he would have delivered if Verres had not fled. This should not diminish his achievement, or make us forget that had someone less industrious and skilful been involved then Verres may well have escaped punishment and continued his career. If the case had involved a province much further afield, making it more difficult to gain reliable information and call witnesses – many of Verres' victims had fled to Rome of their own accord – then things might also have been different. The entire system favoured the governor, but even so some men were prosecuted and some convicted. At best this possibility was a deterrent on future governors from committing similar crimes – a warning which clearly had not deterred Verres and plenty of others. Obviously the victims of brutality could not be brought back to life, and the only punishment for the governor was exile and the end of his career. It was hard to recover the money and other things stolen by a man like Verres, and it is doubtful that his Roman and Sicilian victims got back very much of what they had lost. Cicero claimed that the governor had extorted more than 40,000,000 sesterces, but it looks as if no more than 3,000,000 were recovered.[25]

PEACE AND ITS PRICE

Cicero claimed that the moral qualities of Rome's leaders went into sharp decline after the outbreak of the first civil war in 88 BC and the subsequent dictatorship of Sulla, so that many more exploited provincial commands. Before that era

> . . . our *imperium* could be called more accurately a protectorate of the world than domination. This policy and practice we had begun gradually to modify even before Sulla's time: but since his victory we have departed from it altogether. For the time had gone by when any oppression of the allies could appear wrong, seeing that atrocities so outrageous were committed against Roman citizens.[26]

Modern scholars are reluctant to follow the Romans' emphasis on morality and character in explaining events, but most would admit that there was some truth in this. Some of the men who thrived at a time when citizen was killing citizen were scarcely likely to conform to better standards of behaviour when placed in charge of a province. The ever-spiralling cost of winning office added to this unhealthy mix, creating more and more senior magistrates desperate for quick profit to deal with their debts. Yet we should not exaggerate or paint too grim a picture. There had been good and bad governors in the past, and there were still plenty of senators who shared Cicero's views on the proper conduct of a governor. Throughout his career Julius Caesar championed the cause of provincials, leading at least two prosecutions of former governors, admittedly without success, and reframing the law regulating their behaviour in 59 BC. The modern instinct is to focus on his aggressive warfare during his tenure in Gaul, but by Roman standards his administration appears to have been efficient and honest.[27]

The men who led the Republic in its final decades had a different understanding of Rome's *imperium* to earlier generations, since they grew up when it had come to mean not simply power, but the physical territory ruled as provinces. They boasted of wielding power over 'the whole globe' and were quite open about the profits and comforts this brought to the people of Rome. In various speeches Cicero singled out Sicily as the great supplier of grain to Italy, and Asia as the richest of all provinces. In 66 BC he spoke in support of a law granting Pompey the Great a special command against Mithridates of Pontus, and stressed the importance of this conflict, for

> . . . it involves the glory of Rome, which has come down to you from your forefathers great in everything but greatest of all in war: it involves the safety of your allies and friends, in whose defence your forefathers undertook many great and serious wars: it involves the most assured and the most considerable sources of the public revenue, the loss of which would cause you to look in vain for ornaments of peace or the munitions of war: it involves the property of many citizens whose interests you are bound to consult both for their own sake and for that of the commonwealth.[28]

These four motives were intertwined. The provinces provided a bounty for the state and for individual businessmen operating there. Glory was important, not least because a belief in Rome's strength and power was the best way to deter attackers. On top of that was an obligation to protect allies, since if they were assaulted then glory would be damaged and so would profits. Cicero and Julius Caesar alike assumed that it was the duty of the Republic to keep peace in the provinces, protecting them from invasion, suppressing open rebellion and lower levels of banditry and violence. This had grown from the traditional obligation to defend allies, so often used to justify wars, into a clearer need to maintain the territorial integrity of the provinces and promote peace and prosperity within them. In 56 BC Cicero told the Senate that he felt the 'assignment of the provinces should aim at a maintenance of a lasting peace'. This was the proper and the profitable thing to do. The process was gradual, and allies and provincials alike were still expected to play a significant part in their own security. Only when the threat proved beyond their capacity to defeat did Rome step in, for instance when it set up a garrison in Macedonia.[29]

The presence of warlike tribes prone to raiding was an obvious threat, to be curbed by 'victories and triumphs'. In the same speech the orator attacked the current proconsul in Macedonia, whose corruption and neglect of his army meant that

> . . . this province is now so harassed by barbarians, whose greed has made them break the peace that the people of Thessalonica, dwelling in the very heart of our *imperium*, are forced to abandon their city and fortify their citadel, that our great military road [the Via Egnatia] through Macedonia as far as the Hellespont is not only endangered by raiding barbarians, but even studded and dotted with Thracian encampments.[30]

The peace the Thracians had shattered in this way was the Roman Peace that came through the Republic's victory and strength. Cicero claimed that he could otherwise 'now speak of every region of the world, of every kind of enemies. There is no race which has not either been so utterly destroyed that it hardly exists, or so thoroughly subdued that it remains submissive, or so pacified that it rejoices in our victory and rule.'[31]

Aggression needed to be met with greater force, but although Rome's resources were considerable they were not infinite. It took time, effort, expense and often defeats and large loss of Roman and allied lives to deal with enemies. Victory was not necessarily permanent, as the recent failures in Macedonia demonstrated.

Some problems took a long time to be taken seriously and even longer to resolve. As we have seen, the Romans weakened the Hellenistic kingdoms which in the past had curbed piracy, allowing it to flourish in the second century BC. Allied communities all along the coastlines were prey to raiders, robbing and taking captives to sell as slaves, many of them passing through the markets at Delos and being sold to Romans and Italians. Over time the problem spread further and further west, and it may have been this that eventually persuaded the Senate to do something about it. In the last years of the second century BC a proconsul was tasked with assembling a fleet and attacking the pirates, and in 102 BC Cilicia was allocated as a province. Little changed in the long run, and another effort made in 74 BC ended in the defeat of the Roman commander. Italy itself was raided, Ostia attacked and two praetors and all their attendants abducted. Cicero lamented that Roman power had fallen so low:

> We who in former days, besides keeping the whole of Italy safe, were able to guarantee the safety of all our allies in the farthest coasts by the prestige of our empire . . . Delos, though set far from Rome in the Aegean sea, and visited by men of every country with their merchandise and their cargoes, packed though the island was with riches, small though it was and defenceless, had nothing to fear.[32]

In 67 BC Pompey the Great was given unprecedented power and resources and swept the Mediterranean free of pirates in just six months. Punishment was tempered with generosity, and he resettled many of the piratical communities away from the coast and on better land so that they should not need to resort to raiding in the future. Piracy was not eradicated altogether, but the scale was drastically reduced, an achievement reinforced as more and more of the lands around the Mediterranean coastline came under direct Roman rule.[33]

Roman dominance of a region scarcely altered existing patterns of war and other forms of large- or small-scale violence, but the establishment of provinces did change things. Within these regions, the Romans were unwilling to permit inter-state disputes to turn to conflict or to allow violent changes of power within states. Dealing with banditry, slave insurrection and other problems was still a task that fell to the provincial communities, only now this was under Roman supervision and might be backed by the far more substantial might of the legions. Allied kingdoms and states bordering the provinces were less regulated, but even so the Romans were more likely to intervene than in the past. They also gradually assumed responsibility for securing long-distance communication and trade routes, encouraging peace over a wider area. By the middle of the first century BC the provinces were more peaceful than in the past and many were prosperous, and the same was true to a greater or lesser extent of the lands around them.

This came at a price. Roman war-making was brutal, and the period of conquest might well be marked by destruction of settlements, ravaging of farm land and the mass killing and enslavement of the population. It is hard to give precise figures for the numbers of dead and enslaved during the creation of Rome's empire. After the Third Macedonian War, the consul Lucius Aemilius Paullus rewarded his soldiers and gave a stark object lesson in the danger of opposing Rome by the seizure of some 150,000 people from the cities of Epirus. While it is possible that some were ransomed by relatives, thus providing the Romans with cash instead of captives, most were sold as slaves. Major conflicts were rare and flooded the market with cheap slaves, but the demand was constant and had to be fed by other means, including piracy and abduction – the *publicani* were also known to enslave those incapable of paying taxes. None of these practices were wholly new, but the arrival of Rome, and the concentration of the profits of empire in Italy with its slave-worked estates, greatly increased demand.[34]

Hundreds of thousands were enslaved in the second century BC and even more in the first century BC, paying a heavy price for the spread of Roman power. Conditions were worst for those sent to work the mines run by the *publicani* in Spain and elsewhere. Life expectancy was only a little better for those destined for the rural estates, some living chained in barracks, their numbers supplemented by free citizens kidnapped while travelling. Household slaves did better, but lacked legal rights and were simply property at the disposal of their owners. Slaves could run, but it was hard to escape and the punishments were severe for those recaptured. All of the servile rebellions were crushed – that of Spartacus ending with the massed crucifixion of 6,000 men along the Appian Way from Rome to Capua as a ghastly warning.[35]

There is nothing to suggest that the Romans treated their slaves more brutally than the Greeks or Carthaginians, who also accepted slavery as normal. As far as we can tell, the slave rebellions aimed at personal freedom rather than the abolition of slavery as an institution. In one respect the Romans were more generous, for they freed many more slaves than any other ancient state and also granted the freedmen far more rights. By the first century BC it was believed that most of Rome's population included freed slaves among their ancestors. Yet freedom was far more likely for household slaves, who spent more time around their owners, and for skilled craftsmen or specialists such as teachers and actors. For a few it led ultimately to a comfortable, even wealthy, life, but that should never blind us to the grim fate of the majority.[36]

Conquest was often savage and its consequences terrible for many of the conquered. Yet plenty of other leaders and communities never fought against the Romans, allying with them from the start, and drawing them steadily closer to involvement in a region. After his victory in the Second Macedonian War, the proconsul Titus Quinctius Flamininus announced the 'freedom' of the cities of Greece. Similar declarations were made by the Romans for other parts of the Hellenic world on other occasions. This had been a frequent element in the propaganda of the Hellenistic kingdoms, and in part was intended to exclude them from the affairs of the city-states. Even so the Romans did not interfere in the affairs of these communities or tax them. When provinces were created there was still a range of legal statuses allotted to peoples, based mainly on the nature of their past relationship with Rome. Free cities were exempt from taxation, although they might be obliged to aid their Roman allies and were often subject to lesser duties such as tolls on trade. Other communities were taxed directly in money or produce.[37]

The burdens placed on the provincials were more or less heavy, and subject to the abuses of governors and *publicani* – and of their own leaders. Rome profited from the empire and openly paraded this fact. She did not otherwise interfere greatly in the lives of provincials, who in the main continued to use their own political systems and laws. The power of governors was such that rights and privileges were sometimes ignored, although with time and effort it was possible to send envoys and persuade the Senate to reassert these, and the better governors upheld them without the need for such reminders. There was a tendency whenever a Roman official was involved for him to frame legal questions in ways familiar to him from Roman law, even if the actual decision was based on local precedents. Rome's influence grew slowly and was surely inevitable. Near the end of his tenure in Cilicia, Cicero joked that because he adhered to his edict and let the cities resolve disputes according to their own laws with judges drawn from other communities within the province, then the Greeks could believe 'they have self-government (literally *autonomy*)'.[38]

Cicero knew that this was an illusion. The provinces were Rome's, exploited for her benefit, and short of rebellion the provincials had no means of changing this situation. Revolts were rare, the punishment terrible, and under the Republic no province was able to free itself permanently by armed force. Nor did any external power prove capable of invading and holding on to any province for more than a few years. In the long run, there was simply no choice other than submitting to the military might and determination to dominate of the Roman Republic. This meant the unpredictable conduct of governors, and the activities of moneylenders and *publicani* which were more or less tolerable depending on circumstances. With independence also went the freedom to fight neighbours and stage coups, and instead there was a greater degree of peace and stability. On the whole this fostered prosperity, which is not to say that all benefited equally.

Over time the leaders of the Roman Republic began to think of its *imperium* as not simply power, but something closer to our concept of empire. Keeping the peace within the provinces and defending these and their other allies was one of their priorities, if not always the most important. The motive was never altruistic, but pragmatic, for Rome was wealthier from its overseas territory and it was a good thing to maintain and increase this wealth. Around the end of the second century and the opening decades of the first century BC many senators seem to have felt that their imperium was genuinely under threat from enemies like the Cimbri and Teutones, and then Mithridates of Pontus. The Social War against the Italian allies was also an extremely serious and costly conflict. With hindsight and more sense of the limited strength of such enemies, we can see that they had little chance of destroying Rome, but that was not obvious at the time. Romans of all classes felt threatened, and it may well be that coming through this apparent crisis reinforced the sense of the empire as something to protect.[39]

Then Rome's civil wars began, and from 88–30 BC created by far the biggest threats to peace and prosperity throughout the Mediterranean world. The first war raged mainly in Italy, but spilled over into Sicily, Africa and the east, and spawned another conflict fought out for several more years in Spain. In 49 BC Caesar crossed the Rubicon and began the next prolonged conflict, with little fighting in Italy but two campaigns in Spain, two in Africa and the decisive encounter in Greece. It also sparked large-scale operations in Asia and Egypt. Subsequent conflicts which stuttered on from Caesar's assassination in 44 until 30 BC followed a similar pattern. Provinces became war zones, and even those spared this were called upon to provide soldiers, equipment, mounts, warships, food and money for the war efforts of the rival commanders.[40]

It had always been difficult to reach sufficient influential men to persuade the Senate to listen to a petition. Now it became even harder to know just who was leading the Republic, and there was always a chance that by the time a deal was done those men would have been overthrown. The career of Cleopatra is instructive. Brief joint rule with her brother ended with her expulsion and an unsuccessful attempt to reinvade Egypt. If Caesar had not arrived, become her lover and restored her to power, then the odds were that she would have been exiled or killed by the age of twenty-one. Caesar's backing came at a price drawn from the wealth and rich harvest of Egypt, but was lost when he was murdered. Having arrived in Rome to confirm their alliance, the queen stayed there for a month after the assassination, trying to find out who was now in charge and deal with them. When Brutus and Cassius came to the east to raise armies, Cleopatra obeyed their instructions to supply them with resources, although she later claimed to have done so half-heartedly. After they were defeated, she went in spectacular style to Tarsus and won over Mark Antony, acting as a good ally to him – as well as his lover. In time this meant she was caught up in another Roman civil war which led to defeat at Actium in 31 BC. At the very end, she tried to cut another deal with the victor, surviving for some ten days after Antony's suicide. Only when it was clear that she would not be allowed to retain her throne or pass it to her children did she take her own life.[41]

Cleopatra never fought against Rome, in spite of the depiction of her in Augustan propaganda as a great threat. Throughout her career she was a loyal ally – it was just that the bloody changes of power in the Republic meant that she ended up on the wrong side. Much the same story could be told of other communities and client rulers, who did their best to prosper under Roman rule. In Cleopatra's case clinging to power was the only way to ensure her survival in the murderous politics of the Ptolemaic court. Apart from the brother who died fighting Caesar, she murdered a younger brother and had Antony execute her sister and last remaining sibling. To stay in power she spent lavishly from the resources of her realm to satisfy the demands of successive Roman war leaders and their subordinates. Doing so kept her alive, and she was also able to add to her power by regaining territories once owned by her family. This came at the expense of other allies of Rome, such as Herod of Judaea, a man who managed to back Antony and still convince Augustus to trust him. He remained in power and survived to die of natural causes some three decades later. There were winners as well as losers among the allies and provincials in Rome's civil wars, but all were affected.[42]

In the last half-century of the Republic, the greatest enemies of peace and stability were the Romans themselves. It remained to be seen whether the last of the warlords left standing could change this.

PART TWO

PRINCIPATE

EMPERORS

'You, Roman, be sure to rule the world (these be your arts), to crown peace with justice, to spare the conquered and overcome the proud in war.' – *Virgil, c.20 BC.*[1]

POWER WITHOUT LIMIT

The men who murdered Julius Caesar called themselves 'the Liberators', and claimed to have restored the freedom lost when the Republic was ruled by a dictator. Soon Cassius was minting coins featuring the goddess Libertas, while Brutus produced a series depicting a freedman's cap on the reverse – the same symbol once used by Prusias II of Bithynia to show his subservience to Rome. This freedom was not for provincials, but for Romans, and in truth just for the aristocracy who *ought* to share high office and decision-making rather than see this monopolised by one man, whatever his personal merits. This was the only occasion in the long cycle of Roman civil wars when one side claimed to be acting on principle, and not simply battling with rivals for power. It was a cause with no relevance to the lives of provincials, and yet as loyal allies they were expected to play their part in the war that followed. As they raised armies in the eastern Mediterranean, Brutus and Cassius treated communities who failed to meet their demands for resources and money as rebels. Rhodes was attacked and forced to submit, several communities in Judaea sold into slavery, and the city of Xanthus in Lycia stormed and sacked, prompting the mass suicide of many inhabitants.[2]

Cassius and Brutus were defeated and took their own lives in the autumn of 42 BC. Communities who had resisted them were praised by the victors and received some reparations. Mark Antony ordered those sold into slavery in Judaea to be freed, gave new territory to Rhodes, and this island and all of Lycia were granted exemption from paying tax to Rome. In a letter to Hyrcanus, the allied ruler of Judaea, he spoke of Brutus and Cassius as 'enemies of the Roman people', and 'oath-breakers' (for they like all senators had sworn to protect Julius Caesar) who had committed crimes against men and gods:

> Now that these men have been punished, we hope henceforth we shall enjoy peace and give Asia respite from war. We are therefore ready to let our allies also participate in the peace given to us by God; and so, owing to our victory, the body of Asia is now recovering, as it were, from a serious illness. Having, therefore, in mind to promote the welfare both of you and your nation, I shall take care of your interests.

Not all communities did so well, and the ones who more readily had met Brutus' and Cassius' demands for money and other resources were now obliged to give even more to the victors.[3]

The 'respite from war' was short-lived. In the winter of 41–40 BC the Parthian invasion feared by Cicero at long last happened. Asia was raided, Syria and Judaea overrun. Many individual leaders and communities resisted as far as they could, while others welcomed the invader. Hyrcanus was deposed by a rival backed by Parthian cavalry, who was in turn defeated with the aid of the legions as the Romans recovered and drove the invaders out. As ever, local ambitions did more than anything else to determine actions. For Judaea this was one further episode in a long-running civil war mainly fought by rival claimants from the Hasmonean royal family, with Roman – and in this case Parthian – aid being sought out in an effort to gain a decisive advantage. Yet for all the power struggles within allied kingdoms, it was the Roman civil wars that dominated these years. One by one the rival warlords were eliminated, until finally Antony fought Julius Caesar's heir and namesake and was beaten, taking his own life in August 30 BC.[4]

The victor was not quite thirty-three years old, but would never again face a serious challenge and remained in control of the Roman world until his death in AD 14. As Imperator Caesar Augustus – he was granted the semi-religious name by the Senate in 27 BC – his power rested ultimately on his control of an army which had grown to more than sixty legions by the time that he defeated Antony. Many soldiers were due for discharge, and it was Augustus who set them up in colonies and gave them land to farm. The rest were formed into about twenty-eight permanent legions, supported by non-citizen auxiliaries and naval units. All were now long-service professionals – by the end of his reign legionaries served for twenty-five years – and all were paid by him, rewarded and promoted by him, and swore a solemn oath to be loyal to him. Discipline was strict, and the troops were less pampered than during the civil war years. It was his army, and he and his successors took great care to preserve this mono-poly of military force. In the second century AD, a senator renowned for his oratory was asked why he let the Emperor Hadrian publicly correct his use of a particular word. The man joked with his friends that surely everyone must 'acknowledge that the man who controls thirty legions is the most learned of all'.[5]

Imperator Caesar Augustus, the son of the divine Julius, did not call himself king or dictator. Instead he was *princeps* – the first senator, the first citizen and the foremost servant of the state. His constitu-tional position developed over time, through trial and error rather than any long-term design, as offices, honours and privileges were awarded to him. The trend was for more and more of his powers to be personal, granted directly to him and not tied to a particular magistracy and so lapsing when the term of office expired. Each was awarded through due legal process, but there was no means of taking them back, and only Augustus himself could choose to give them up. From the beginning the Greeks called him *Autokrator* or autocrat, and there was no real question that he was anything other than a monarch, regardless of the title he used. Scholars refer to the system he created as the Principate, and describe it as a veiled monarchy.[6]

It was a thin veil, and it is unlikely that anyone was really deceived.

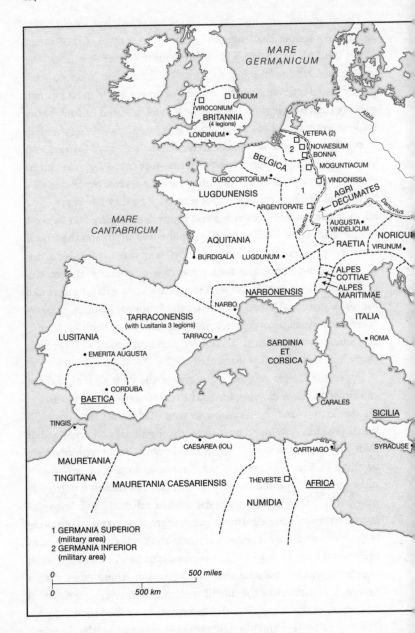

The Roman Empire in AD 60

Under Augustus the Popular Assemblies still convened to elect magistrates, and there was often genuine competition, frequent bribery and occasional intimidation in the worst traditions of the last decades of the Republic. Yet Augustus recommended a significant number of candidates and these invariably won, and his successors transferred elections from the assemblies to the Senate. This was one of several additional powers gained by the Senate, which continued to meet and was treated with great respect and dignity, while losing all independence. By 30 BC its numbers had swollen to almost 1,000 members, and Augustus pruned them of the most unsuitable men who had been enrolled during the civil wars until it returned to around 600. The old aristocratic families were well represented, at least once a new generation grew up to replace the losses from the decades of violence. Senators provided the vast majority of provincial governors, including those for all the major provinces with the exception of Egypt, but when they commanded an army it was as a legate of the emperor, a *legatus Augusti* – representative and subordinate of Augustus with *imperium* delegated from him. (Africa was an exception, and the proconsul there had charge of a single legion, but even this was changed under Augustus' successors.)

A man could still win office and honours, but a successful career required the approval of the *princeps*. New men reached the consulship and ennobled their families, while the scions of the old houses were able to add to the record of their lines. None were permitted to compete with Augustus or his successors, and there were limits to what was possible. The last triumph by a man unrelated to the imperial family was celebrated in 19 BC, and after that even the most successful had to satisfy themselves with the insignia of triumph – the *ornamenta triumphalia* – and were not allowed to parade through the City. Augustus held three triumphs and two ovations (a lesser form of the honour, when the general rode on horseback rather than in a chariot), and refused a succession of other offers of triumphs awarded to him when a war was won by one of his legates. He was also consul thirteen times, the son of a god, the father of his country, and held a long string of other honours.

The City of Rome was remodelled on a far grander scale to celebrate Augustus' glory as leader of the Roman people. As the years passed, communities in Italy and the provinces set up more and more monuments to him and his close family. Some were given as benefactions to them, but many more were local initiatives. Augustus' image and name were on every gold and silver coin throughout the empire – and on many of the bronze issues as well. Traditionally, Roman coins bore the heads of gods and goddesses, or distinguished but dead men from earlier generations. Julius Caesar was the first living Roman to be depicted on many, though not all, coins during his dictatorship. After his death other leaders did the same thing, including Brutus, but none could match the sheer quantity of coin series issued by Augustus. Whether on coin or as a bust, statue, sculpted relief or painting, the image of the *princeps* was everywhere. It was idealised and carefully controlled, the face that of a serenely handsome young man, and it never aged, in stark contrast to the Roman tradition of realistic, often grim-faced portraiture. More images of Augustus survive from the ancient world than of any other Roman emperor, or indeed any other human.[7]

In 27 BC the *princeps* accepted an immense provincial command. He pretended reluctance for such a burdensome responsibility, but it is clear that the charade played out in the Senate was carefully orchestrated, as they begged the foremost servant of the state to take on the most important tasks for the wider good. At first Augustus controlled all of Spain, Gaul, Syria and Egypt, the first three ostensibly because they were regions where Roman control was least secure, either because they were not fully 'pacified' or because there was a threat from outside. North-western Spain was not yet conquered, Gaul was subject to raids from German tribes beyond the Rhine, and Syria had been badly disrupted during the civil wars and bordered on Parthia. The command was voted for ten years, but then extended by periods of five or ten years throughout his life. The remaining provinces were controlled by the Senate, with proconsuls selected by lot from former magistrates in the traditional way.[8]

Within a decade, Transalpine Gaul and the new province of

Baetica in southern Spain were transferred to senatorial control. Both were settled and peaceful, and this helped to confirm Augustus' claim that he only took the dangerous provinces out of a sense of duty to Rome and would not cling on to them once they were secure. Instead he took responsibility for newly acquired provinces, notably in the Balkans and in Germany. Virtually all the army was stationed within his provinces, and so under his direct control or commanded by his legates. From 54 BC onwards, Pompey the Great had controlled the Spanish provinces in this same distant manner, remaining near Rome and never visiting his command, but employing legates to govern and lead the legions. During the years of their alliance Antony, Lepidus and the young Augustus had divided up the empire between them in a similar way, letting representatives act on their behalf in the provinces allocated to them. The Augustan system developed from this, but was on a far larger scale.[9]

PEACE AND WAR

The art and literature of the Augustan age – much of it encouraged and sponsored by the *princeps* and his associates – celebrated the return of peace. Augustus boasted that he 'had extinguished the flames of civil war'. Among the many images of him, relatively few, especially of the statues, busts and reliefs, depict him as a general. The *ara pacis augusti* – the altar of the Augustan peace – decreed by the Senate in 13 BC and dedicated in 9 BC, is one of the most striking monuments celebrating his achievements, and depicts the *princeps* and his family walking in procession along with leading members of the Senate. The men are in togas, the women in formal dresses, all quintessentially Roman, but also as Roman civilians honouring the gods in time of peace. There are no soldiers on the monument, the only direct hint of military life being the cloak worn by Augustus' stepson Drusus.[10]

This peace was a Roman Peace brought by Augustus. First and foremost it came from the end of civil war. The poet Horace spoke of his own 'unholy generation whose blood is accursed' turning on each other and threatening to bring Rome down.

> Why are you drawing swords that have only just been sheathed? Has too little Latin blood been shed on land and sea – not to enable the Roman to burn the arrogant stronghold of jealous Carthage, or to make the Briton, so long beyond our reach, walk down the *Sacra Via* in chains, but to ensure in answer to the Parthians' prayers this city shall perish by its own hand?[11]

He and the other poets rejoiced when civil strife was ended through the final victory of Augustus at the Battle of Actium. Ovid described the *ara pacis Augusti* wreathed in 'Actian laurels', and for all its echoes of civil war, Actium was evoked time and time again in art, literature and in trophies and symbols on buildings.[12]

Peace came from victory and strength, and prestige so over-whelming that in future no aggressor would dare risk going to war. This was how Augustus had ended civil war, and this was how he and the Romans would eventually achieve peace in the wider world. Fond of reintroducing archaic ritual as part of his religious, cultural and moral revival of Rome, Augustus took great pride in a ceremony to close the gates of the Temple of Janus, a god with two faces, one looking back and one forward. The doors of this small shrine were shut when the Roman people were not at war, a rite performed just twice before Augustus. Under his leadership the Senate three times gave orders for this to be done, although in the third case news of a fresh outbreak of war on a distant frontier prevented it. On both of the other occasions the doors were reopened within barely a year. For all the talk of peace, Rome under his leadership was almost per-manently at war somewhere in the world, just as it had been under the Republic.[13]

Much of this warfare was aggressive, taking the legions into regions never before entered by the army of the Roman people. Augustus added more territory to the empire than anyone else in Rome's history. Often this involved difficult campaigns in harsh terrain. Thus he conquered the rest of the Iberian Peninsula, and the Alps, stopping the local tribesmen from extorting money from travellers. The campaigns in the Balkans were similarly hard-fought and involved significant Roman losses, but these extended Roman control up to the River Danube. Further north, the legions crossed the Rhine and began to set up a new province reaching as far as the Elbe. Elsewhere Augustus' commanders went down the Nile and struggled through the deserts of Arabia, although in this case the territorial gains were minimal.[14]

The professional army created by Augustus provided his regime with victory after victory. After 26 BC, when he had fallen ill during operations in Spain, the *princeps* never again commanded an army in the field, but he was often in the wider theatre of operations. In almost every major conflict command went to a family member, most of all his old friend and eventually son-in-law Agrippa, and his stepsons, Tiberius and Drusus. Smaller-scale operations were entrusted to legates, but in every case the credit for victory went to him. On fifty-five separate occasions the Senate ordered public thanksgiving to commemorate a fresh victory, amounting to a total of 890 days of celebration. In the *Res Gestae divi Augusti*, the list of his own achievements Augustus wrote and ordered to be set up outside his mausoleum, he listed his many victories, and the same poets who sang of peace also sang of victory. Virgil boasted that it was the Romans' destiny and great art 'to spare the conquered and overcome the proud in war'. Horace claimed that

> Augustus will be deemed a god,
> on earth when the Britons and the
> deadly Parthians have been added to our empire.[15]

Victory followed victory, and defeats were avenged by eventual success. At the heart of the Forum of Augustus, dedicated in 2 BC, was the Temple of Mars Ultor – the war god Mars in his role as 'the avenger', in this case both of the murdered Caesar and of the Roman people as a whole. The empire grew larger and by AD 14 there were twenty-five provinces in total, with seventeen allocated to the *princeps* and eight under senatorial control. Even so, as in the past, not every successful war led to territorial gain. Nor, in spite of the enthusiasm of the poets, did Augustus invade Britain to follow in Julius Caesar's footsteps or attack Parthia as Caesar had planned to do. Instead the *princeps* ignored Britain and used diplomacy backed by a substantial display of military force to negotiate a treaty which was presented as the king of Parthia submitting to Rome. The precious eagle standards lost by Crassus and Mark Antony were returned and eventually deposited with great ceremony in the Temple of Mars Ultor.

Pride was restored, a defeat avenged, and a former enemy made humble acknowledgement of Roman superiority – turning the Parthians from the proud who needed to be overcome into the conquered who should be treated with mercy. As in the past, Rome's victory did not require permanent occupation of territory unless this was considered to be advantageous. Displays of submission did not need to yield significant profit or have concrete results, and the *res gestae* listed people such as the Indians and Britons as part of Rome's empire simply because they had sent embassies to Augustus.[16]

The *princeps* expanded the empire where he felt this was necessary or for the common good and did so over almost half a century of military activity. If it were not for what happened under his successors when conquest all but came to a halt, we would not trouble too much about his motives. Rome had fought wars for many centuries and had expanded, even if provinces were only added every now and then. In the first century BC, men like Pompey and Julius Caesar had gained unprecedented resources and long terms of command and had overrun large areas quickly and turned them into provinces. Augustus did much the same, and had even greater resources, far more time and the freedom to act as he wished. He claimed that his wars were just, responding to past or current aggression, much as Pompey and Caesar had done, and by Roman standards they probably were.

Augustus was a Roman aristocrat, and so like all his class craved glory – military glory most of all. For a man who had seized power by force during a civil war, victories over the foreign enemies of all Romans offered clean honours untainted by the blood of fellow citizens. Augustus conformed to tradition in proving his worth by defeating the enemies of Rome. This was service to the state and, as with victors in the past, the spoils of successful wars were spent in public works in Rome itself. The *princeps* built temples, monuments, aqueducts, bath houses and entertainment venues in the City and, as with so much that he did, it was only the scale that outstripped his predecessors.

Glory was important, and no doubt he was sometimes an opportunist in seizing a chance to add to his achievements, but there does seem to have been more thought to his war-making than this. Similarly, while Virgil promised the Romans *imperium sine fine*, Augustus' restraint in not invading Britain or Parthia makes it clear that he did not invariably want war, even if many Romans felt that it would be justified. Some of what he did made the empire more coherent and secure, and the disposition of the army is a guide to the areas considered most likely to see fighting in the future. The conquest of Spain involved at least five legions, but within a few years of its completion the garrison of the entire Peninsula was reduced to three, and would then drop to one under his successors. Permanent occupation of the Alps greatly improved communications, and it was only his campaigns in the Balkans that created a secure land route to the eastern provinces. Augustus probably was not operating to a rigid plan, but there is no doubt that these accessions of territory made the empire a more coherent unit. On the other hand it is harder to say whether a frontier based on the Elbe rather than the Rhine would have been more secure since it lasted such a short time. The first may look neater on a map, but it is unclear how well the Romans understood the physical geography of the world, and they certainly paid far more attention to the political geography of tribes and peoples.[17]

LIMITS

Augustus suffered many disappointments, most of all the premature deaths of so many close family members, and the scandals that led him to exile his daughter and only legitimate child, Julia, and later two of her children; but his sorest military trials came in the last years of his life. In AD 6 his armies had already begun a great advance into what is now Bohemia when rebellion erupted in the Balkans, forcing a withdrawal so that troops could be sent to deal with this. It was not an easy task, and there were heavy Roman losses and three years of tough fighting before the revolt was suppressed. At one point no fewer than ten legions, along with numerous auxiliaries, were concentrated in a single camp – a force representing more than a third of the entire army. Then, when the war was finally won, rebels in the new province of Germany ambushed and killed the provincial legate Publius Quinctilius Varus, wiping out three of Augustus' legions, the *XVII*, *XVIII* and *XIX*. The Romans fell back to the Rhine and launched a succession of punitive expeditions over the years to come, but they never retook the lost territory. For the first time, a province rebelled against Rome and won permanent freedom.[18]

Augustus was in his seventies, his health already failing, and this blow struck him very hard – a man whose whole career had been based on victory after victory struggled to cope with defeat. He did not shave for weeks, and is said to have wandered the palace calling out 'Quinctilius Varus, return my legions!' When he died five years later he left written advice for his adopted son Tiberius to 'keep the empire within its present boundaries'. The cynical historian Tacitus, himself a senator, tells us of this, wondering whether it was 'through fear or jealousy'. Tiberius succeeded to Augustus' position and powers, many of which he had already been awarded, and largely followed this suggestion. The same was true of most of his successors.[19]

In AD 43 the Emperor Claudius launched an invasion of Britain and created a province in the southern part of the island. Expansion continued on and off there for the remainder of the century, but there was never permanent occupation of the very north of what is now Scotland, and much of the Lowlands were only occupied for a few decades. In AD 101–102 the Emperor Trajan attacked the strong kingdom of Dacia (an area roughly equivalent to modern Romania), and created a new province there after winning a second war fought in AD 105–106. He also added Arabia to the empire and invaded Parthia, intending to create provinces of Mesopotamia and Media. However, his hold on these new conquests was shaky and he was soon faced with a spate of rebellions. In AD 117 Trajan died of natural causes while trying to suppress these revolts, and his new eastern provinces were abandoned. Marcus Aurelius also appears to have intended creating one or two new provinces, in this case in central Europe, but again the plans were abandoned at his death in AD 180. Earlier in his reign he had added some Parthian territory to Syria. At the end of the second century AD Mesopotamia was made a province by Septimius Severus.

Expansion did not stop with the death of Augustus, but it did become far less common, and the contrast with the intense bout of expansion under the first emperor is striking. Augustus' reign was in this respect much like the last decades of the Republic. Pompey and Caesar were also great conquerors, but then the political situation gave them unprecedented opportunities in their commands. Then and earlier the vast majority of senators who fought campaigns as provincial governors dealt with unrest within a province or raiding from the outside. Many attacked peoples outside the empire, but the aim – apart from the acquisition of personal wealth and glory – was to make these enemies submit, not to annex them. Wars of this sort had become the most common form of conflicts as soon as the Romans took and held overseas provinces, and they continued under the Principate. In this sense Augustus was the anomaly, as were Pompey and Caesar to a lesser extent, in presiding over so much acquisition of new territory. Even so, far less expansion occurred after AD 14 than in the third and especially the second centuries BC. Allied kingdoms were turned into provinces until almost all of the lands in the empire were directly ruled, but to a very great extent its size stayed much the same as it had been under Augustus.[20]

Something had changed, but there has been very little agreement over what it was and why this happened. It is unclear precisely what Augustus meant in his advice to Tiberius, and whether he felt that the empire should never again expand or should not do this for the moment. The big rebellion in AD 6 and the loss of Germany in AD 9 inflicted heavy casualties on the Roman army which could not be easily replaced. On both occasions Augustus purchased male slaves and freed them so that they would serve as distinct units in the army. These conflicts came after decades of almost constant warfare, during which he had already increased the length of military service from sixteen to twenty years, and finally to twenty-five years to save on the costs of discharge and also to retain experienced manpower. The military resources of the empire were at a low ebb after such heavy employment. Tiberius ordered three campaigns across the Rhine at the start of his reign, but at the end of AD 16 he called a halt to these operations. One of the reasons was that Gaul and the other western provinces were no longer capable of supplying the army with replacement cavalry mounts and pack and draft animals. For the moment, there were simply not the resources to continue such intensive campaigning, and hence there was a need to consolidate.[21]

This would explain a temporary reduction in Roman aggression, but not a long-term change, and some scholars have wondered whether the empire had reached its natural size. An older view was that Augustus conquered so that he could establish the best and most defensible frontiers, and that once that was achieved, then further expansion was neither necessary nor desirable. This is an extension of the old view of defensive imperialism and so jars with the more recent emphasis on Roman aggression. At the very least the willingness to accept the loss of the German province suggests that any such design changed with circumstances. More importantly, there is no direct ancient evidence for such a plan, and many scholars question whether the Romans possessed the geographical knowledge and had the capacity to think and plan on such a grand scale of strategy.

1 GERMANIA SUPERIOR
2 GERMANIA INFERIOR
3 ALPES ATRECTIANAE
  ET POENINAE
4 PANNONIA SUPERIOR
5 PANNONIA INFERIOR

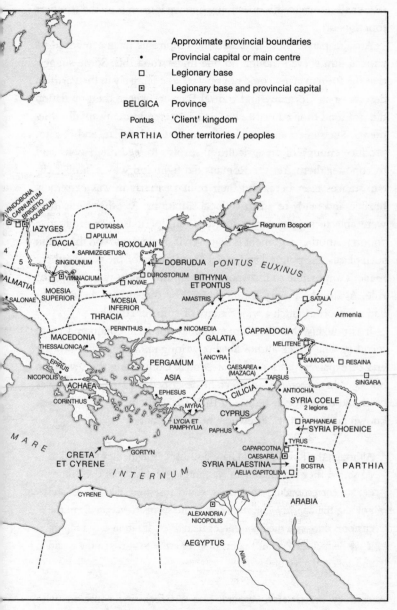

The Roman Empire at the death of Septimius Severus, AD 211

(We shall return to this question when we look at how the frontiers functioned.)

An alternative view is to see the empire as having reached its natural limits, even though no one understood this. Some suggest that the Roman army could not operate as effectively in the Parthian deserts or in Germany and central Europe, where the population did not tend to live in cities but was scattered in many small settlements. Such enemies were harder to find and defeat, and did not produce enough of an agricultural surplus to feed the legions sent to conquer them. Yet the Romans did fight and win in similar circumstances elsewhere, and their military machine was extremely flexible and ready to adapt to local situations. At other times they were able to supply armies for very long periods in unproductive country. Another argument is that even if the legions won the war in such places, the political and social organisation of the peoples there made it impossible to incorporate them into the Roman system of rule. Again, the theory is undermined by the success the Romans had in absorbing such a wide variety of cultures elsewhere.[22]

It is unlikely that the Romans could not have conquered more territory. The Greek author Strabo, writing under Tiberius, saw the end of expansion as a matter of choice. Concluding the seventeen books of his *Geography*, in which he described the lands and peoples of the known world, he noted that 'the Romans occupy the best known portions of it'. Elsewhere he claims that

Although the Romans could have possessed Britain, they scorned to do so, for they saw that there was nothing to fear from the Britons . . . No corresponding advantages would arise from taking over and holding the country. For at present more seems to accrue from the customs duties on their commerce than direct taxation could supply, if we deduct the cost of maintaining an army to garrison the island and collect the tribute.[23]

A century or so later, Appian, also a Greek and someone who worked in the imperial administration at Rome, expressed a similar sentiment: 'Possessing the best parts of the earth and sea the Romans have, on the whole, aimed to preserve their empire by the exercise of prudence, rather than to extend their sway over profitless tribes of barbarians.'[24]

Similar sentiments were voiced on other occasions, and many may have felt that there was little to be gained from further expansion. Yet in spite of Strabo's judgement, Claudius did invade Britain. It was rumoured that Nero thought about abandoning the island because the garrison was too expensive compared to the revenue from the province, but he decided against it. The balance of profit and loss could be overruled by other concerns, and the glory of victory and conquest remained admirable motives for the actions of an emperor.[25]

The Principate was a monarchy, and it was the emperor who controlled the army and made the key decisions over whether or not to expand. Augustus justified his rule through service to the state, and most of all through victories in foreign wars. At the start many people disliked him, remembering his bloody climb to power, but they were willing to accept that he led Rome well, that there was internal peace and prosperity and external success, and over time they became accustomed to his dominance and the existence of a *princeps*. After forty-four years it had become the natural order, since no one could remember a Republic that had functioned well. A *princeps* was necessary, and he was expected to guide the state. All took the title *imperator* and were expected to be victorious in war, whether via their legates or in person. The aristocracy felt a deep nostalgia for the days of the Republic, when their class had led the state and no one man stood out from them, but nobody expected those days to return. After the murder of Caligula in AD 41, the Senate debated a restoration of the Republic for just a few hours before they turned instead to choosing a replacement for the emperor from their own ranks.[26]

Augustus spent most of his reign away from Italy, touring the provinces, organising them, dealing with petitions, travelling and working hard even when he was an old man. He supervised many of the major campaigns, and the rest were led by a close associate, usually a member of his extended family. Tiberius was close to his fifty-sixth birthday when he succeeded Augustus, and had a long record of active and successful military command so he did not have to prove himself as a general. He also had little appetite for travel, or indeed for the dull routine followed by Augustus, and after a few years spent more and more time in the country. In AD 27 he went to live on the island of Capri and did not return to Rome for the last ten years of his life. In the early years of his reign, his nephew and adopted son Germanicus commanded in Germany and the east, acting in place of the *princeps* much as Tiberius and others had done for Augustus. Germanicus died in AD 19, and Tiberius' own son Drusus was only briefly used in a similar way and then in turn died four years later. The *princeps* did not choose to employ any other family members in a similar fashion.

It is important to stress just how far Tiberius' style of rule differed from that of Augustus, for this would do far more to influence the behaviour of later emperors. Augustus spent much of his long reign on the move, visiting almost every province at least once, and employing close associates and family to act in the same way in other parts of the empire. Of his successors, only Hadrian travelled on anything like the same scale. None were able to find so many family members to act in their stead. Usually this was a question of trust, for Augustus was the son of the divine Julius, the victor of Actium, the father of his country. His relatives won glory for themselves, but at the same time reinforced his far greater prestige. They were not and could not be equals or rivals, even when granted some of his powers. In many ways this was the leadership of two or more *principes* rather than one *princeps*, but the dominance of Augustus was unquestioned. No one else was ever as secure.

Lacking trustworthy relatives, the alternatives were to go and preside over a major war in person, or to entrust this to a senatorial legate, but that risked giving that man fame and glory, perhaps even allowing him to subvert the loyalty of the soldiers under his command. Tiberius was already a proven commander and by now had

had enough of life in the field. Unwilling to campaign in person, he did not trust family or senators to hold too many major commands. Ordinary provincial legates never controlled more than four, later three legions, and did not on their own have enough military force to overthrow the emperor. They could only do so if several joined together, and the competitive instincts of Roman aristocrats made this unlikely in most circumstances. Wars were fought to maintain the empire, but significant expansion would require greater resources than those at the disposal of a legate governing a single province.[27]

Caligula was young, had no military experience, and spent some time with the army but achieved nothing. Claudius was older, just as inexperienced, and had been proclaimed as emperor by the praetorian guard – household troops formed by Augustus to have a military force at his immediate disposal since he did not want to station any legion in Italy. In AD 43, two years after coming to power, Claudius launched an invasion of Britain, entrusting command to a legate, Aulus Plautius. Even so, the elderly and infirm emperor travelled to the island to command in person for the capture of the main tribal capital. Claudius spent just sixteen days in Britain, but made sure that the chief credit for the victory was his, although he was also generous with honours to all those senators involved in any way. This adventure satisfied his need for glory. A few years later Cnaeus Domitius Corbulo, one of his provincial legates, had begun to advance deep into Germany, but was recalled by the emperor. The man made the rueful comment, 'How lucky Roman generals were in the old days' of the Republic, but obeyed.[28]

Nero showed little interest in war, although he was praised for waging war against the Parthians rather than accepting a 'shameful peace' and entrusting a major command to Corbulo. Even so, a few years later he summoned the latter and ordered him to commit suicide. Nero's death in AD 68 prompted the civil war in which Galba, Otho and Vitellius reigned in turn until Vespasian managed to restore some stability in AD 69. A year later his older son Titus presided over the capture of Jerusalem, breaking the heart of the Jewish rebellion, and this success was paraded as justification for their rule as emperors – for instance with the construction of the Arch of Titus and the Colosseum. Proven commanders, neither man chose to go on campaign while they were emperor, but they did permit aggressive warfare and expansion by their legates in Britain. Vespasian's younger son Domitian came to power when Titus died suddenly after only a short reign. He could not boast a military record, and spent several years campaigning against the Germanic tribes and the Dacians. There were some gains in territory – or at least an advance of the army's line of bases facing the German tribes – but he suffered at least two serious defeats at the hands of the Dacians and accepted a peace treaty which involved paying money to the Dacian king and giving him other aid. This further damaged his already poor reputation among the senatorial class.[29]

Domitian was murdered in AD 96 in a palace conspiracy, and the Senate chose the elderly and inoffensive Nerva as *princeps*. He then adopted Trajan, legate in command of one of the Rhine provinces and its army, who succeeded to power two years later. Although he had spent an above-average amount of time serving with the legions, the new emperor could not boast of any major successes. This soon changed when he embarked upon full-scale war against the Dacians, culminating in the creation of the new province. Dacia was wealthy from its mineral deposits, and Dacian gold paid for the lavish construction of the Forum of Trajan in Rome, which covered an area bigger than Caesar's Forum and Augustus' Forum put together. The prestige won on the Danube encouraged Trajan to launch his great eastern expedition, which at least in part was inspired by the dream of matching the glory of Alexander the Great. The Romans reached the Persian Gulf and the emperor compared himself to Alexander, but rebellions soon broke out in much of the newly conquered territory, and at the same time there was a revolt by the substantial Jewish populations of Egypt, Cyrenaica and Cyprus.[30]

Trajan's health failed him and he died. It was claimed that in his last days he announced that he planned to adopt his relative Hadrian and name him as successor, but there was suspicion that this was a story invented as his widow and palace officials looked around for someone to succeed the *princeps*. Given the doubts about this, it is unsurprising that Hadrian wanted to get back to Rome rather than spend years in difficult operations to suppress rebellions, and so he abandoned the new provinces and withdrew. Much of his reign was spent touring the empire, and especially the military provinces, inspecting the army and watching the soldiers train. In several cases this led to redeployment of the units and most famously the construction of Hadrian's Wall in northern Britain. There were no fresh wars of conquest, but there were operations on the frontiers and a long and difficult campaign to suppress a rebellion in Judaea.[31]

In AD 137 Hadrian died – it was claimed that he was such a skilled astrologer that he predicted the day and the hour – and was followed by Antoninus Pius, who was so secure in spite of his lack of any real military experience that he never left Italy and let provincial legates command in all the wars of his reign. None of these involved substantial conquest, although Hadrian's Wall was decommissioned almost as soon as it was completed and the army moved north to the Antonine Wall on the Forth–Clyde line. At the end of his reign the Parthians attacked Rome's eastern provinces – perhaps the only time under the Principate when they began a conflict. Antoninus Pius' successors, Marcus Aurelius and Lucius Verus ruling as colleagues, responded, the latter presiding over an expedition that went and sacked the Parthian capital city of Ctesiphon, just as Trajan had done. They did not revive that emperor's new provinces, and the expeditionary force brought back with it a plague that devastated the empire over the next few years. Verus died young, and Marcus Aurelius spent the second half of his reign almost permanently on campaign against the Germanic peoples living between the Rhine and Danube. New provinces were planned, briefly occupied, and then abandoned when he died in AD 180, his son Commodus preferring to return to Rome. He never again led an army in the field, even though he was young and active.[32]

Commodus' murder on the last day of AD 192 led to civil war within a matter of months, and this time it took four years to resolve the conflict, as three provincial legates battled for power. The victor,

Septimius Severus, twice embarked on major foreign wars, first in the east and then in Britain. It was no coincidence that these were the bases for his two rivals for the imperial throne, and one purpose of the campaigns was to confirm the loyalty of the armies based there. Dio Cassius, a senator of Greek extraction, was a contemporary and reports that Severus claimed that his new province of Mesopotamia was a 'bulwark' or 'shield' for Syria, making that province more secure. Dio was unconvinced, seeing the seizure of so much territory from the Parthians as provocative and too expensive.[33]

Rome under the emperors justified its war-making as it had always done, claiming to fight only in defence of its interests and allies. There were plenty of pretexts for war but, as under the Republic, the reasons for embarking on it often had more to do with domestic politics than anything else. Augustus received appeals from exiled British leaders to restore them to power and did not act upon them because he had plenty of other concerns. Claudius received a similar appeal at a time when he was insecure and desperate to win military renown and so invaded. Our sources do not suggest that senators or anyone else felt that the cause was not a just one. Dio also felt that Trajan responded to a real threat in breaking Domitian's treaty with Dacia and going to war, but was less convinced that the Parthian expedition was anything more than a quest for glory. *Imperium sine fine* did not absolve Rome's duty to act honourably, and genuine challenges or even insults to Roman supremacy were cause for war, while war for the sake of glory and nothing else was not honourable. Yet the dream remained, for emperors and senators still read Virgil and all the other authors who spoke of Rome's destiny, and they thrilled at the stories of Alexander the Great and his victories, and indeed of Caesar and Augustus. As always, wars expanding Roman power did not have to mean the acquisition of new provinces, simply the humbling of enemies, as well as glory and plunder.[34]

Territorial expansion was unusual after AD 14. A few emperors needed military victories and so conquered new lands, but made sure that they gained the lion's share of the credit. The best way to do this was to go to the war in person, which most were not inclined to do, while at the same time they were afraid to let a subordinate take charge. None ever assembled a team of senior colleagues and assistants to match those of Augustus, and so large-scale aggressive warfare became rare. Yet politics and war had always been intimately linked at Rome, and the emperors had to appear successful militarily. If wars occurred they must be won, and if they did not break out, then this must be because the might of Rome was so great that no one dared to be hostile. The growing sense that it was the duty of Rome to keep the peace and allow its allies and subjects to go about their business in safety became a central attribute of the emperor. Strabo claimed that 'Never have the Romans and their allies thrived in such peace and plenty as that which was afforded them by Augustus Caesar, from the time he assumed absolute authority, and is now being afforded them by his son and successor, Tiberius.'[35]

Not only was war banished from the greater part of the world, but internally the provinces were safer and more settled because of the peace brought by Rome and its emperors. Velleius Paterculus, who served as an army officer and senator under Augustus and Tiberius, spoke in glowing terms of the world under their rule. 'The *pax augusta*, which has spread to the regions of the east and of the west and to the bounds of the north and of the south, preserves every corner of the world safe from the fear of brigandage.' Bandits were hunted down, pirates driven from the seas, and everywhere was peace and prosperity based on the strength and continued military power of the emperor. That at least was the proud boast of imperial propaganda.[36]

REBELLION

'Passing to your present passion for liberty, I say that it comes too late. The time is past when you ought to have striven never to lose it. For servitude is a painful experience and a struggle to avoid it . . . is just. But the man who having once accepted the yoke then tries to cast it off is a contumacious slave, not a lover of liberty.' – *Josephus' version of King Herod Agrippa II's unsuccessful attempt to deter rebels in Jerusalem in AD 66.*[1]

'MUST EVERYONE ACCEPT SERVITUDE?'

While the pace of conquest slowed after Augustus, when it did occur the process was much the same as ever, save that it was more tightly controlled. Only the emperor could give the order and commit the necessary resources, which were usually substantial. For his invasion of Britain, Claudius mustered four legions supported by auxiliary infantry and cavalry, as well as transport ships and their crews and some warships. If the units were anywhere near their theoretical strength, then something like 40,000–50,000 men participated in the invasion. Julius Caesar had as many, and perhaps somewhat more men, in the later campaigns in Gaul, but few proconsuls under the Republic were ever given command of so many troops. The forces operating on the frontier with Germany after AD 9 were substantially larger, and the defeat of the Pannonian rebellion required twice as many soldiers, but even so this was a large force, amounting to at least 15 per cent of the entire Roman army.[2]

Roman wars were fought against political groups – states, kingdoms, tribes – and not simply to control ground. In AD 43 the first target of Claudius' great expeditionary force was a confederation of tribes, centred around the Catuvellauni and Trinovantes, their heartland north of the River Thames. These were defeated in several battles and their capital at Camulodunum (near modern Colchester) was stormed. The Emperor Claudius made his brief visit to Britain to be present at this dramatic moment, before recrossing the Channel to Gaul and beginning the long journey back to Rome and his victory celebrations. Once the confederation had been broken up, the opposition was focused instead on individual tribes acting independently and fielding smaller armies.

To deal with the new situation, the expeditionary force split into several battlegroups, each based around a single legion and auxiliaries, to wage war at a slightly lower level. Some tribes were politically united and might be defeated in a single battle or by the capture of a central capital, while others had a much looser sociopolitical structure. The future emperor Vespasian commanded *Legio II Augusta* and operated in southern Britain, where he 'fought thirty engagements, overcame two powerful tribes, more than twenty walled towns, and the Island of Vectis (the Isle of Wight)'. One of the tribes was the Durotriges, whose territory is filled with the remains of hill-forts, many of them large and surrounded with more than one line of ditches and ramparts, all of which suggests the presence of many rival chieftains rather than a strong central leader. The sites at Maiden Castle and Hod Hill have both revealed signs of Roman attack, and the latter was subsequently garrisoned by a detachment of Vespasian's men.[3]

The Roman army adapted to defeat different opponents, changing the scale of its operations and the focus of its effort, but it did not fight for the sake of fighting. Diplomacy preceded the legions, and in Britain as everywhere else there were always local leaders and communities eager to ally with Rome. The dominance of the Catuvellauni and Trinovantes in the south-east was achieved after Julius Caesar's forays to Britain by the subjugation of other peoples. Augustus and Caligula both received exiled British rulers driven out during these power struggles, and it was one such fugitive, King Verica, who fled to Claudius and provided the public justification for

Roman intervention. When Camulodunum fell, the emperor personally received the honourable submission of eleven British rulers. Some may well have been allies before the Romans invaded, perhaps receiving subsidy or other support. Others decided to join the stronger power, or preferred alliance with Rome to the domination of the tribal confederation. As elsewhere, particular leaders and the factions around them made these choices on the basis of personal advantage or because a rival within or from another tribe committed to the other side. Many leaders and some whole tribes seem never to have fought against Rome.

There is also no good evidence to suggest that the Catuvellauni and Trinovantes were hostile to Rome before AD 43. There was a lot of trade between the tribes of Britain and the empire, and the leaders of the confederation were as eager as other chieftains and kings to benefit from this and to gain access to the luxury goods that helped to bolster their status. The community of Roman merchants living semi-permanently on the Thames in what would become Londinium existed quite happily with their neighbours. Exiles were received by the emperors, but it was only Claudius' need for glory as proof of his right to rule that prompted large-scale military intervention instead of simply diplomatic activity. The leaders of the confederation may well have been just as surprised as Ariovistus was in 58 BC at the sudden change in Roman attitude and the arrival of the legions.

Two brothers, Caratacus and Togodumnus, led the Catuvellauni and Trinovantes when the Romans attacked. Togodumnus died in the early fighting, but his brother survived and continued to fight. Existing alliances, new friendships or his reputation as a war leader and personal charisma allowed him to move to what is now Wales and rally the tribes there to join his own followers. Eight years later he was defeated in battle, once again escaping and this time going to the Brigantes, a very large tribe living in northern England. Their queen was a Roman ally and decided that it was in her best interest to maintain this link, so handed over the fugitive as a prisoner. In Rome he was brought before Claudius and carried himself with dignity, declaring that, if circumstances had been different, he would surely have been welcomed as a worthy ally. As it was, the hard fight he had made only added to the glory of Roman victory. 'I had horses and warriors, arms and wealth – can you wonder that I wanted to keep them? For if you wish to rule the world, must everyone accept servitude?' The words were written by the Roman historian Tacitus, but whatever was actually said, Claudius spared the lives of Caratacus, his family and followers and gave them a comfortable captivity. The defeated leader was no longer a danger, allowing the emperor to make this public display of mercy.[4]

THE QUEEN

The Iceni were one of the tribes to welcome the Roman invaders. They lived in East Anglia, north of the Catuvellauni and Trinovantes, and no doubt saw them as the greater danger. Early on they became Roman allies, and it is more than likely that one or more of the rulers who submitted to Claudius came from this tribe. Avoiding war with Rome, their leaders kept their power and prospered as allies. Others were doing the same thing, most notably a certain Togidubnus, a king of the Atrebates. (His name was originally restored as Cogidubnus, but this now seems less likely.) An inscription from Chichester makes it clear that he received Roman citizenship from Claudius and describes him as 'king and legate of the emperor in Britannia' (regis legati Augusti in Britannia), while Tacitus tells us that other tribes were placed under his rule. Another man who was probably a chieftain granted citizenship around this time was Tiberius Claudius Catuarus, known only from a gold ring found near the site at Fishbourne in Sussex.[5]

Some of the Iceni wavered from their alliance when Aulus Plautius, the leader of the invasion, was replaced as governor sometime in AD 47. His successor decided to disarm communities within the Roman province whose loyalty was suspect. We do not know the basis for his suspicions, because the only account of this incident comes from a brief and confused passage of Tacitus. It was not normal Roman practice to disarm the population of the provinces. A token handing-over of weapons could form part of a surrender, but total disarmament was neither practical nor desirable. As under the Republic, provincial communities were expected to police their own areas, and in many cases were called upon to provide allied soldiers or equipment to support the Roman army. A group of Iceni persuaded warriors from other tribes to join them and rebelled, occupying an earth-walled settlement. We do not know whether these were led by men who had originally sided with Rome, or leaders whose rivals had done so and who had accordingly lost out in local politics. The Roman governor responded quickly, leading a force composed solely of auxiliaries against the town and storming it. This success ended the rebellion, which in itself suggests that the numbers involved were small, making it doubtful that more than a section of the Iceni took part.[6]

One leader who stayed out of this early rebellion was Prasutagus, king of all or some of the Iceni and according to Tacitus 'distinguished by his long prosperity'. We do not know whether or not he was also granted citizenship, but when he died in AD 60 the king made his two daughters joint heirs with Nero, 'an act of obsequiousness which he thought would place his kingdom and household safe from harm'. The emperors did not automatically grant to allied kings the right of naming a successor and his hope may well have been to guide the Roman decision. Unfortunately, Nero's reckless spending made him desperate for increased revenue from the empire. Whether or not they acted on direct orders, officials on the spot decided to interpret the will as permitting the immediate seizure of royal property. They were led by Decianus Catus, the imperial procurator, a post created by Augustus to act for his legates much as quaestors acted for proconsuls in senatorial provinces. However, unlike a quaestor, the procurator was very much the emperor's man, able to report directly to him, and could be used to check the behaviour of the provincial legate.[7]

In AD 60 the legate of Britain was Caius Suetonius Paulinus, but he was at the opposite side of the province, leading a campaign which culminated in an attack on the Isle of Mona (Anglesey) and the destruction of the shrines there sacred to the druidic religion. As well as taxation, the procurator was responsible for imperial property in a province, and in this case he was also the man on the spot. To make matters worse, existing debts to other prominent Romans were called in, including some owed to the emperor's close advisor, the philosopher Seneca. Like the cities and leaders of Cicero's province, the royal house may not have been capable of paying, but many chieftains were faced with demands for immediate repayment. Decianus Catus probably assisted in some of these cases, helping friends and friends of friends, and his actions were both insensitive and highly aggressive, responding with brutal force to any resistance as he seized royal property 'as if it were booty'. The king's widow Boudicca was publicly flogged, and his daughters raped. With the bulk of the provincial army far away, its distant threat weighed little against such dreadful humiliation. The Iceni rebelled, led by Boudicca.[8]

They were soon joined by other tribes. Their neighbours the Trinovantes had fought against Rome in AD 43, but after seventeen years only the older men could remember what it was like to face the legions in battle and suffer defeat. All ages knew about the reality of occupation. A legion had garrisoned Camulodunum until AD 48, when it was moved to rejoin the campaign. In its place a colony was established for discharged army veterans, with the former soldiers being given land confiscated from the Trinovantes, so that they could farm and support their families. Augustus had banned soldiers from marrying, but some would have brought unofficial wives with them, while others found local girls. With all the confidence of conquerors, this often brash and overbearing foreign presence was a constant reminder of defeat. Rubbing salt into the wound was a high statue to the goddess of Victory, and the Temple of the Divine Claudius – a grand building whose solid foundations were later used by the Normans when they built Colchester Castle. This great structure and the sacrifices required to honour the cult of the deified emperor in a suitable manner were expensive and, whether the priests were retired officers from among the colonists or tribal aristocrats compelled to take part, the price was ultimately paid from levies on the tribe.[9]

The burden of taxation was felt elsewhere and most likely persuaded others to rise against the Romans. Then there were the leaders who had done badly since the occupation and wanted to regain power, and those who had done well, but now hoped to do better again if the invaders were expelled. We cannot say whether the attack on the druids and their sacred groves provoked widespread hatred of the Romans. Julius Caesar wrote about the importance of the druids in Gaul, particularly in the spiritual life of communities, but also their legal and diplomatic role in arbitrating disputes between tribes, but he did not depict them as leading resistance against him. Augustus banned Roman citizens from participating in the druidic cult, and presumably also banned the human sacrifice that formed part of it, but otherwise did not act against it. Tiberius made the religion illegal and suppressed it in Gaul, and this was surely extended to Britain after the invasion. Caesar claimed that in his day some Gauls went to Britain to receive the highest levels of druidic teaching.[10]

The Romans found human sacrifice unpalatable (while happily watching public executions and gladiatorial sports). As importantly, druids with the authority to regulate the relationship between different tribes, and the formidable power to expel individuals from participation in the ritual life of their own community, offered an alternative to the political system created in the provinces. The Romans preferred to act through the wider warrior aristocracy in Gaul and Britain, rather than the separate and smaller druidic elite. Suetonius Paulinus destroyed the cult sites on Mona, and this was clearly one, if not the sole, objective of his operations in Wales. It is hard to believe that news of this blow to the traditional religion and to old certainties about the world did not add to the mood of anger, hatred and desperation. What is clear is that from the beginning the rebels acted with a savagery that was extreme even by the brutal standards of the ancient world. It is equally obvious that the Romans did not expect this outburst of rage.[11]

The colony at Camulodunum was the first to feel this fury. It had no defences – walls were expensive and time-consuming to build, and more effort had gone into the public buildings appropriate for a city of Roman citizens. The colony's magistrates asked the procurator for help, but all that arrived were some 200 soldiers without proper equipment, most likely men detached from their units on staff or police duties. Added to the small garrison and the veterans armed with whatever was available, it was a pathetically inadequate force to defend an unwalled town. Some barricaded themselves in the Temple of Claudius and held out for two days, but no more help came. The town was burned to the ground – archaeologists have found a thick layer of burnt material on the site dating to this period, and in it are badly scorched coins, pottery and other debris. No prisoners were taken. The same was true when the rebels moved on to destroy Londinium – now grown from a trading colony into a large and more formal town – and Verulamium, the tribal capital of the Catuvellauni (modern St Albans). There seemed every chance that the province would be lost to Rome.[12]

Decianus Catus fled to Gaul, but Tacitus repeated a report that some 70,000 people died in these massacres or when smaller communities in the countryside were destroyed. A later historian raised the number to 80,000. Such figures cannot be proved or disproved, but there is no doubt that the losses were very heavy and a total in the tens of thousands is more than likely. Tacitus expressed surprise that the rebels did not want captives to sell or ransom in 'the usual way of war', but dealt in slaughter, crucifixion, gibbets and fires. Writing a century and a half after the events, Dio offered some gruesome details which may or may not be accurate:

The worst and most bestial atrocity committed by their captors was the following. They hung up naked the noblest and most distinguished women and then cut off their breasts and sewed them to their mouths, in order to make the victims appear to be eating them; afterwards they impaled the women on sharp skewers run lengthwise through the entire body. All this they did to the accompaniment of sacrifices, banquets and wanton behaviour.[13]

The first major response from the Roman army came when the legate in command of *Legio IX Hispana* led part of his command south to attack the rebels. There are few details, but the result was a disaster. The legate escaped with his cavalry, but everyone on foot was slaughtered by the Iceni and their allies. A few months later 2,000 legionaries were sent from the Rhine garrisons to reinforce *IX Hispana*, which may give some idea of the losses, although no doubt there were heavy casualties among the auxiliaries as well. It took time for the news of the revolt to reach Suetonius Paulinus, and longer still for him to march his army back to face the rebels. The governor and a small escort reached Londinium before it fell, but he did not have the troops to hold the town and so abandoned it to its fate, taking only those civilians capable of keeping up with him.

Paulinus had barely 10,000 men when he confronted Boudicca's much larger host on ground of his own choosing. There were so many people with the queen's forces that they could not stay in one place for any length of time before supplies ran out, so she could not afford a long campaign. The Britons were eager and confident, but mixed aristocrats and their followers with greater numbers of enraged farmers, lacking training or proper equipment. Behind the masses of fighters their womenfolk watched from a line of wagons at the rear. The Romans were veterans, used to victory, as well as disciplined and practised in working as a team. They were also enraged by the sights and stories of the atrocities committed by the rebels. The fighting was heavy and prolonged, but in the end the Britons broke and were slaughtered as they tried to flee. Legionaries and auxiliaries cut down warriors and the watching women alike, and even slaughtered the enemy's baggage animals. Such merciless and indiscriminate killing was rare, if only because slaves and beasts were worth money and the soldiers could expect their share of the spoils.

The tide had turned, although the war was not over. Boudicca died soon after the battle – taking poison in one version and dying of disease in another – and no names are given for other leaders

1 Calleva
2 Londinium
3 Verulamium
4 Camulodunum

BRIGANTES
PARISI
DECEANGLI
CORNOVII
CORITANI
ORDOVICES
ICENI
CATUVELLAUNI
TRINOVANTES
DEMETAE
DOBUNNI
4
3
SILVRES
2
ATREBATES
1
CANTIACI
BELGAE
REGINI
DUMNONII   DUROTRIGES

0   100 miles
0   150 km

The British tribes and the rebellion of Boudica, AD 60

who continued the struggle. Paulinus devastated the lands of the tribes who had rebelled, killing and burning. Food was short because agriculture had been so badly disrupted, and so hunger and disease inflicted even greater loss. Deaths among the Iceni and their allies were most likely far higher than the casualties they had inflicted. A new procurator named Julius Classicianus had replaced Decianus Catus – sadly we do not know the latter's fate – and this man did not get on well with the legate. He complained to the emperor that Paulinus was too vindictive in his punishment of the rebels, and an imperial freedman was sent to investigate the matter. Paulinus was replaced, ostensibly for the loss of some warships to bad weather rather than any criticism of his strategy. His successor proved far more conciliatory – or lazy and lacking in spirit according to the cynical Tacitus – and peace returned. Classicianus died during his tenure as procurator, and the inscription from his tomb is now in the British Museum.[14]

In time – probably faster than we might expect – the burnt towns were rebuilt and soon flourished anew. We do not know how many tribes joined the Iceni and Trinovantes, but some certainly did not. Leaders like Togidubnus and Catuarus, and no doubt many others whose names are lost, remained loyal to their alliance with the Romans. If they fought at all, then it was against the rebels, and plenty of Britons were among the victims of Boudicca's army – the bulk of the population of Verulamium were locals. Many, perhaps most, Britons did not rebel in AD 60, whether through loyalty, fear of reprisals or fear of domination by the other tribes, or because they did not have personal experience of such brutal behaviour by Roman officials. Whatever the reasons, the continued loyalty of a large section of the provincial population was a major factor in the Roman victory. Even more striking is the fact that after Boudicca, there is no evidence for any significant revolt in lowland Britain until the end of Roman rule more than three centuries later. Most of this area shows every sign of stability and prosperity, although the territory of the Iceni was turned into one of the poorer regions of southern Britain.[15]

TAXES AND ILL-TREATMENT

There are quite a few similarities between the rebellion of Boudicca and the great rising under Vercingetorix in 53–52 BC. In each case the initiative came from tribes and leaders who had not fought the Romans during the early period of conquest. They were allies and had often gained power, influence and wealth through the association. Only later, a realisation that Roman rule was permanent caused them to think again. Julius Caesar's killing of Dumnorix and the public execution of Acco, and in AD 60 the plundering and brutal treatment of Boudicca and the royal household of the Iceni, demonstrated that no one was safe if they upset Rome's representatives. Occupation brought this risk, meant the loss of liberty and also of many of the opportunities of independence. Natural rage at her own and her daughters' awful abuse by the Romans fired Boudicca's urge to rebel, but in most cases calculation went alongside emotion. Caesar was known to be south of the Alps in the winter of 53–52 BC and so away from his army. In AD 60 Paulinus and the main Roman field army were also off on campaign and would not be able to intervene for some time. The great Pannonian revolt under Augustus was said to have been encouraged when the peoples there mustered allied contingents to send to the Roman army and realised how great their own numbers were.[16]

The rebellion in Germany in AD 9 was the most successful revolt against Roman rule under the Principate, and it was no coincidence that it began just as the war against the Pannonians came to an end. That it had taken three years, considerable casualties, and more than a third of the entire Roman army to suppress this rising suggested that the Romans were not invincible. Even more importantly, the conflict had drawn in the bulk of fresh recruits at a time when these were hard to find. Germany was not the first priority, and so got a much smaller share of resources and talented officers of all ranks. It still had a sizeable garrison of five legions, while the provincial legate was Publius Quinctilius Varus, who had governed the imperial province of Syria and in 4 BC led his army to crush insurrections in Judaea. Now in his fifties, his wife was Augustus' great-niece, and this may well have been the most important factor in his selection.[17]

The main advance into Germany had begun in 12 BC and for a long time was a family affair, with armies led by Augustus' stepsons Drusus and Tiberius. At first Roman armies operated across the Rhine during the spring and summer, before returning to bases on the Rhineland each winter. It was a while before they risked wintering in the new province of Germany which stretched to the River Elbe, but soon this became normal. Civilian settlements grew up around the forts and more permanent communities were established when the army moved on. Excavation has revealed an entire town at Wald-grimes, founded at the end of the first century BC or the very start of the first century AD. Most of the area was peaceful, and after a burst of fighting in AD 5 there were only minor outbreaks of violence. This was not always directed against the Romans, for the tribes had a long tradition of raiding each other, but after Varus arrived in AD 7 he was pleased to see disputes between leaders and peoples being settled in court rather than battle.[18]

Varus may have tried to rush the process of establishing the province, and levied a regular tax on the tribes. This probably involved a census to assess their property and obligations to pay – something which was often a source of resentment. If conducted fairly it still imposed new burdens on communities, and there was always the chance of graft among the officials carrying it out. A little earlier, an imperial freedman working in Gaul had invented two extra months to each year and increased the tax accordingly. His excuse was that the last month of the year was named December, which means 'the tenth month'. The name came from the old lunar calendar replaced by Julius Caesar in 46 BC with the solar calendar used to this day. The name was kept because of important religious and political dates, such as 31 December when the consuls laid down their office. The freedman explained to the provincials that there must obviously be an eleventh and twelfth month and forced them to pay for these as well.[19]

There is no evidence that Varus engaged in such blatant profiteering, although the historian Velleius Paterculus claimed that during
his time in Syria he had gone 'to a rich province as a poor man, and
left a poor province as a rich man'. Later he was blamed for assuming
that the German province was securely settled, and for despising the
tribesmen, seeing them as 'human only in shape and speech, and
that though they would not be subdued by the sword would nevertheless submit to law'. This was the wisdom of hindsight, and it is
hard to know whether or not Varus was unusually contemptuous
and complacent. The arrogance, brutality and extortion so commonly encountered in provincial government under the Republic
did not vanish with the coming of the Principate. One of the leaders
of the great Pannonian revolt against Augustus complained that
'You Romans are to blame for this; for you send as guardians to your
flocks, not dogs or shepherds, but wolves.'[20]

Taxation was a common cause of friction, whether from its sheer
scale or the way that it was collected. The Frisii, one of a handful of
Germanic peoples living east of the Rhine who stayed under Roman
control after AD 9, were subject to an annual levy of ox hides and
appear to have paid this without excessive hardship or resentment
for more than a generation. In AD 28 the army officer put in charge
of supervising the levy announced that from now on each hide must
be of a set size and chose the immense forest aurochs as the standard.
The Frisii were unable to supply these in quantity – Tacitus noted that
cattle in Germany were smaller than those in the empire, something
confirmed by archaeology. When the Frisians werre unable to meet
their obligations, the Romans began to seize their land as well as
women and children to sell as slaves in lieu of the debts. As was often
the case, the explosion of resentment was not instant, but when it
came it was especially savage. The soldiers supervising the levy were
crucified, although, like Decianus Catus, the officer in charge made
his escape. The legate of Lower Germany responded with a punitive expedition, but the campaign was mishandled and resulted in
heavy losses. Two detachments were left behind when the column
retreated, one to be wiped out and the other preferring suicide to

capture. Tacitus accused the Emperor Tiberius of suppressing the scale of the casualties because he did not want to entrust anyone with the responsibility of fighting a major war on this frontier to avenge the defeat.[21]

Levies might be in money, kind or a quota of recruits for the *auxilia*. A rebellion occurred in Thrace under Tiberius when a rumour spread that Thracian auxiliaries would no longer serve in neighbouring provinces, but be sent to the far corners of the empire. Some tribes rebelled, but others stayed loyal and aided the Roman army, which arrived and broke the rebels' spirit in a rapid campaign. In AD 70 the previously loyal Batavians – a Germanic tribe who had migrated across the Rhine and been settled in what is now Holland – were provoked by the 'greed and licence' of the officers in charge of recruiting. This was the only tax burden placed on these communities, and Batavian auxiliaries had a reputation as some of the finest soldiers in the army. One trick was to conscript the elderly and infirm, forcing their families to pay for them to be released and to provide a substitute to serve in their place. There were also cases where underage boys were enrolled and then raped by the recruiting officer. The levy was ordered during the chaotic year and a half of civil war after the death of Nero, which may have encouraged the men in charge to think that they could act as they wished without fear of punishment. Anger at this mistreatment grew, fighting against a long habit of loyalty, and it took the grievances and ambitions of a number of local leaders to convert discontent into rebellion. All of these men were Roman citizens, many equestrians, and representatives of a local aristocracy who had gained a good deal through joining the empire.[22]

The same was true in AD 9. Plenty of German leaders had welcomed the Romans as strong friends or, after resisting for a while, had submitted and come to terms. A number of German aristocrats were regular dinner guests at Varus' table. Arminius of the Cherusci was in his twenties and already a Roman citizen and an equestrian, having led auxiliary soldiers from his people in a number of campaigns. Fluent in Latin – he may well have been educated in the empire or Rome itself – he appeared to be the perfect example of Rome's talent for winning over local elites. Yet at some point he decided to turn against Rome, and became the leader of a group of other nobles who met in secret and plotted rebellion. Another German chieftain openly accused him to Varus, but the legate dismissed this as no more than mud-slinging between rivals for his favour.[23]

The plan was carefully prepared and carried out, reflecting Arminius' considerable skill and his experience of the Roman army. In the summer of AD 9 Varus marched with a force of three legions and nine auxiliary units to parade Rome's military might around the province. Arminius and his confederates persuaded him to send out small detachments to different communities on various pretexts, weakening his force, and then lured him back to the eastern end of the province to deal with an outbreak of rebellion which faded away as soon as he approached. It was late in the season when the Roman column began to march back to its winter quarters. Arminius was with them, leading a force of tribesmen who acted as guides and scouts until they left to join the rebels, who were waiting in a series of carefully prepared ambushes. Stumbling along, the Roman column was whittled down in several days of fighting on ground where everything favoured the Germans. Varus was wounded and then despaired and killed himself – something no Roman nobleman was supposed to do when fighting a foreign enemy. All three legions – XVII, XVIII, and XIX – were wiped out along with the auxiliaries, with only a few fugitives managing to get away. Senior officers taken prisoner were sacrificed, other captives tortured to death or kept as slaves.[24]

In the weeks that followed, the detachments throughout the rest of the province were slaughtered or chased back to the Rhine. The province between the Rhine and Elbe was lost and never regained. Roman armies drove deep into Germany several times in the next seven years and Arminius was beaten in battle, but never decisively. Lack of resources in the short term and lack of political will in the longer term meant that the effort to conquer Germany was never renewed. Arminius fought and defeated a rival Germanic leader,

Maroboduus of the Suebi, only to be murdered by a group of his own noblemen who resented the permanent dominance of one man. At the end of the first century AD Tacitus said that the Romans had still not achieved victory in the struggle with the Germans, which had already lasted 210 years, but still seemed to expect that one day this victory would be achieved. It never was.[25]

Arminius won a great victory on the battlefield. If Vercingetorix had defeated Julius Caesar or Boudicca had managed to destroy Suetonius Paulinus' small army, then their rebellions may also have succeeded. The Romans were surprised by the outbreak of all three rebellions, not least because they began among peoples and leaders considered to be securely under their rule and because their attention was currently elsewhere. Their military response was always the same, gathering whatever troops could be mustered and striking at the heart of the rebellion as soon as possible. Varus did this in AD 9, heading immediately for the reported rising in the east of the province. It was late in the season, his army was encumbered with more than the usual amounts of baggage and camp followers because he was planning a return to winter quarters, but even so his instinctive response was to strike at the threat. He had done much the same on his interventions in Judaea in 4 BC.

Julius Caesar also hurried to his army and began an immediate counter-attack against Vercingetorix, just as he had hastened to relieve the legion besieged by rebels in the winter of 54–53 BC. In each case his army was scattered and not concentrated for the campaign, so that he had far fewer soldiers than he would have liked. The forces available were not prepared for operating in the field, having little time to gather supplies and few opportunities to forage from the winter landscape. One of the reasons Caesar attacked the Gallic *oppida* in early 52 BC was to seize their stocks of grain and feed his soldiers.

At the start of a rebellion much of the wider population was watching to see what happened. In the past the Romans had proved unbeatable – after all, a revolt could occur only after they had come to dominate a region. Only the truly desperate and thoroughly disaffected would risk open resistance and the inevitable retribution of Rome. Varus' march to Jerusalem in 4 BC was marked by burning settlements and mass crucifixions. If terrible punishment of this sort happened quickly, then it confirmed the invincibility of Rome and deterred the uncommitted from joining the rising. If the Romans waited to muster their strength, then with each passing day the confidence of the rebels would grow and belief that they might succeed would spread.[26]

Delay favoured the rebels, while a rapid counter-attack meant a display of Roman confidence and force which might be enough to crush the rising before it gathered momentum. It was a risk, since it often meant taking the field with a small and poorly supplied force. Sometimes this was enough, as when the Iceni and their allies were defeated in AD 48 by a column composed solely of auxiliaries – the governor even dismounted cavalrymen so that they could help to storm the ramparts of the town. Roman soldiers were professionals, the army had drills and a clear command structure, making it much more flexible than clumsy tribal armies, and often this was sufficient to let them smash far more numerous rebel forces. At times little fighting was needed, and the mere appearance of Roman soldiers was enough to overawe opposition. Reputation counted for a lot, and even a small force represented the army that had conquered much of the world and was known to be stubbornly determined and ruthless in its pursuit of victory.[27]

Yet the aura of invincibility projected by the empire and its army could be broken. Military reverses elsewhere weakened it, and those on the spot could shatter it altogether. This was the great gamble in responding so quickly to a rebellion. In AD 60 the 200 men sent by Decianus Catus to Camulodunum could do no more than perish with the garrison and colonists. The intervention by a detachment of *Legio IX Hispana* was a far more serious effort and if the Iceni and their allies had been less numerous, less determined or less lucky, then it might have worked. Only part of the legion was involved, along with some auxiliary forces, but at most there were a few thousand men and it is unlikely that they were prepared to fight a long war of manoeuvre. It was not enough, and instead they were cut to pieces. Roman delay strengthened the rebels and bolstered their confidence, but a disaster like this was an even faster way to recruit more rebels.

Suetonius Paulinus did not have as strong a field force as he wanted when he faced Boudicca. He had summoned an additional legion to join him, but it did not arrive because its acting commander chose to disobey the order. We do not know why this man acted as he did, although belief that he could not safely move away from the area he garrisoned in the south-west is most likely. (He took his life in the aftermath of the revolt as penance for letting his legion miss the great victory.) Whatever the reason, when Suetonius Paulinus fought the most decisive battle on the island since AD 43 he commanded an army less than a quarter of the size of the original invasion force. Up until now Boudicca's warriors had been successful wherever they went. Avoiding a battle would seem like fear and give them even more momentum, perhaps persuading still loyal tribes to join the queen – it was late in the campaign of 52 BC when the Aedui defected to the rebels. Paulinus had little to gain by delay, since this was unlikely to add significantly to his forces, and Dio claims that he was also running short of food. The Roman commander gambled on a battle and won. In AD 9 Arminius so skilfully orchestrated the rebellion that Varus was given no real chance.[28]

WINNING AND LOSING A PROVINCE

Arminius' victory overthrew Roman rule between the Elbe and the Rhine and the province was never retaken. Caesar broke the back of the rebellion in 52 BC by winning at Alesia, and Suetonius Paulinus' defeat of Boudicca did the same in AD 60. Both Roman commanders then spent many months attacking the homelands of the rebellious tribes, forcing each in turn to submit. The punishment for rebellion was terrible, but alongside this came conciliation – if only in Britain after the recall of Paulinus. It is unlikely that the entire population of any province ever rebelled, not least because the provinces were artificial creations of the conquering power with little to unify their inhabitants. The Romans thought in terms of Gauls, Germans and Britons, but these knew themselves to be members of a particular tribe, clan, community or loyal to a particular leader. A charismatic leader and shared resentment might unite them for a while, but strain was always likely. In 52 BC some peoples rebelled, but preferred to fight on their own rather than join the common effort, while others like the Aedui bickered over who would command. Arminius was not always able to persuade other leaders to follow his plan, and in the end was murdered because he tried to unite several peoples under his own rule.[29]

In AD 9 Arminius' brother remained loyal to Rome and continued to serve in the Roman army. The man who warned Varus about the rebellion was also a prince of the Cherusci and Arminius' father-in-law. After the first great success he joined in the rebellion, feeling that he could not resist the enthusiasm of his warriors. His son had been enrolled as a priest of the cult of Rome and Augustus established for the new province, but proved far more eager and was with the rebels from the very start. It was rumoured that he mistreated Varus' corpse in the aftermath of the massacre. Later father and son defected to the Romans and were installed in comfortable exile to the west of the Rhine. Few leaders were implacably pro- or anti-Roman, and very few of the latter were beyond reconciliation as long as they were willing to submit to Rome.[30]

All three rebellions occurred relatively soon after initial conquest – within a generation. Arminius won his war where Vercingetorix and Boudicca lost. The lowlands of Britain were untroubled by any other serious revolts. While Gaul never again experienced a rising on the same scale as 53–52 BC, it took longer for it to become wholly peaceful. Julius Caesar was able to withdraw most of his army to fight the civil war without threatening Rome's hold on the newly conquered province. Details are few, but there was trouble in Gaul during the dictatorship, and on several occasions under Augustus. In each case the unrest came from no more than a handful of tribes and there was no great alliance to expel the occupying Romans. The sources link many of these rebellions with attacks by Germanic raiders from across the Rhine. The failure of the Romans to prevent them from happening made them seem less reliable allies and also suggested that their military dominance was no longer so strong. It is more than likely that some of the Germans came as allies to ambitious leaders from Gaul, following in the footsteps of Ariovistus.[31]

A succession of censuses and the taxation that followed encouraged ill-feeling. Many nobles complained to Augustus about the freedman who collected extra money for his two invented months and this was stopped. The man claimed that he had taken the money for the good of the empire, since it prevented the noblemen of Gaul from having the wealth to fund rebellion. We do not know whether or not the cash was returned to them or went into the state treasury. The leaders of an outbreak of rebellion in AD 21 were all heavily indebted aristocrats. These tribal noblemen were Roman citizens and, as Tacitus points out, their families had gained the honour when it was still a rare thing. Maintaining prominence among their tribes as part of a Roman province was expensive, and this rather than the overall burden of taxation may have placed them irrevocably into debt. There is no hint of unusual abuses in levying of tax in Gaul at this time.[32]

Desperate aristocrats from many tribes began to communicate and meet in secret, for once again this was not a spontaneous outburst but a slowly matured plan, formed in the belief that Tiberius' rule was unpopular and the legions disaffected. The leaders were Julius Florus of the Treveri and Julius Sacrovir of the Aedui – the Julius in each name showing citizenship granted either by Augustus or Caesar – but at the beginning they remained behind the scenes. Groups rebelled in two tribes and were swiftly suppressed by the Romans' routinely quick counter-attack. In one case the urban cohort – a paramilitary force guarding the imperial mint at Lugdunum (Lyons) and numbering at most 1,000 men – was sufficient to crush the rebels. A detachment of legionaries from the Rhineland dealt with the other. These were aided by local allies, including a contingent led by the still openly loyal Sacrovir, who fought bare-headed, boasting that he wanted his bravery to be seen by all. Prisoners claimed that he did it to be recognised so that he did not get hurt. Tacitus blamed Tiberius for ignoring these warnings.

Florus attempted to suborn a cavalry regiment or *ala* raised from his own tribe, but few joined him to swell the band formed by his own clients and some desperate debtors. All were quickly hunted down by columns sent from the armies on the Rhine, including many loyal auxiliaries. One of the most active officers chasing the rebels was himself a Treviran nobleman, a certain Julius Indus who was a long-standing personal rival of Florus. (A cavalry regiment known as the *ala Gallorum Indiana* existed in the Roman army for many generations and was probably named after him.) The insurgents were hunted down and killed or caught. Florus was at large for a while, but was eventually cornered and took his own life.[33]

The Treveri and the other peoples of Gallia Belgica lived within easy reach of the strong garrisons in the Rhineland and so were vulnerable to reprisals. The Aedui lived far from any major concentration of troops and had the additional advantages of considerable numbers and greater wealth. Sacrovir rallied enough supporters to seize the tribal capital at Augustudunum (Augst) – the city founded by Augustus to replace the old *oppidum* of Bibracte. Young aristocrats from all over Gaul received a properly Roman education in the city, and Sacrovir took these as hostages, hoping to persuade their families and home communities to join him – an echo of the Aedui seizing the hostages in Caesar's baggage train in 52 BC. Soon the rebel army numbered some 40,000, but of these barely 8,000 were properly equipped in Roman style. Apart from a contingent of gladiators under training who were freed and enlisted, the rest of the army wielded hunting spears and whatever other weapons could be improvised. As we have seen, the Romans did not actively disarm provincials, but as society became more peaceful, military equipment naturally became rarer. In Gaul aristocrats competed through priesthoods, local magistracies, property and wealth as well as imperial service, and no longer based their status on the number of warriors in their household. Although Sacrovir had arranged for arms to be manufactured in secret, the need to avoid suspicion had limited what could be achieved.[34]

The numbers were impressive, but experience was in as short supply as proper equipment. Some encouragement came when the legates of Upper and Lower Germany bickered over who should take charge of the campaign, delaying the Roman response. Tacitus says that in the neighbouring areas there was private sympathy, but a fear of open commitment to rebellion. Some of this was no doubt a pragmatic calculation of its chances of success. Yet it also suggests that debt and resentment were not so widespread, or at least not to a degree that made the entire population desperate enough to seek any way out regardless of the risks. When the Roman commanders sorted out their differences, a force was sent from the garrisons of Upper Germany and hastened to Augustudunum. In a hopelessly one-sided battle, the rebels were routed and the rebellion ended in a matter of hours. Sacrovir committed suicide. In Rome, Tiberius had made no formal announcement of the revolts in Gaul, allowing wild rumours to flourish. He waited until news of the victory reached him before writing to the Senate to tell them of both the revolt and its utter defeat.[35]

This was the last rising in Gaul where there was any real attempt to rally the tribes en masse, and even then only two of the four Gallic provinces were involved and the enterprise failed utterly. In fact, after this there is little evidence for any revolts even of individual tribes. In AD 69 the temples on the Capitoline Hill in Rome were set on fire during the fall of the Emperor Vitellius and all, including the hallowed shrine to Jupiter Optimus Maximus, were seriously damaged. As the news spread, Druidic prophecies of the end of the Roman Empire circulated widely in Gaul. They were repeated with great enthusiasm, but did not prompt rebellion. The year before, Mariccus of the Boii had raised some 8,000 followers, proclaiming himself to be a god and the 'champion of Gaul'. He was not from the aristocracy of the tribe, and instead seems to have been a mystical leader. Significantly, this rising was defeated mainly by the aristocrats of the Aedui, who organised a tribal militia backed by some auxiliary cohorts. Mariccus was thrown to the wild beasts in the arena, and his reputation briefly revived when these refused to harm him. Vitellius, on his way from the Rhineland to make himself emperor, watched as the rebel leader was then executed by more mundane means.[36]

The Batavian rebellion in AD 70 was a more serious matter, which began as part of the Roman civil war and grew into a self-proclaimed Gallic Empire. It did not spread much beyond the Rhineland, and even there many communities and individual leaders remained loyal to Rome. The rebels gained more allies from the German tribes beyond the frontiers than from the provinces themselves, and within little more than a year the rising was put down. It does appear that a province on the frontier was less stable for much longer than one surrounded by other parts of the empire. Once the heavy Roman military presence was established on the Rhine, Gaul became much more peaceful, in spite of the loss of the German province in AD 9. Some regions, for instance parts of North Africa or northern as opposed to lowland Britain, never achieved this stability, but elsewhere there simply does not appear to have been any serious prospect of large-scale rebellion against Roman rule. Later, especially from the third century AD onwards, revolts were not anti-Roman, but efforts to make a locally popular leader emperor.

As far as we can tell, after the phase of conquest, which might be quick as in Britain or take generations as in Spain and Gaul, there was often a major rebellion before the province was fully secure. After that, serious revolts were extremely rare and did not occur in most provinces. Tiberius concealed the risings in Gaul until they were defeated and later hid the seriousness of the reverse at the hands of the Frisii, prompting some scholars to wonder whether revolts against Roman rule are under-reported in our sources. An obvious weakness of this theory is that we are told what he did by one of these very sources. It is certainly true that the literary evidence is poor for many periods, including the bulk of the second century AD. Yet it strains belief that major rebellions would not be mentioned or leave some other trace. Smaller risings like that of Mariccus might well vanish from the record, and we only know of it because Tacitus wrote a detailed account of the period of the civil war after Nero's death which has survived – unlike the remainder of his *Histories*, which carried on from AD 70 to the death of Domitian in AD 96. Thus it is possible that incidents on this scale in other years and provinces do not appear in our sources. Such things did not threaten Roman rule, and indeed may often have been aimed at defeating local leaders rather than the empire as a whole.[37]

None of the rebellions against Roman rule won universal support in an entire province. Even when led by local aristocrats who had profited from the alliance with Rome, but now shifted in their allegiance, there were always significant numbers of similar men who remained loyal. It does not much matter whether these acted from genuine affection for Rome, from fear of the consequences of revolt, from rivalry and dislike of the rebel leaders or because they hoped to be rewarded. Roman rule was never so unbearable to everyone in a province that all chose to reject it. Over time, in each area it looks as if fewer and fewer were inclined to risk active rebellion. Once again we must remind ourselves of the absence of something akin to a sense of nationalism in the provinces. Equally, there is no trace of fellow feeling between different provinces uniting in hatred of the imperial power. If the army was seen to be weak or was simply thought to be too busy elsewhere, rebels were encouraged to see an opportunity to act, but their aims remained local. There is no evidence for co-ordinated planning to divide the resources of the empire or for any active assistance capable of matching the force the empire was able to wield. Individually, even if a rebellion managed to include the bulk of the population, no single province could cope with the military might of Rome.

In AD 9 Arminius managed to win a great enough victory to push the Romans back to the Rhine, and in the years that followed he avoided a decisive defeat until Tiberius called a halt to operations. It was possible to abandon a province on the edge of the empire. Had Vercingetorix or Boudicca matched Arminius' success then it is possible that the Romans would not have returned to conquer Gaul and Britain. Under the Principate the key to this was the attitude of the emperor, and his willingness to pour resources into regaining lost territory. Germany was not reconquered, but provinces in the heartland of the empire were a different matter, and it was unlikely that their loss would ever be accepted. It might take time, until the manpower and logistic support were available, but there was simply no prospect of giving up a lost province.

The historian Josephus, who had himself joined in a rebellion against Rome before changing sides, attributed a speech to Herod Agrippa II in which the king tried to persuade the people of Jerusalem not to rebel in AD 66. The principal argument is that the might of Rome made any such revolt doomed to defeat and ghastly retribution. It would be folly to go to war simply because of a cruel and rapacious governor. 'Granted that the Roman governors are intolerably harsh, it does not follow that all Romans are unjust to you any more than Caesar.' Tacitus makes the man who suppressed the Batavian rebellion express similar sentiments. Rome was too powerful to defeat, and although there were bad and rapacious governors there were good ones as well. Fear, and a sense that Roman rule was usually tolerable even if it was more or less oppressive, may well have convinced most provincials against rebellion.[38]

A STRONGER SENSE OF IDENTITY?

The history of Judaea and the other substantial Jewish settlements in the east seems to provide a partial exception to the pattern seen elsewhere. Varus, as legate of Syria, intervened in Judaea twice in 4 BC, and one of his successors in the post did the same in AD 6. This latter disturbance was provoked by anger at the imposition of the Roman census. Judaea was an equestrian province governed by a prefect who did not command any legionary troops and instead had a force of around six or seven auxiliary units. These were locally raised from Samaria and the Gentile population of the region and Syria. On numerous occasions they fought short, usually one-sided,

operations to suppress a mixture of charismatic religious leaders
and men dubbed as bandit chiefs. Deep-seated hostility between
Jewish and Samaritan communities, or between Jewish and Gentile
communities, especially in Caesarea on the coast of Judaea and in
Alexandria in Egypt, sometimes spilled over into violence on a grand
scale, leading to heavy-handed military intervention.

In AD 66 – sixty years after the imposition of direct Roman rule
– there was a major rebellion, which began with fighting between
Jew and Gentile in Caesarea and Alexandria. The governor – by now
called a procurator rather than prefect, but distinct from the procurators of major imperial provinces – was unpopular and brutal. He
had been sent by Nero with explicit orders to increase the revenue
from the province, probably as part of the same desperate need for
money that helped to provoke Boudicca's rebellion. He handled the
situation badly, and was defeated and forced to withdraw from Jerusalem. The amount of inter-communal violence rapidly increased,
spreading around the wider area. When the legate of Syria mustered
all available soldiers, including allied contingents, and marched on
Jerusalem he encountered more resistance that he had expected. As
he withdrew, his column was badly cut about, losing more than 5,000
men and the eagle of *Legio XII Fulminata*. Judaea was a Mediterranean province and not on some distant frontier, and so in AD 67 a new
commander, the future emperor Vespasian, was sent with a much
stronger and better prepared army to begin its reconquest. Delayed
by the outbreak of civil war a year later, in which he emerged as
the eventual victor, Jerusalem was not taken until AD 70 and the last
strongholds were only mopped up a few years later.[39]

For a while there was an independent Jewish state, minting its
own coins – and spending a good deal of its time and resources in
wasteful power struggles. In AD 66 many members of the Jerusalem
aristocracy centred around the high priestly families chose to join
the rebels – the young Josephus among them. Even so, not everyone
was ever fully committed to the revolt. In Galilee some communities with significant Jewish populations fought against the rebels,
while others capitulated as soon as possible. The rebels were never

able to form an effective field army, and relied on the small, highly motivated bands of the main leaders backed by large numbers of undisciplined, untrained and poorly equipped volunteers from the wider population. In the open they could not hope to stand against even small numbers of Roman regulars. The lost province was re-captured in a succession of sieges, and the area controlled by the rebels steadily shrank. At each stage the Romans followed their usual practice of encouraging defection and surrender wherever possible. When it was not, engineering skill and determined aggression took each fortified place in turn, including Jerusalem after a three-month siege in which the Temple was destroyed. The siege-works at Masada by the Dead Sea give a good impression of the doggedness of the Roman army. Wherever the rebels went, and no matter how strongly fortified a position they held, the legions would come and would destroy them.

From AD 115 to AD 117, the Jewish populations of Egypt, Cyrenaica and Cyprus rebelled in a war marked by atrocities and allegations of cannibalism. The spark seems to have come once again from mutual animosity with their Gentile neighbours. It took considerable re-sources, at a time when most of the army was heavily committed to Trajan's eastern expedition, but once again the rebellion was crushed. There is no evidence for any fighting in Judaea or Galilee and it looks very much as if the communities there remained peaceful. Judaea re-belled again in AD 132–135 under the leadership of the charismatic Bar Kochba. The sources are poor, but there seem to have been heavy Roman losses – the Emperor Hadrian is supposed to have written to the Senate omitting the conventional formula of 'I am well, and so is the army'. This independent Jewish state lasted less time than in the earlier rebellion, but for a while minted coins and organised some basic bureaucracy. It does look as if Galilee largely remained free of rebellion in these years, and the archaeology suggests that the communities there suffered little and continued to prosper. In Judaea itself the Romans wore down the rebels in a long succession of raids and sieges of walled towns and villages – Dio claims that fifty towns and 985 villages were stormed and razed to the ground. Jerusalem was turned into a Gentile city, with the cult of Jupiter established on Temple Mount, causing the spiritual heart of Judaism to shift to previously marginal Galilee.[40]

The Jews had a sense of identity which long predated the arrival of Alexander the Great, let alone the Roman Empire. Their faith bonded them and reinforced their sense of nationhood, while providing examples of miraculous victories over stronger enemies and escape from slavery. Jewish ritual made it harder for them to be absorbed into the Roman system – for instance they were exempt from military service, ending quite a long tradition of providing mercenaries. Some of this sense of their own difference may well have already begun to grow stronger before the arrival of Rome, and the belief in their ability to overthrow a conqueror was greatly reinforced by memory of the Maccabees' victory over the Seleucids in the second century BC which established the Jewish kingdom of the Hasmoneans. By any rational calculation, the people of Judaea, even if united and able to win over all the Galileans and Idumaeans – and doing all of this was unlikely, to say the least – could not hope to defeat the power of the Roman Empire. They were bound to lose, which was of course the argument Josephus put into the mouth of Agrippa II in AD 66. It is possible that they hoped for aid from the Parthians, for there was a substantial Jewish population in Babylon and elsewhere, and until the destruction of the Temple many of these travelled to Jerusalem for the great festivals. If so, then this hope was never realised, and it should be remembered that the Parthians were never able to take and hold permanently any part of the Roman Empire.[41]

The Jewish religion was not incompatible with living as subjects of Rome. After AD 135 there were no more revolts, and even before that most of the time Jewish populations in Judaea and the wider empire did not teeter on the brink of revolt. The outbreak in AD 66 was far from inevitable. Attitudes hardened after that rebellion, but before it there is little trace of strong anti-Semitism in Roman society and especially in the attitudes of its elite, which is better characterized by disinterest or mild amusement at their curious practices. It is quite likely that there were serious social and economic problems in first-century AD Judaea, creating a desperate rural population willing to risk rebellion whenever strong leaders emerged, but difficult to know whether the situation there was so much worse than in other areas where rebellion did not occur. The cost of rebellion was dreadful, yet it is harder to see permanent devastation of much of the country in the archaeological record. The Jewish population was not removed from Judaea after the rebellions, although losses were terrible and some went abroad. Galilee remained openly Jewish, especially in the countryside, and in both areas this population never again rebelled on any major scale.[42]

The three major Jewish rebellions at first sight appear to show a significantly more protracted and determined struggle to win freedom from Roman rule compared to other provinces. Yet if the Trajanic revolts are treated as separate, then the difference is much less striking. Ultimately, the Jewish subjects of the Roman Empire accepted imperial rule and ceased to rebel. Even during the revolts, it does appear that as much or more of their hostility focused on non-Jewish neighbours rather than on the empire.

RESISTANCE, RIOTING AND ROBBERY

'The people called the Bucoli began a disturbance in Egypt and under the leadership of one Isidorus, a priest, caused the rest of the Egyptians to revolt. At first, arrayed in women's garments, they had deceived the Roman centurion, causing him to believe that they were women of the Bucoli and were going to give him gold as ransom for their husbands, and had struck him down when he approached them. They also sacrificed his companion, and after swearing an oath over entrails, they devoured them. Isidorus surpassed all his contemporaries in bravery.' – *Dio Cassius, early third century AD.*[1]

'PEACEFUL AND QUIET'

Over time major rebellions against Roman rule ceased, even if this took a little longer in Judaea. Small-scale revolts did occur in a number of provinces, although even these were rare. In AD 171 or 172, a group called the Boukoloi (or Bucoli) – 'cowboys' or 'herdsmen' – rebelled in the Nile Delta. Our sources are poor, with the fullest little more than a paragraph from a much later epitome of Dio's account, whose collator focused on the lurid and bizarre. He claims that some of the Boukoloi disguised themselves as women, so that they could get close to the centurion sent to collect money from them. The Roman officer was taken by surprise and hacked down, and a companion butchered as a sacrifice, his entrails being eaten to bind the rebels in a dreadful oath.

Joined by a group led by a priest named Isidorus – described as 'the bravest of them all' – the rising gathered momentum. The Romans responded in the usual way and attacked, but the force sent against the rebels was defeated. By this time Egypt was garrisoned by a single legion, supported by at most a dozen auxiliary units. Some of these troops were stationed on the province's southern frontier, guarding the Upper Nile, and others patrolled the roads to the Red Sea ports or were dispersed in small detachments, guarding quarries or granaries, and acting as policemen and administrators. Such a deployment makes it unlikely that the column sent to deal with the rising was either large or consisted of the best-trained and motivated troops in Egypt, making the defeat less surprising.[2]

Success encouraged the rebels to advance on the great city of Alexandria, although clearly this was some months later, for they were blocked by forces sent from Syria and led by the legate of that province, Caius Avidius Cassius. Senators were forbidden from visiting Egypt, and this intervention must have been ordered by the Emperor Marcus Aurelius, requiring a report to reach him, an order to be sent to Syria, and time for a force to be mustered and then moved to Egypt. Cassius avoided a major battle and instead wore the rebels down, fighting many smaller actions and defeating each of the rebel groups separately. This suggests that they had either dispersed as raiding bands or each settled down to defend their own homes.[3]

Many important details of the episode elude us. For instance, the attack on the centurion suggests that Roman levies were resented, but it is not clear whether this was the main cause of the revolt. A gruesome human sacrifice and the mention of the priest Isidorus both hint at religious fervour, whether simply as a unifying force and reminder that they were ruled by foreigners of a different culture, or as a promise of divine aid like that Mariccus offered to his followers among the Boii. Yet we should be cautious, given so brief an account. Greeks and Romans alike saw the people of Egypt as excessively superstitious and alleged that they practised strange and savage rituals, and so were inclined to depict their behaviour in this way. The Boukoloi also appear in ancient fiction, turned into a caricature of wild barbarians given to human sacrifice and cannibalism, and this fictional imagery may well have seeped into historical narratives.[4]

For all our doubts about the rebellion, some aspects are revealing. As was often the case, it appears to have taken the Romans by surprise, in the long as well as the short term, for the gradual reduction in size of the garrison of Egypt in the later first and second centuries AD suggests that no major trouble was anticipated. Whoever the Boukoloi really were, and whether or not they were truly as savage as the sources claim, they were just one group within the wider population of rural Egypt. Others joined them, but the revolt was not by a unified people with a common sense of identity, and instead consisted of multiple communities loosely banded together. If the scale of the revolt is unclear, there is no hint that it involved anything more than a small minority of the provincial population, and while the rebels were clearly hostile to Rome, the move on Alexandria suggests little sympathy for other subjects of the empire. That city was always described as Alexandria 'near Egypt' rather than 'in Egypt' and was a metropolis with a population of several hundred thousand. Founded by Alexander the Great, its inhabitants were mixed, but the dominant group was legally and culturally – if not necessarily ethnically – Greek. Groups like the Boukoloi and the rural population in general had little affection for this 'foreign' city, any more than the Alexandrians had any liking for them.[5]

The mix of populations within a province was one of the main reasons why even the major rebellions struggled to unite the entire population of a single province against the imperial power. Lesser rebellions tended to focus on small regions or groups, and found it difficult to spread, because other provincial communities were antipathetic or openly hostile to them. Few of the areas in the empire had experienced peace and stability before the Romans arrived, and memories of past feuds remained strong. The experience of conquest reinforced some divisions among the indigenous population, as did any subsequent real or perceived favouring of particular leaders and sections of the population. In the eastern Mediterranean, where the Romans were merely the latest in a succession of conquerors, their arrival did not remove every long-standing division created or exacerbated by earlier empires. Even if the Alexandrians and the Egyptians from the countryside both felt alienated by Roman rule at the same time and rebelled, there was no prospect of them joining together. In fact, throwing off Roman rule was likely to make them eager to revive far older quarrels.

During the civil war after the death of Nero, the hatred between Lugdunum and Viennensis (modern Vienne) in Gaul flared into new life, and led to skirmishes 'too savage and frequent for anyone to believe that they fought on behalf of Nero or Galba'. Later, the leaders of Lugdunum tried to persuade an army on its way from the Rhine frontier and fighting for another claimant to the throne to sack Viennensis as a place 'foreign and hostile' and also rich in plunder. The people there managed to placate the soldiers by a dramatic display of submission and by handing over money and weapons to them. Later during the same power struggle, the cities of Oea and Lepcis Magna in North Africa went from disputes between peasants stealing each other's cattle and crops to 'proper weapons and pitched battles'. Oea enlisted the aid of some of the Garamantes to the south, 'an ungovernable people well practised in raiding their neighbours', and so gained the upper hand. Eventually a force of auxiliaries arrived and drove off the Garamantes, recapturing the plunder they had taken, apart from the goods already sold off to distant communities, and peace was restored.[6]

Even Italy was not free of rivalries between its cities. During some fighting in this same civil war, the 'most splendid' amphitheatre outside the city walls of Placentia (modern Piacenza) was burned down. No one was quite sure whether the blaze was started by the besiegers or by the defenders hurling burning missiles at them, but afterwards the 'common folk of the town' alleged that the building had been packed with combustible material by unknown agents of other Italian cities who envied Placentia its magnificent monument. The games were a great opportunity to parade civic pride, both in the grandeur of the venue and the scale and style of the gladiatorial fights and other shows. In AD 59 this exploded into violence between Pompeii and its neighbour and rival Nuceria at a show staged in the amphitheatre at Pompeii. A few bits of graffiti from the city hint at long-standing hostility – 'Good luck to the Nucerians and the hook for Pompeians and Pitheucusans'. At first there was simply chanting and mutual abuse of the type common enough between rival fans at many sporting events, but Tacitus then says that this was followed by 'stones, and finally cold steel'. A famous wall painting from a house in Pompeii showing gladiators fighting in the arena while other figures battle it out on the streets outside surely depicts the disturbances that followed. The visiting Nucerians were heavily outnumbered and soon had the worst of it, with many being killed or wounded. Some of the injured were taken to Rome, and the matter was brought to the attention of Nero, who ordered the Senate to hold an enquiry into the whole incident. They found against the Pompeians and banned the city from holding games for ten years.[7]

Fighting on this scale was unusual anywhere in the empire and especially in Italy, and we know too little of the background to identify what sparked the trouble. The Senate exiled several leading culprits, including the man who staged the games, who had been expelled in disgrace from their own ranks before this incident. Although competition between cities was common throughout the empire it was mainly peaceful, if only because there were few occasions when large crowds of hostile communities would meet. More common was bickering over the boundaries of their jurisdiction, where the risk was of small-scale violence and theft. An inscription from Sardinia records the formal end of hostility between two villages after 185 years, the peace deal being imposed by the Roman authorities in AD 69, centuries after the region became a province. This only occurred because the Romans threatened to use heavy force against one of the rivals. For many provincials Rome was a distant presence, resented rather less than the ongoing annoyance of living close to old enemies.[8]

KINGS AND BAD NEIGHBOURS

The fullest evidence for local enmities and the violence springing from them comes from Judaea and from Jewish communities in neighbouring provinces. The Jews were different, monotheists in a polytheistic world, followed unusual customs and kept themselves apart from the rest of the population, observing forms of ritual purity which made it hard for them to mix. Yet the hostility was more than simple anti-Semitism, or fear and suspicion of a group so obviously different. The Hasmonean dynasty, established when the Maccabees threw off Seleucid rule, was highly aggressive, conquering Galilee to the north and Idumaea to the south and forcibly converting its inhabitants to Judaism. In Samaria, much of the population was descended from marriages between Jews and others, and came to follow a religion that had developed out of Judaism but was now seen as distinct. The Hasmoneans were hostile to them and destroyed the Samaritans' great temple on Mount Gezerim, the centre of their cult, just as the Temple at Jerusalem was for the Jews. Mutual loathing between Samaritans and Jews became proverbial and underlay Jesus' story of the Jewish man robbed and beaten, who was 'passed by on the other side' by a priest and a Levite, only to be helped by a Samaritan.[9]

Adding to the mix were various Gentile communities, survivors of earlier populations or from more recent colonies established by Alexander the Great and his successors, and at various times many of these were subjected to the rule of the Jewish kings or lay on their borders. Other monarchs and some of the great cities were just as eager to expand their own territory, so that control of some regions changed hands several times, and the fortunes of individual communities rose and fell depending on how much they were favoured by the currently dominant power. Mark Antony took land from Herod the Great and from the king of Nabataea to the south to give to Cleopatra when all were allies of Rome, but did not give her all that she requested – in earlier times the Ptolemies had sometimes held sway over much of this territory. Under Augustus Herod regained all that he had lost and was rewarded with additional territory.[10]

Herod was an Idumaean, considered not fully a Jew by the Jerusalem elite, and he had also a deep interest in Hellenic culture. Caesarea Maritima on the coast and Sebaste in Samaria – both names honouring Caesar Augustus, for Sebastos was the Greek equivalent of Augustus – were overtly Gentile cities, filled by the king with statues and temples built on a grand scale. There and in the other Gentile areas he did his best to appear as a tolerant, benevolent and Hellenised ruler, and he also made generous donations to famous Greek communities further afield and to the Olympic Games. There were Thracian, Germanic and Gallic soldiers in his army, and their veterans were given land on discharge. Jews who had fled from Babylon also served him in a military capacity, and were granted their own colony. Judaean or Galilean Jews did not serve in the army, which over time took on a foreign and increasingly Gentile character. Yet for all this, Herod took care to obey Jewish law, and he and his descendants insisted that any marriage of his family into another royal dynasty would only occur if the person involved converted to Judaism. For all his benefactions to Gentiles, Herod lavished as much money or more on monuments in Jerusalem, and in particular the completion of the Great Temple.[11]

Kingdoms with such varied populations made it difficult for a ruler to keep each separate community content with – let alone enthusiastic about – his rule, for each was suspicious of any honours or favours paid to others. To make this even harder, most of these communities were themselves divided into factions – something best attested with the Jews, but likely to have been the case with most others as well. At the very least there were rival leaders vying for power and influence with the higher authorities and the wider population. Herod the Great tried with little success to balance all these demands, and his successors rarely did much better, even though they were granted smaller, less heterogeneous kingdoms. Herod Archelaus was removed from his kingdom by Augustus and Judaea turned into a province in AD 6, passing the problems of controlling its volatile population to an equestrian governor. Galilee remained under a king, and from AD 41 to 44 much of Herod the Great's kingdom, including Judaea and Samaria, were reunited under the rule of his grandson, Herod Agrippa I. Jewish opinion of him was mixed, but some of his Gentile subjects believed that he was pro-Jewish and loathed him accordingly. When he died, mobs in Caesarea and Sebaste publicly rejoiced in the news, and some of his own soldiers – men until recently auxiliaries in the Roman army but recruited mainly from these cities – joined them in feasts of celebration. Statues of the king's daughters, which were in themselves distinctly Hellenic and contrary to Jewish custom, were 'carried . . . to the brothels, where they set them up on the roofs and offered them every possible sort of insult, doing things too indecent to be reported'.[12]

Allied kings depended on Roman support, something subject to the whims of emperors and their advisors, but ultimately resting on their ability to keep their subjects under control. Imperial decisions gave and took away territories and thrones themselves – Agrippa I was a close associate of Caligula and Claudius and benefited from their affection. There were risks and opportunities, and on a day-to-day basis the Romans paid even less attention to what went on in the kingdoms than what happened in the provinces. Domestic squabbles and power struggles within royal households continued, and there were acts of public opposition to the rule of many allied kings. Under Herod the Great real or suspected plots at court resulted in many murders and executions of family members and aristocrats – Augustus joked that he would 'rather be Herod's pig than his son' – and if this was extreme, it was far from unique.[13]

Relations between neighbouring rulers were often poor and occasionally led to open warfare, even when both were allies of Rome. Herod the Great fought a war against the king of Nabataea and won, but then nearly lost the battle over how the matter was reported to Augustus in Rome. The emperor was the ultimate arbiter and his decision could confirm or reverse military victory. Herod Antipas also fought the Nabataeans and this time lost. The legate of Syria was about to lead an expedition to Nabataea to impose a peace when news arrived of the death of the Emperor Tiberius and he withdrew to await further instructions. Two years later Caligula deposed Antipas and replaced him with Agrippa I. Both conflicts began with raiding across the borders between the kingdoms, each side accusing the other of harbouring and perhaps directing these activities.[14]

Herod the Great was often engaged in military operations against leaders characterised as bandits, although in several cases these men were dynastic rivals with connections to the Hasmoneans. Most of the Roman prefects and procurators also suppressed bandits, and several had troubled relationships with the wider population and especially its leaders. Pontius Pilate – prefect from AD 26–c.36/7 – caused offence when he brought a cohort of auxiliaries up to garrison Jerusalem and had them carry the *imagines* (images of the emperor) along with their other standards. This was probably ignorance of local sensibilities rather than deliberate provocation, although since the unit marched into the city during the night it was seen as suspicious. Perhaps they were simply late or he wished to avoid a formal entrance which might disrupt the life of the city. By the time the news spread, the prefect had returned to Caesarea, where he spent much of his time in the more comfortable surroundings of this Gentile city by the sea. A deputation of senior figures from Jerusalem went to see the governor, prostrating themselves around his tribunal for five days and nights when he refused to order the removal of the standards. Pilate surrounded the crowd with a line of soldiers, who drew their swords at his signal. The Jewish deputation remained peaceful and offered their necks to the blades, saying that they would rather die than permit their religious laws to be broken. Pilate relented and ordered the standards to be removed.[15]

This was not the only successful use of passive resistance. In AD 41 Caligula ordered that his statue and other imperial symbols should be erected in the Temple at Jerusalem, reversing a long-established Roman policy of respecting Jewish sensibilities. The emperor was clearly aware that this was highly provocative, but was not acting solely out of deranged vanity. He had received a report that Jews had destroyed an altar erected by some Greeks in a predominantly Jewish community near the coast. The altar was makeshift, and had been set up as a deliberate insult, but the official informing him of the incident presented the Jews in the poorest light, a stance reinforced by several of the emperor's advisors, including a man from Alexandria and another from Ascalon, one of the main Philistine cities in the

Old Testament era. The legate of Syria was sent with his army to ensure that the statue was installed but was met by crowds of protestors, who again said that they were willing to be killed rather than permit this desecration of their most sacred site. To his credit, the legate hesitated and wrote to the emperor asking that he reverse his decision. Caligula ordered the man's execution, but was murdered shortly afterwards. Fortunately the ship carrying the order was delayed until after another letter had arrived from Claudius, cancelling the execution and the original instructions about the statue.[16]

Such peaceful and determined protests were rare, as was the restraint shown by the Romans. Pilate made use of Temple funds to construct an aqueduct improving the water supply of Jerusalem. It was the sort of amenity generally considered good for the whole community, but at some point the source or the way the money was being used provoked angry demonstrations. The prefect disguised parties of soldiers as civilians and let them mingle with the crowd, before unleashing them at a given signal. They attacked using clubs rather than proper weapons, but in spite of this attempt to avoid lethal force some of the protestors died from the blows and others were trampled to death in the ensuing panic. Pilate's actions were deliberately aggressive, but we should not forget the problems in controlling and dispersing crowds. Even with such modern inventions as water cannon and tear gas, the response of the authorities can often seem heavy-handed.[17]

Pilate's tenure in his province lasted for more than a decade, and our sources only record the few moments of major friction. The last of these involved Samaritans rather than Jews and focused on Mount Gerizim. A demagogic leader gathered many people, most of whom were armed, and led them to the site of the destroyed shrine, promising to uncover rich treasures buried there by Moses. Pilate met them with a force of cavalry and infantry, blocking the path up the mountain. Fighting broke out when the first of the Samaritans tried and failed to force their way past the auxiliaries. Pilate launched a vigorous pursuit, killing many and taking prisoners, some of whom were subsequently executed. Leaders from the

Samaritan community went to the legate in Syria and protested at this heavy-handed action, which prompted him to order Pilate to return to Rome to explain himself to the emperor. However, Tiberius died before he arrived and none of our sources tell us whether or not the former prefect was investigated for his actions in office.[18]

Large numbers of people gathering in the open country appear to have triggered an aggressive Roman reaction more often than demonstrations in the cities. Under Cuspius Fadus (procurator AD 44–46), a 'charlatan named Theudas persuaded the majority of the masses to take up their possessions and to follow him to the Jordan River. He stated that he was a prophet and that at his command the river would be parted and would provide them with an easy passage.' Fadus sent a cavalry *ala* which killed or captured them – some 400 people according to the New Testament. Theudas was executed and his head sent back to Jerusalem.[19]

Under Felix (AD 52–60) another false prophet, this time an Egyptian Jew, gathered far more followers – 30,000 according to Josephus, although only 4,000 in Acts – and led them 'out into the wilderness'. His plan was to march to the Mount of Olives and then storm Jerusalem, but they were met in open country by Felix and some auxiliary infantry backed by civilian – and so presumably Jewish – volunteers from the city. The Egyptian and some of his close associates escaped the ensuing massacre, and the rest were killed, captured or slipped away to their homes. In this case the group involved were surely armed and certainly intended revolution. This is less clear with Theudas and some of the other leaders who appeared, or indeed with the Samaritans on Mount Gerizim, but the accounts are too brief to reveal how the fighting began. It was possible for large numbers of people to gather in the countryside and listen to charismatic religious leaders like John the Baptist or Jesus without provoking a military response from either the Roman governor or one of the Herods if the gathering occurred in their territory. Neither the aristocratic Josephus, writing after the failure of the Jewish Rebellion, nor the New Testament authors show any sympathy for those killed or arrested in such incidents where a group became violent.[20]

The auxiliary forces controlled by the equestrian governors were predominantly local men, recruited from the Gentiles of Caesarea and Sebaste. None were well disposed to the Jews, and it is unlikely that a leavening of soldiers from other parts of Syria did anything to change this. Jerusalem was garrisoned by most of one cohort, reinforced by another unit for the great festivals when the city was crowded with pilgrims from all over the world and its population volatile. It was normal practice for sentries to stand guard on top of the porticoes around the Temple and the attached Fortress of Antonia. During the procuratorship of Ventidius Cumanus (AD 48–c.52), one of these men was seen to bend over, lift up the skirts of his tunic and make an obscene noise. Complaints were made, only to be dismissed by Cumanus, especially annoyed because rumours were circulating claiming that he had encouraged the soldier. The next day he paraded his entire force in full armour on the walls of Antonia, causing panic among the worshippers and a stampede in which large numbers were injured or killed – if scarcely the tens of thousands claimed by Josephus.[21]

Soon afterwards, a force of auxiliaries was sent to punish a village for robbing an imperial slave travelling along the road nearby. Its leading men were arrested, probably on suspicion of harbouring or aiding the criminals, and the houses searched and plundered. One of the soldiers found a copy of the Jewish scriptures and launched into an obscene tirade against the Jews, before tearing up the scroll and throwing the remnants into a fire. The protests that followed were so strong, and probably made by large numbers of important men from Jerusalem, that Cumanus ordered the soldier to be beheaded.[22]

The next incident brought out all the latent hostility between Jews and Samaritans. A party of Galileans were travelling through Samaria on their way to Jerusalem. There was trouble, and one or more of them were killed by villagers. A formal complaint to the procurator achieved nothing, either because he was too busy or had listened to – and perhaps taken money from – the Samaritans. Frustrated, some of the Galileans began urging people in Jerusalem to take action. Gangs of vigilantes assembled and joined with established bandit leaders to raid Samaria. Some of the attacks occurred before the official protests had run their course. As is so often the case throughout history, these reprisals were inflicted on villages unconnected in any way with the original offence and were particularly vicious, killing old and young indiscriminately. Cumanus mustered contingents from four cohorts of infantry and his *ala* of cavalry and defeated the largest Jewish band, taking many prisoners. Leaders in Jerusalem helped to calm the situation and persuade the remainder to disperse and return home. In the meantime the Samaritans took their complaints about Cumanus to the legate in Syria, who came to investigate the matter in person, fearing that a rebellion was brewing. He blamed the Samaritans for the initial outbreak and crucified a number of them, before executing several Jews for their part in stirring up trouble. Cumanus was sent to Rome, along with deputations from both sides so that Claudius could investigate the matter fully.

The emperor concurred with his legate in placing most blame on the Samaritans, and ordered several more executions. He also blamed Cumanus for mishandling the situation and sent him into exile. The commander of his cavalry regiment, the *ala Sebastinorum*, was clearly felt to have behaved with excessive vindictiveness in suppressing the Jewish militants. He was sent back to Jerusalem, where he was publicly humiliated by being dragged around the city and then executed. This was a remarkably severe punishment for a Roman officer of equestrian status. He was either a local notable or had simply absorbed the deep loathing of many of his soldiers for their Jewish neighbours. It does seem to have been clear to Claudius that these predominantly Sebastenian and Caesarean soldiers were a source of trouble, being too ready to humiliate and attack the Jewish community. Earlier in his reign Claudius toyed with the idea of posting all of the auxiliary units in Judaea to distant Pontus and replacing them with other army units, less likely to join in local squabbles. He relented when the two cities sent ambassadors to him asking him to reconsider. Discharged soldiers often settled in the province where they had served, and the city elders may have feared losing so many

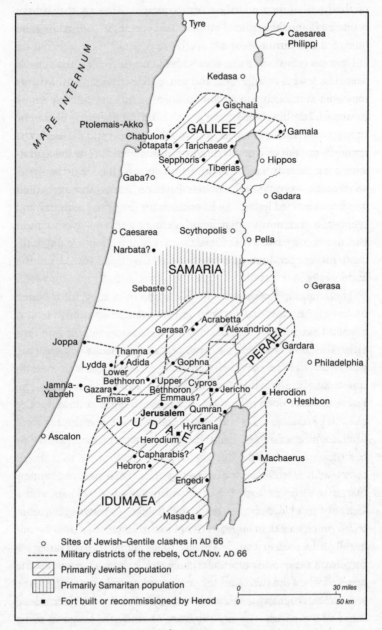

Tyre

Caesarea
Philippi

MARE INTERNUM

Kedasa

Gischala

GALILEE

Ptolemais-Akko
Chabulon
Jotapata • Taricheae •
Gamala

Sepphoris •
Tiberias •
Hippos

Gaba? •

Gadara

Caesarea
Scythopolis •
Narbata? •
Pella

SAMARIA

Gerasa •

Sebaste •

Acrabetta •
Gerasa? •
Alexandrion ■

Joppa
Thamna •
Gophna •
Gardara •

Lydda •
Adida •
PERAEA
Philadelphia •

Lower
Bethhoron •
Upper
Cypros ■

Jamnia-
Yabneh
Gazara •
Bethhoron
Emmaus?
Jericho •

Emmaus •
Jerusalem
Qumran •
Herodion ■
Heshbon •

J U D A E A
Hyrcania ■

Ascalon •
Herodium ■

Capharabis? •
Machaerus ■
Hebron •

Engedi •

IDUMAEA

Masada ■

○ Sites of Jewish–Gentile clashes in AD 66
------ Military districts of the rebels, Oct./Nov. AD 66
▨ Primarily Jewish population
▥ Primarily Samaritan population
■ Fort built or recommissioned by Herod

0   30 miles
0   50 km

Judaea in AD 66

of their young men and their regular wages. They may also have wanted to keep the regional influence that came from providing the bulk of the governor's forces.[23]

On most occasions, successive Roman emperors favoured appeals from the Jewish community, and especially the Jerusalem aristocracy. This was furthered by the influence of the Herods, especially Agrippa I and his son Agrippa II, whether they were in Rome or ruling kingdoms in the east, and whether or not Judaea itself was currently in their charge. Their concern extended to Jews living elsewhere, particularly the large numbers in Alexandria, where there was a substantial, prosperous and well-established community, governed by its own elected leaders and distinct from the Greek majority and the Egyptian minority. That many Alexandrian Jews were fluent in Greek and conversant with Hellenic culture and literature did nothing to prevent persistent hostility between Greek and Jew. Alexandria had long been a turbulent city, frequently subject to rioting which had overthrown and even killed Ptolemaic monarchs. Little changed under Roman rule, and there were men who made careers out of manipulating the mob and using organised bands of partisans to stir up trouble. When Agrippa I visited on his way to his kingdom, some of the Greeks staged a mock royal procession of their own, dressing a local lunatic in a parody of kingly robes. Riots followed, and the Roman prefect sided with the Greeks and blamed the Jews for the trouble, punishing and plundering them. He was eventually recalled, disgraced and exiled, although Caligula's distrust of him played as much part in this as his conduct.[24]

Caesarea was another flashpoint, where a smaller but commercially successful and wealthy Jewish minority lived alongside the Gentile majority in an overtly pagan city. The governor spent more of his time there than anywhere else, increasing the chances for important local men to influence his decisions, and the troops under his command were local men or Sebasteni felt to be on the side of the non-Jewish citizens. Around the middle of the first century AD, the sense that all this gave a marked advantage to their rivals convinced some of the Jewish leaders in the city to lobby for Caesarea to be declared a Jewish community. The tenuous argument rested on its refoundation and development by Herod the Great, ignoring the fact that from the beginning it was overtly 'Greek'. As in so many divided cities throughout the ages, tension increased as partisans of each side demonstrated and did their best to intimidate their opponents, allowing small matters and real or imagined slights to become important. Younger men formed gangs, jeering at each other, and sometimes threw stones or fought, and over time skirmishes became frequent, in spite of the best efforts of local magistrates and the older leaders in each community. The main Jewish gang gained the advantage, and after one victory failed to disperse when ordered by the procurator Felix. It surely did not help that the soldiers with him were associated with their hated and lately vanquished rivals. The governor ordered his troops to use force, which they did with great, and perhaps excessive, zeal. Felix sent deputations from both sides to Nero, who decided in favour of the Gentiles. In the past emperors had usually favoured Jewish petitions, so this was a surprise even if this time their case was poor.[25]

Nero declared that Caesarea remain a formally Gentile city, but its population was bitterly divided. Some of the Jews purchased land for a new synagogue, but tried and failed to persuade the Gentile owner of an adjacent plot to sell to them so that they could build an even larger structure. In the end they gave up, modified their plans and by AD 66 had built to the limit of the ground they owned. At the same time, their neighbour decided to develop his site for industry, so that people attending the synagogue would have to file through a narrow alley past rows of noisy, smoke-filled workshops. He was perfectly within his rights to do this, and his motives may have sprung from commercial decisions rather than deliberate provocation. Some young Jewish men tried to drive away the workmen erecting the sheds, until the procurator, Florus, stopped them. At this point a number of prominent Jews paid the governor a substantial sum to have the work stopped, but Florus pocketed the money and left for Sebaste without doing anything to fulfil his side of the bargain.

On the following day, which was a Sabbath, when the Jews assembled at the synagogue, they found one of the Caesarean mischief-makers had placed beside the entrance a pot, turned bottom upwards, upon which he was sacrificing birds. This spectacle of what they considered an outrage upon their laws and a desecration of the spot enraged the Jews beyond endurance. The steady-going and peaceable members of the congregation were in favour of immediate recourse to the authorities; but the fractious folk and the passionate youth were burning for a fight. The Caesarean party, on their side, stood prepared for action, for they had, by a concerted plan, sent the man on to the mock sacrifice, and so they soon came to blows.[26]

A Roman officer intervened, removing the pot, but failed to prevent further rioting, which prompted some of the Jewish community to flee the city.

This was the incident that helped to spark off the great Jewish Rebellion, when anger at the news, at Florus' continuing failure to intervene, and then at his seizure of funds from the Great Temple in Jerusalem sparked rioting and, later, armed conflict. The heavy-handedness of the locally recruited auxiliaries and the deep hatred felt for them by many Jews inflamed the situation. One cohort eventually surrendered in Jerusalem, only to be massacred with the sole exception of their commander, an equestrian officer spared perhaps because he was not from Sebaste or Caesarea and also because he promised to convert to Judaism. When news arrived that Jerusalem was openly in rebellion, a mob massacred large numbers of those Jews still living in Caesarea. This in turn provoked 'parties of Jews' to attack the Greek cities of the Decapolis – the ten towns of the King James Bible – and any other Gentile settlements within reach, including towns such as Gaza and Ascalon on the coast.[27]

Josephus tells us that

. . . in the vicinity of each of these cities many villages were pillaged and immense numbers of the inhabitants captured and slaughtered.

The Syrians on their side killed no less a number of Jews; they, too, slaughtered those whom they caught in the towns, not merely . . . from hatred, but to forestall the peril which menaced themselves. The whole of Syria was a scene of frightful disorder; every city was divided into two camps . . . They passed their days in blood, their nights . . . in terror.[28]

Jewish sympathisers were suspected, but allegiances were not always simple, nor did every city succumb to infighting. Tyre killed many of its Jewish inhabitants and imprisoned the rest, but at nearby Sidon there were no executions and no imprisonments. Predictably, rioting erupted in Alexandria, but Antioch was peaceful. At Alexandria the Jewish mob gained the upper hand over the Greek mob until Roman troops were sent in and routed them after a stern fight. The governor of Egypt, a Jew who had left the strict practice of his faith for imperial service, called off the soldiers once peace was restored, but found it harder to restrain Greek civilians from further attacks. At Scythopolis (modern Beit She'an or Beth Shean), the only city of the Decapolis on the western bank of the River Jordan, the Jewish inhabitants of the town joined their neighbours to drive off bands of Jewish raiders. In spite of this, they were then asked to prove their loyalty by camping outside the city. After three days some of their neighbours turned on them and killed them. It is impossible to know what determined events in each place, since local history and the personalities of leaders at the time surely played the central role. For Josephus fear was as important as hatred, and often it was simply greed, with the troubles used as a pretext to murder and plunder wealthy neighbours without fear of consequences. The man acting as regent while Agrippa II was away sent troops to murder a deputation from the Jewish communities in Batanaea who had come asking for protection. Josephus claimed that he did so simply to rob them.[29]

MURDER, PLUNDER AND POLITICS

The disruption caused by civil war or revolt created opportunities for enrichment, and it is striking that plunder featured in all of the incidents we have discussed. That does not mean that the hatreds and rivalries were any less real, for the desire to injure and kill people belonging to opposing groups is obvious in the sources. In some ways it was a reversion to the conditions in much of the world before the Romans arrived, where raiding was the normal form of warfare, embarked upon whenever there was an opportunity and disliked neighbours – or indeed anyone else worth robbing and who was not considered a friend – appeared vulnerable. When central authority weakened, whether it was Rome's hold on a region or in areas on the borders between allied kingdoms which did not co-operate well, then raiding broke out, especially where the communities had a tradition of hostility.

Such activity might be led by well-established bandit leaders, given more opportunities by the confusion of the times. During Cumanus' procuratorship the Jews raiding Samaria enlisted the help of Eleazar, son of Deinaeus, 'a brigand who for many years had had his home in the mountains', to lead them. Similar men emerged in AD 66, and in each case others joined them. When Josephus was appointed by the rebel government in Jerusalem to take command in Galilee he hired large numbers of bandits to serve as mercenaries, on the basis that this gave him some control over them. In the troubled years before the rebellion in AD 66, many leading Jerusalem aristocrats, including the high priests, raised bands of armed followers. Another group to appear were the *sicarii* – the name comes from the Latin *sica* or dagger – assassins carrying concealed knives who would strike and then vanish back into the crowd. Their targets were high-profile, which suggests a political agenda, although Josephus claims that they could be hired, even alleging that Felix paid them to kill a high priest. There are also mentions of men able to manipulate the mobs in cities like Alexandria, and some of the

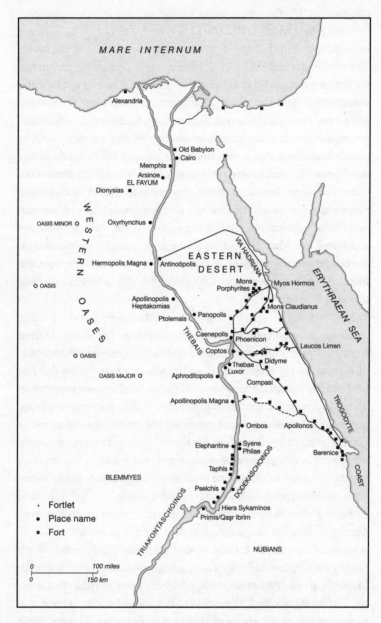

Egypt and the Red Sea ports

gangs of youths who appear were clearly organised and orchestrated.[30]

The Latin *latro* (plural *latrones*) and Greek *leistes* (plural *leistai*) are often translated as bandit – or pirate if they happened to operate on water – although the word lacks the strength of the ancient terms. Such men were not simply robbers, for there was always the expectation that they would use violent, often murderous force. They were stock characters in ancient novels, whisking off heroes and heroines and placing them in dreadful peril so that they could be rescued at the eleventh hour. A degree of romanticism sometimes spilled over into historical accounts, and a charismatic bandit leader, more than half Robin Hood for his boldness, mastery of disguise and ingenious plans, appears now and then in historical sources as foil to a bad emperor. Such sympathy is very rare, and even then partial. *Latrones* and *leistes* were damning terms for bad men using violence illegitimately. According to Roman law, 'Enemies are those on whom the Roman people has formally declared war, or who have themselves declared war on the Roman people; the rest are described as bandits or robbers.'[31]

This distinction assumed that bandits were criminals rather than combatants representing a people or state. It did not matter whether they came from inside the empire or from beyond its borders, or whether they operated in large numbers: such predatory groups were not granted even the limited rights given to foreign enemies, but were effectively outlaws, subject to far harsher punishment. A citizen captured by enemies in a war lost his or her status, becoming a slave of the captor and having to undergo a process to be reaccepted into society. Someone taken by bandits remained a citizen because the capture did not happen during a war.[32]

Bandits and pirates were criminals rather than legitimate foes worthy of respect, so it became increasingly common to brand opponents as such outlaws in order to demonise them, something made easier by the prevalence of raiding as the most common form of military activity. Thus Pompey's great operation against the pirates in 67 BC involved fighting many organised cities and states, a great number of which were annexed. In Rome's civil wars, rivals were dubbed bandit leaders – Augustus depicted Sextus Pompeius as a pirate leading a fleet of runaway slaves. Men challenging allied kings were similarly dismissed as bandits, even when their aims were primarily political.[33]

Banditry appeared in many areas of the empire, although it was more common in frontier provinces, or where terrain offered places of refuge. The conquest of Spain was completed under Augustus, but under Tiberius there were raids launched by the inhabitants of the Cantabrian mountains and these may well have continued on and off for some time. A legion remained based in Spain for centuries, something hard to explain since there was no external frontier nor any hint of widespread rebellion. The area around Mount Amanus where Cicero had campaigned similarly remained troublesome, as did other mountainous or barren and inaccessible regions. In each case the locals continued to raid and plunder just as they had done in the past unless forcibly restrained. It was an assertion of independence, although less an attack on Roman rule than a desire to follow their traditional habit of preying on neighbours and travellers.[34]

Something rather different was the banditry in more settled, urbanised regions, simmering away in normal times, and rapidly increasing during disturbances. Josephus wrote of many *leistai*, sometimes as named individuals, seeing their activities as adding to the tension which provoked the rebellion in AD 66. He was uniformly hostile in his description of them, but admitted that at least some claimed to act for a cause rather than simply for profit. As we have seen, some fought Herod to challenge his right to rule, while others rejected him as a foreigner and similarly resented Roman rule and taxation. How a good Jew should act on such matters was a much-debated issue in these decades. 'Tell us, therefore, what thinkest thou? Is it lawful to give tribute unto Caesar or not?' was the question some Pharisees and Herodians asked Jesus in Matthew's Gospel. The range of answers to this and other questions was very wide, but a significant minority advocated resistance and even rebellion. Among Jesus' disciples were Judas Iscariot – a member of the *sicarii*, although Josephus claims they appeared later – and others such as the brothers

James and John, called 'the sons of thunder', whose names hint at past revolutionary associations. Barabbas, the man released by Pilate instead of Jesus, was a *leistes* 'who for a certain sedition made in the city, and for murder, was cast into prison'. The two robbers crucified on either side of Jesus were also *leistai*, for theft without violence did not warrant execution.[35]

Herod and his heirs, and then successive prefects and procurators, campaigned against bandits and enjoyed many successes, but failed to solve the problem and others soon appeared to replace those killed, arrested or executed. Some of this resilience came from belief in a cause, whether political or religious – the two are hard to separate in Judaea in this period. There were also serious social and economic problems, creating men who turned bandit, a number of whom had more hatred for absentee aristocratic landlords than for more distant Rome, although it is equally clear that some of the *leistai* were no more than armed robbers out for personal gain. These underlying factors fed off each other, encouraging people to seek a way out through protest, religion or violence, helping the situation to spiral out of control. There were counterparts to some of these men in Gentile areas, if perhaps fewer of them and few indeed wanting freedom from Roman rule. In AD 66 genuine bandits combined with political revolutionaries, and the enthusiastic or desperate from the wider population, to spread disorder over a wide area. Similar groups very probably played a major part in the rebellions under Trajan, where inter-communal attacks are widely attested, and also under Hadrian.[36]

Politically motivated banditry aimed in the long run at political change, most likely involving rebellion against Rome. Yet after Hadrian there were no more Jewish rebellions, and revolts were unknown in most other provinces before this time. As early as Tiberius' reign, the soldier, senator and historian Velleius Paterculus boasted that the Roman world was kept 'safe from the fear of brigandage (*latrociniorum*)'. Successive emperors boasted of the peace their guidance of the state brought to the world, much as modern governments claim to reduce the levels of serious recorded crime.

In spite of this, crime continues and is not always perceived as less prevalent.[37]

From the Roman period there is plenty of evidence to show that banditry continued in many areas, and this was certainly the case in Judaea. Once again, our evidence for the Jewish experience under Roman rule is better than that for any other people, and some scholars suggest that in spite of the failure of the rebellions, some bandits acted from resentment of Roman rule rather than simply a desire for profit. This is worth considering, since if some Jewish bandits were men resisting the empire for a cause, then it is possible that some of the ones attested in other regions similarly aimed at throwing off Roman rule. If that was so, then the failure to escalate this resistance into all-out rebellion may suggest a Roman army being used very effectively as an occupying force to hold down provincial populations, even when troops were not stationed in an area.[38]

The argument depends heavily on Talmudic literature, collections of sayings and judgements by rabbis not written down until long after our period, but claiming to represent the wisdom of earlier teachers. Its late date and the moralistic style of these texts make it very hard for us to date or to judge whether incidents recounted were real or hypothetical. Bandits appear often, while the attitude to foreigners and the Romans in particular is at best ambivalent. While it is not all pervasive, a sense of occupation by a brutal and rapacious foreign empire is evident in some of these writings, for instance in this comment on a passage from Deuteronomy:

> . . . these are the oppressors who have taken hold of the land of Israel . . . but tomorrow Israel inherits their property and they will enjoy it as oil and honey. 'Curds from the herd': these are their consulars and governors; 'fat of the lambs': these are their tribunes; 'And rams': these are their centurions; 'herds of Bashan': these are their *beneficiarii* [senior soldiers on special service away from their units] who take away [food] from between the teeth; 'and goats': these are their senators; 'with the finest of the wheat': these are their women.[39]

Roman soldiers are rarely depicted in any favourable light, save in a story where the garrison in Sepphoris turns out to deal with a fire in a neighbouring village on the Sabbath. The owner of the property on fire sends them away, and a rainstorm extinguishes the blaze for him, but even so once the Sabbath is over he sends them a gift of money. The man in question appears to have been important locally, so some would see this as no more than favour shown by the authorities to the rich and well connected. Otherwise the troops come across as alien and often sinister. If a woman was captured by soldiers it was assumed that she might well have been raped or consented to have sexual intercourse with them, but if she was a hostage of bandits then it was assumed that she would not be violated. Bandits are portrayed as likely to behave better than soldiers in this respect. Even so, the former kill and steal and most of their victims are Jewish. One condemned bandit sent word to a prominent rabbi to say that he had murdered the man's son, wanting the family to know that he was dead rather than missing; to interpret this as a sign that bandits were more than simple criminals and had a political or religious agenda strains the evidence. A curious ruling over a man following a nazarite vow who had been forcibly shaved by robbers to violate this may be hypothetical, but suggests a level of deliberate brutality on their part, if only to promote fear.[40]

Bandits were often associated with caves as hiding places, and excavation at a number of sites in Judaea has revealed carefully dug tunnel complexes with living space and store rooms underneath villages. According to Dio, during the Bar Kochba revolt, the rebels 'occupied the advantageous positions in the country and strengthened them with mines and walls, in order that they might have places of refuge whenever they should be hard pressed, and might meet together unobserved under ground; and they pierced these subterranean passages from above at intervals to let in air and light'. Some of these hidden bases may well be associated with that rebellion, but by their nature they are very hard to date and it is more than likely that some were used at other periods and may well have remained in use for a long time.[41]

The garrison of Judaea more than doubled in numbers and increased significantly in quality after the first rebellion, and rose to two legions plus auxiliaries in the second century AD. This was a large concentration of troops for the size of the province, even when it was enlarged to become Syria Palestina, and in itself suggests that the emperors considered the area to be troublesome. Marcus Aurelius is said to have commented on the intransigence of the troublesome Jews. Given, too, the matter-of-fact acceptance in the Talmudic texts of bandits plaguing the roads and even raiding at night into villages, it does seem fair to say that Judaea had a significant problem with banditry for most of the Roman period. As fellow Jews, the rabbis were more likely to speak of them as individuals and concern themselves with their affairs and the conduct of their families – for instance whether the wife of a condemned man should have sex with him. They appear to have seen some bandits as behaving better in at least certain circumstances than Roman soldiers – or perhaps behaving less badly would be more accurate. There was no ringing endorsement of the bandits as fighters for the common good against an oppressive power or as defenders of Jewish culture.[42]

In one story Roman troops surround a village and threaten to sack it if the villagers do not hand over to them a wanted bandit who had taken refuge with them. A rabbi made the man give himself up, but the moral of the story was that Heaven disapproved of his action. Some caution is necessary with this and other hints of sympathy for the bandits – or shared antipathy to the authorities – for the rabbis and the bandits or rebels all came from the same society. If there was some instinctive fellow feeling, there was also a good deal of intimate knowledge. Roman retribution was terrible, but tended to be clumsy. The vengeance of an angered bandit could be far more cruel in its precision, especially when such men mingled with the communities or even lived in hideouts beneath their villages. In plenty of modern trouble spots it would be difficult to find anyone willing to risk speaking out openly to condemn the armed militia or terrorist group in effective control of a region.[43]

After Hadrian, there is no evidence for concerted resistance targeting only the Romans or those seen as collaborating with them, and neither is there the same sense of organised violence against Gentile communities in the wider area. The bandits were there, but they preyed on the rest of the community, robbing and killing Jew and Gentile indiscriminately. If some claimed to resist the imperial oppressors, this does not seem to have altered their behaviour, and none ever gained much momentum or had any prospect of inspiring rebellion in the rest of the population, even if they ever thought of this. No doubt many Jews resented Roman rule and lamented the destruction of the Temple, but they did not look for leaders to help them shake off this oppression, from among bandits or anyone else.

It is unlikely that the picture was very different elsewhere, among communities with less sense of common identity and separateness from the wider world. Evidence for concerted resistance simply does not exist for most of the provinces, and even the few exceptions suggest that it was extremely limited. A collection of stories known today as the *Acts of the Pagan Martyrs* records individuals in Alexandria who stood up to the Roman authorities and were alleged to have mocked repressive governors – and even bad emperors like Commodus – face to face. A theme of anti-Semitism pervades these texts, with the Romans condemned less as an occupying power and more because they are seen as pro-Jewish. There is a nostalgia for a time before Rome ruled, but it is wistful and does not promote rebellion. For such material to have circulated and survived, some Alexandrians must have shared the sentiments of such stories, but as always this was not enough to persuade them to do anything about it, still less to unite with others in common cause against the empire.[44]

All in all, there is no convincing evidence for banditry as a form of prolonged resistance to Roman rule anywhere in the empire once provinces became settled. Even in Judaea, any trace of a political or religious agenda became no more than a pretext for straightforward robbery and violence once the major rebellions were over. Banditry was a constant threat, usually small in scale in most areas most of the time, but apt to increase rapidly during any crisis of central authority.

It did not strike more at representatives of Roman authority than anyone else.

Much of the evidence for this chapter has come from Judaea or other areas with significant Jewish populations. There is far less evidence for inter-communal violence in other parts of the empire, although as we have seen there is some. This may be because local hostility was rarely so bitter, or perhaps because there were fewer opportunities for it to erupt into such large-scale violence. The region that eventually became the province of Syria Palestina consisted of a jumble of different populations living side by side and sometimes in the same cities, but divided by religion and a long history of conflict. As power over each region passed from allied king to Rome and back again, its structure often made little administrative sense. For a while in the first century the Decapolis was part of the province of Syria even though it was not joined to the rest of the province, but was effectively an island surrounded by the territory of allied rulers. Alexandria was exceptionally large, with three major sections within the population, none of them fond of the others. Even so the frequency of rioting there should not be exaggerated, just as in the long run we cease to hear of inter-communal violence in Judaea and the surrounding areas.[45]

Other cities were less turbulent, even if the possibility of rioting remained. This could be political, as leaders vied for office and employed any means to intimidate their opponents and control elections. Another threat to public order came if food supplies ran short, when angry crowds were apt to turn on anyone believed to be hoarding grain supplies in the hope of selling when the market price was at its highest. In each case the same causes had provoked unrest and violence long before the Romans arrived. Like much of the banditry, and wider raiding by mountain tribes and opportunistic piracy, these were well-established features of life in much of the ancient world. It is now time to look at how the empire under the emperors was governed, and how far it was able to check such things.

IMPERIAL GOVERNORS

'He took such care to exercise restraint over the city officials and the governors of the provinces that at no time were they more honest or just, whereas after his time we have seen many of them charged with all manner of offences.' – *Suetonius, speaking of the Emperor Domitian, early second century AD.*[1]

'FIRMNESS AND DILIGENCE'

Around 160 years after Cicero landed at Ephesus on his way to govern Cilicia, another former consul arrived there on his way to his own provincial command of Bithynia and Pontus. Pliny the Younger (Caius Plinius Caecilius Secundus) had not dawdled like the reluctant Cicero, but even so arrived later than he hoped, his ship delayed by bad weather. More delays followed as he pressed on to his province. The heat was excessive, making overland travel by carriage arduous, and Pliny went down with fever and had to stay some days at Pergamum, but when they took passage on trading ships operating along the coast they were again held back by the weather. It was not until 17 September AD 109 that the new governor reached Bithynia, allowing him to celebrate the birthday of the Emperor Trajan on the next day.[2]

Pliny was a 'new man' like Cicero, his family coming from one of the towns of Italy, in his case Comum (modern Como, on the picturesque lake of the same name). He was also a highly successful advocate in the courts and a prolific author who published nine books of edited letters in conscious emulation of his famous predecessor. Pliny's correspondents included many of the distinguished senators of the era, notably the historian Tacitus, and dealt with domestic themes, literature, admirable behaviour by prominent men and women, and the conduct of some of the important trials in which he was involved. There were also a number of letters soliciting favours for himself or his associates. Wholly absent is Cicero's concern for the outcome of elections, for building political friendships with others, for the changing balance of power and influence within the Senate and with the details of legislation. The reader of Pliny's *Letters* can be left in no doubt that this was a state controlled by a *princeps*, whose influence – malign in the case of Domitian and benevolent in the case of Trajan – was everywhere. It is no coincidence that the only one of Pliny's published speeches to survive is a panegyric of Trajan, for senators under the Principate were dependent on imperial favour to a degree that Cicero could scarcely have imagined, even during Caesar's dictatorship.[3]

It was as a representative of the emperor, as *legatus Augusti* on a special commission, that Pliny went out to Bithynia, his appointment made by Trajan and not subject to senatorial debate or lot. Even so his authority was greater than that of anyone else in the province, except in the highly unlikely event of the *princeps* coming in person. However, the greater power of Trajan could not be ignored. Pliny took with him a set of instructions (*mandata*) issued by the emperor, which were longer and more prescriptive than the suggestions the Senate made to someone like Cicero. It would be difficult for provincials to appeal over his head to Rome unless they had his permission, but it was certainly not impossible. There was also a procurator overseeing the imperial estates and some of the taxation of the province and this man corresponded directly with the *princeps* and his advisors. In this case the relations between the two men were good.[4]

Bithynia and Pontus was not a major military province and was garrisoned by at most a handful of auxiliary units – one *cohors equitata* consisting of infantry and a small force of cavalry is definitely attested, a second is almost certain, and there may have been other regiments. In normal times the province was under senatorial control, its governor a proconsul selected by lot from a list drawn up by the Senate of sufficient men to fill the number of posts coming vacant in the public provinces. Sometimes the *princeps'* advice on selection was sought, and even when it was not it is clear that they would not choose anyone who was obviously out of favour. In office, these governors had limited independence and their decisions could be overruled by the *princeps* if a matter was brought to his attention. They were also bound by rulings made by past emperors, and would need to seek approval to change these. Augustus may at first not have issued *mandata* to proconsuls, but probably began to do so later in his reign and this became normal under his successors.[5]

In the early second century AD Bithynia and Pontus was a troubled region. Several of its former governors were prosecuted for corruption, while there were bitter rivalries for dominance within its major cities and widespread misuse of public money. Trajan decided to intervene, temporarily adding the region to his provinces and sending Pliny there as his legate. He was *princeps* and the Senate could not refuse, although in this case it is unlikely that it resented the move, since it still meant that one of their number was given the command.[6]

On the whole, proconsuls and imperial legates did much the same job, and successful senators served in both capacities at different stages in their careers. The essentially civilian role of the proconsul was emphasised in the wearing of the toga on ceremonial occasions, while the overtly military legates wore a sword, military cloak and cuirass. The former were accompanied by six lictors bearing *fasces*, the latter probably by five, marking their lesser *imperium* as representatives rather than magistrates in their own right. Both types of governor held essentially identical authority over the garrisons of their provinces in every important respect, and it was simply that the proconsuls had far fewer troops at their disposal. Their tenure was also shorter, often no longer than the traditional twelve months. In contrast it was rare for a legate to hold command for less than three years, and many were in post for even longer, giving the province greater continuity of leadership and allowing the governor to address more serious problems, whether military or civil. Pliny died

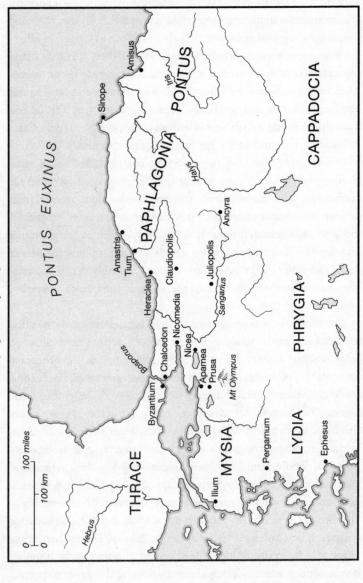

Pliny's province of Bithynia and Pontus

before the end of his third year in the post and we do not know how long he was due to be in the province, but he was sent expressly to restore order to its finances and administration so there may not have been a fixed term.[7]

Throughout his time in the province Pliny wrote to Trajan, often seeking guidance on specific problems. A tenth book of correspondence was published posthumously, consisting of letters to the emperor, and it is dominated by his time as governor – his letters from Bithynia and Trajan's replies make up 107 out of a total of 121. Although we do not know the circumstances of their preparation and release, this must surely have occurred with at least the approval and perhaps the active involvement of Trajan and his advisors. It was an era when many technical manuals were being written, and in some ways the letters from Bithynia have a similar, instructional feel to them, showing the way that a good governor should go about his job. Pliny's approach to a problem involved looking for precedents and past rulings, trying to find the most beneficial solution for the provincial communities, and seeking the emperor's decision on some issues where he was unsure. This was clearly how Trajan wished his principate to be seen, as efficient, benevolent, respectful to local traditions and obedient to the spirit as well as the letter of the law. The Trajan of these letters has the same tone of friendship and interest in the welfare of provincial communities that can be seen in many inscriptions recording replies from emperors to requests from cities and individuals.

All imperial legates sent reports and queries to the *princeps*, and we cannot say whether or not Pliny wrote more often than was normal – or indeed whether there were originally far more letters, some too brief or too mundane to be included in the published version. The tendency to address just one issue in each letter was more likely intended to make it easier for the imperial secretariat to check for precedents and to respond or advise the *princeps* rather than being a sign that letters were extensively rewritten before publication. It is possible that some of the questions were asked in order to permit Trajan to give the official response, although this would assume that it was always planned to publish the letters. One instance is the re-peated requests for specialists such as architects and surveyors to be sent out from Italy or from a military province – the army produced very skilled technicians of all kinds. Only once does the *princeps* agree, saying that he will instruct the legate of Moesia to send a man to supervise a complex canal-building scheme. Otherwise, he invariably assures Pliny that not simply Bithynia but any province will have competent specialists among the population, an answer with a general application.[8]

All in all, the letters in Pliny's tenth book appear genuine and give us our best picture of a provincial governor under the Princi-pate, worthy of comparison with Cicero's letters from Cilicia. As always, the different circumstances of the early second century AD compared to the middle of the first century BC are obvious. No doubt Pliny wrote plenty of letters to friends, relations and other connections while in his province, but none of these were published. What mattered was the relationship between *princeps* and legate and the provincial communities. Throughout Pliny addressed Trajan as *domine* – master or lord – and was in turn called 'my dear Secundus'. Augustus had not cared to be called *dominus*, but under his succes-sors – even ones considered to be good rulers and respectful of the Senate – this became normal. Some of the replies have a formal style, reflecting their drafting by imperial secretaries, but now and again the tone of familiarity or of exasperation at the provincials is surely the authentic voice of the emperor.[9]

BITHYNIA AND PONTUS – WASTE, CORRUPTION AND RIVALRIES

Pliny's province stretched along the Asian shore of the Black Sea, from the Bosphorus in the west to the territory of the city of Amisus in the east. It had first become a Roman province during Pompey's reorganisation of the eastern Mediterranean following the defeat of Mithridates, and many of the arrangements put in place then remained in force. Although much of the region was essentially rural, all important administration focused on the cities, which were Hellenic in culture and would produce several of the second century's most prominent Greek writers. Prior to Roman rule, the cities were controlled by satraps imposed by regional kings, so had less tradition of independence than the Greek communities in some other areas. To the south were the provinces of Asia under the charge of a proconsul and Galatia commanded by a legate.[10]

Part of the coastline of the province was under the command of an equestrian 'prefect of the Pontic shore' (*praefectus orae Ponticae*), under the governor's supervision. This man may have had some troops of his own in addition to ones detached from the garrison of the province, and there was also a flotilla of warships, the *classis Pontica*. Even so, it is unlikely that there were as many as 2,000 military personnel in the province and probably the total was significantly lower – perhaps barely 1,000 or even less if the units were under-strength. The nearest major army was based in Cappadocia and could not have intervened quickly in the case of trouble, so it is clear that the Romans did not expect any serious military problems in what was not a frontier province – hence its normal allocation to a proconsul. Pliny's letters contain not the slightest hint that he considered a rebellion to be remotely possible or that he might need to spend some of the summer on campaign. If there was a problem with banditry, then it was on a far smaller scale than that faced by Cicero in Cilicia. The troops in Bithynia and Pontus under Pliny's command functioned primarily as a paramilitary police force, and as escorts for the governor and other officials and as administrators.[11]

The creation of the Principate did not alter many of the fundamental structures of Roman provincial government. Most day-to-day affairs continued to be left to the provincial communities. We have fewer details about Pliny's staff, but it is unlikely that this was significantly larger than Cicero's cohort in Cilicia. Pliny had a single legate as subordinate, Servilius Pudens, probably chosen by the emperor – in normal times the proconsul was allocated a legate by the Senate. Governors were also free to take personal friends or connections with them to their province, as under the Republic. It was felt right and proper for these to advise him, forming the council (*concilium*) considered appropriate for any magistrate, including the *princeps*. Such men could also be given tasks to perform on his behalf. Later in the second century, another senator and letter writer, Fronto, was allocated the proconsulship of Asia, and immediately began to gather associates to assist him,

> . . . so that the resources of my friends should put me in better position to cope with the demanding business it involved. I summoned from home kinsmen and friends of known loyalty and integrity. I wrote to Alexandria to close friends telling them to make haste to Athens and wait for me there . . . From Cilicia too I urged men of distinction to come . . . [Fronto notes that he had acted on behalf of individuals and communities from that province.] From Mauretania again I summoned to my side Julius Senex, a man who is extremely devoted to me and who is correspondingly dear, to enlist his help, not only because of his loyalty and willingness to work, but for his indefatigable energy as a soldier in flushing out brigands and crushing them.[12]

As in the past, the state provided few professional civil servants, and governors relied heavily on their households and personal connections. In some cases such associates were well suited to their tasks. Fronto noted that his friends from Alexandria – probably including the historian Appian – were 'extremely learned' and so were to have charge of his correspondence in Greek, which would form the greater part of his work in a province where Latin was rarely used. Some men appear to have made a career out of assisting governors as specialists, such as the bandit hunter Julius Senex. In the event, illness prevented Fronto from taking up his post and the arrangements came to nothing.

An inscription recording the visit on 1 May AD 165 of the proconsul of Macedonia to the shrine at Samothrace lists his entourage of four

friends, three lictors and three messengers (*viatores*), fifteen slaves
and five auxiliaries, one a junior officer and another marked down
as a messenger and so probably a cavalryman. There was also an imperial slave and three or four slaves belonging to other members of
the group. The entire entourage took part in the rites at the temple.
There were surely other staff members who were not present, and
the number of civil servants – with only three instead of six lictors
– seems small, as is his military escort, judging from the number
of soldiers often allocated to more junior officials. The prefect of
the Pontic shore was supposed to take only ten picked soldiers, two
cavalrymen and a centurion from the troops under Pliny's command, but in fact had more and claimed to governor and emperor
that he needed them. Pliny let him keep them until Trajan made a
decision on the matter. Pliny also mentions that ten selected soldiers
were allocated to the procurator, but that his assistant the imperial
freedman Maximus insisted that he needed six more and seems to
have acquired them. On request Pliny granted him two cavalrymen
as escort for a journey to collect grain in Paphlagonia. Trajan told
Pliny that he was 'quite right to supply my freedman Maximus with
soldiers for his present requirement', but that in future he should
make do with just four men.[13]

It is striking that a governor would write to the emperor about
the assignment of individual rank-and-file soldiers, perhaps again a
case of asking so that the official response could be given. Trajan
repeats his wish that as few soldiers as possible be detached from
their units, but is willing to relax this rule where necessary. Thus
both officials appear to be permitted more soldiers than originally
allocated. In contrast he orders Pliny to end a temporary expedient
of using soldiers to guard prisons in place of the public slaves, who
were not doing the job well. He also refused to detach a centurion
and some men to regulate the heavy traffic passing through the city
of Juliopolis, saying that this would set a dangerous precedent and
allow many other cities to demand the same favour. This reflected
both the aim of keeping units up to strength and capable of training
for their military role, and also the Roman expectation that local

communities should manage their own affairs rather than presume that the empire would deal with them.[14]

Public provinces like Bithynia and Pontus had very small garrisons, with the units quickly depleted of men, and especially officers, suited to detached service. Educated men were needed for the army's own administration – not least, keeping track of all those posted away on various duties. Usually these provinces contained only auxiliaries, and levels of literacy among such soldiers varied depending on where they were recruited. There were some exceptions. One cohort of *Legio III Augusta* was sent annually from Numidia to serve the proconsul of Africa. Legates of military provinces had far greater manpower at their disposal. Each legion had a legate of its own, as well as one senatorial and five equestrian tribunes, and sixty centurions. It is estimated that about 100 soldiers of lower ranks were also trained for and available to the governor for administrative tasks, joining his staff or *officium*. This means that in a province with three legions the legate had a pool of officers of varying ranks, some of whom could be detached to his staff or act independently, and some 300 military bureaucrats, not including his armed bodyguard of mounted and foot *singulares* drawn from the *auxilia*. Although at first sight an impressive total – to which could be added friends, slaves and freedmen, but fewer public officials than a proconsul – such a command also required maintaining a level of preparedness for warfare and perhaps actual campaigning. Controlling, equipping and supplying an army of three legions and auxiliaries was a major task in itself, even in peacetime, and surely occupied a good deal of the legate's and his staff's attention.[15]

One other addition to the governors' staffs came with the Principate, although it was not a deliberate reform intended to add to their administrative capabilities, nor was it compulsory. Under the Republic a governor might take adolescent or older sons with him, but the rest of his family remained in Italy. A governor did not take his wife to his province, although some took mistresses or found them locally. During the civil wars this started to change and several leaders, such as Pompey and Mark Antony, took their wives to the provinces, although not on campaign. Augustus was accompanied by Livia on most of his travels during his principate, a practice which was followed by several of the younger members of his extended family and soon became normal for most governors and many army officers, especially since tours in the provinces tended to last longer. In Matthew's Gospel, Pontius Pilate's wife was with him in Jerusalem, and her dream prompted him to wash his hands of responsibility.[16]

Under Tiberius a senator with a long record of military service proposed that the Senate should vote to ban governors from taking their wives with them. The man had never taken his wife on any of his forty campaigns or tours of duty, in spite of which they had six children and – at least in his view – a happy marriage. He argued that the presence of women hindered military operations, while some wives were inclined to interfere with military discipline or set themselves up to be courted by the provincials wishing to use their influence over their husbands. There was so much opposition to the motion that it was not even brought to the vote. Pliny took his wife Calpurnia with him to Bithynia, and she endured the sea voyages, the heat and the long journeys by carriage.[17]

The Principate saw no move to create permanent provincial capitals as administrative centres, although in some cases governors acquired comfortable residences in one or more cities. Even so, just like a governor in Cicero's day, Pliny spent his time moving from each assize city to the next. This was one of the reasons why the governor's staff remained modest in size, since it was forced to be itinerant as he made himself available to the provincials. The status of assize centre continued to be greatly prized, and it is unlikely that under the Principate a governor could have followed Cicero's example and held court in one place, making people travel to him. A governor spent a lot of time on the road – or occasionally travelling by river or sea if this was possible.

This was made easier as the system of good, all-weather roads was extended throughout the provinces and by the creation of the Imperial Post, with relays of horses and vehicles for the use of those travelling on official business. Local communities were obliged to support this, and subject to requisition of animals, transport, drivers and guides – at times a considerable burden. Permits to make use of the post were issued by the emperor and some allotted to governors, but it is clear that it was frequently abused. Pliny's final letter to Trajan explained that he had given a permit to his wife, summoned home by the death of her grandfather, and the emperor replied giving his approval. Apart from transport there were also some official residences in major cities, as well as way stations or *mansiones* to accommodate official parties when they stopped for the night. Yet the infrastructure was incomplete, and governors might well stay at inns with civilian travellers, or camp out in the course of their annual tours. Pliny was around fifty when he arrived in his province, and not a robust man, making the demands of his post arduous. Some governors were even older, and it was rare for a man to receive a province before he reached middle age.[18]

Each city had its own courts, which resolved the great majority of legal disputes and trials. The governor had to deal with more serious cases, including many capital crimes, challenges to Roman authority and disputes between communities, or those involving Roman citizens or other prominent men who were not satisfied with local justice and hoped to overturn the result by approaching a higher authority. Litigants dissatisfied with a governor's ruling favouring their opponents might in turn try to take the matter directly to the emperor – or, as in Cicero's day, hope to postpone a resolution until his successor arrived. A set number of days were allocated for the governor to hold court in each assize centre. Normally the cases to be brought to him were announced in advance, although he had freedom to deal with them in any order he chose and to take as long as he wanted or felt necessary with each one. The impression is that there was far more work than could be completed, so that some litigants would wait, perhaps for years or even in vain. As always, the more influential had a better chance of gaining access to the governor and getting what they wanted.[19]

Pliny was about to leave the assizes at the city of Prusa when a magistrate asked him to deal with an accusation brought by one local aristocrat against a rival, the prolific orator Dio Chrysostom. The case involved a public building project Dio had undertaken but not completed, and involved accusations of embezzlement, as well as vaguer claims that as part of the work he had set up a statue of Trajan near some family graves. Given the importance of the men involved, Pliny agreed to delay his departure to hear the case. However, Claudius Eumolpus, the lawyer acting for Dio's opponent, wanted time to prepare the case and asked for it to be dealt with in the assize at another city. Pliny told Trajan that he

> . . . arranged to hold it in Nicaea, but, when I took my seat to hear the case, Eumolpus again began to beg for an adjournment on the grounds that he was still insufficiently prepared, whereas Dio demanded an immediate hearing. After much argument on both sides, some of it referring to the actual case, I decided to grant an adjournment to ask your advice, as the case is likely to create a precedent. I told both parties to present their demands in writing as I wanted to enable you to judge their statements from their own words.

Dio's opponents felt that this would be to their disadvantage and had not produced their written case by the time that Pliny wrote to the emperor. Trajan dismissed the matter of his statue – a charge that might have carried more weight under some of his more nervous predecessors – and focused on the important charges, insisting that Dio produce full accounts of the project for Pliny to inspect. The exchange of letters between Bithynia and Rome must have taken several months, and we do not know when and how the case was ultimately resolved. Then as now, legal disputes could take a very long time and involved much manipulation of the system, with delays, other charges being made to occupy time and damage opponents, as well as seeking out the authority seen as most likely to be favourable.[20]

Pliny's concern for precedent reflected every aspect of Roman government. At times this was purely formal, but important to all involved. The city of Apamea was a Roman colony and in the past proconsuls had not inspected the public accounts. Pliny wished to do this – it was part of his mission to ensure that the finances of the cities in his province were restored to order – and was told that the city authorities were happy for him to see them as long as it was put on record that they had not in the past been obliged to submit to such scrutiny. Pliny forwarded on to Rome the documentation they provided to support this claim; Trajan replied commending the Apameans and Pliny. The legate was to carry out the inspection at the *princeps'* request, an extraordinary circumstance which in no way altered the colony's status and did not set a precedent for the future.[21]

At various times Pliny consulted local laws, established practice and specific rulings including ones by Pompey, as well as several emperors, and also applied his understanding of Roman law. In many cases these dealt with specific communities, and only occasionally were applicable to the province as a whole. Each province had its own laws, rules and conventions, and there was no attempt to impose a standard legal system and civic organisation on the entire empire, so that examples from a governor's past experience elsewhere were not applicable. It was rare for a man to serve in the same province twice in his career, and there is little sign of men with experience in a region being selected for posts on that basis.

Given the itinerant nature of legates and proconsuls, it was impossible for their staff to carry thorough documentation dealing with every law and regulation for the situations they might encounter. Therefore they relied on litigants and local authorities bringing these to their attention and providing documentary proof of authenticity, or on consulting the emperor whose secretariat – limited though it was by modern standards – had access to rulings made in the past at Rome. In his correspondence with Pliny, Trajan always respected decisions made on such matters by his predecessors – even such generally criticised men like Domitian – and preferred to do this rather than establish a new rule. The need to refer questions to Rome was probably common for all governors and not simply Pliny, and can only have meant that many cases dragged out over long periods of time. Disputes between provincials drew the Roman authorities into issues that would not have concerned them at other times.[22]

On the whole the initiative still lay with the populations in the provinces, just as it had under the Republic. They came to Pliny with problems and disputes because he had the power to act. There is no hint of powerful men at Rome pressuring the legate to aid them in their business ventures in Bithynia and Pontus. Companies of *publicani* continued to take on the collection of some levies and tolls, but direct taxation was dealt with by the state, assisted by the provincial communities who in turn often farmed this out to locally based private contractors. In the changed political environment of the Principate, the money of the *publicani* and their backers was no longer an important factor in elections and political competition at Rome. No doubt there was still plenty of corruption within the system, but there was no longer one influential group capable of collaborating to put heavy pressure on governors. As before there were plenty of local interests, who did their best to enlist the influence of important Romans to gain leverage with the governor. More and more important local men were also Roman citizens – although this was at first more common in the western provinces – and so entitled to greater consideration.[23]

The aim of Roman government was to keep the provincial communities stable, prosperous enough to pay their taxes in the long term, at peace with each other and content with imperial rule. The Romans' preference for letting the provincials run their own affairs is strikingly illustrated in the most famous exchange between Pliny and Trajan, two letters that deal with Christians arrested and brought to the governor by the authorities in one of the cities. The legate informs the emperor that he has executed Christians who refused to recant, unless they were citizens whom he has arranged to send to Rome for trial. Everyone who denied being a Christian, and gave proof of this by taking an oath, by making a sacrifice and reviling the name of Christ, was allowed to go free. Trajan approved this procedure, but added that 'these people must not be hunted out; if they are brought before you and the charge against them is proved, they must be punished'.

It was up to the provincial leaders to find and arrest Christians if they chose to look for them. If they were not aware of them, or unconcerned by their presence, then nothing would happen. Nero had declared Christianity to be illegal at the time he made Christians scapegoats for the great fire in Rome in AD 64. Trajan and most other emperors until the middle of the third century AD did not consider them to be a significant threat, either because their numbers remained small or because their activities were unimportant and not dangerous. Pliny's investigations revealed a harmless group guilty only of 'excessive superstition' – hence the curious willingness to execute Christians when brought before the authorities while at the same time deliberately not trying to find them. Persecutions occurred only when important provincials became worried, so were rare and local in their impact. It was all about keeping communities content.[24]

The bulk of a governor's time was spent dealing with issues brought to him – just as, at a higher level, emperors were constantly answering petitions and appeals. Yet it would be wrong to portray either as wholly passive and reactive. Pliny's special legateship was intended to deal with the disorder and financial problems in his province, and from the start he was active in investigating a wide range of civic functions. We have already encountered his short-lived experiment of using soldiers to supervise the public slaves guarding prisoners. Trajan ordered him to bring this to an end and instead ensure that the public slaves did their duty, assuring the legate that this relied on his 'firmness and diligence'. On another occasion, in both Nicaea and Nicomedia he discovered men convicted of serious crimes and sentenced to the effective death sentences of the mines or the arena, but instead acting as public slaves, performing work for the community and even receiving an annual salary. Examination of the records failed to reveal how they had escaped their sentences. Trajan replied saying that this failure of the justice system could not be allowed to stand. Anyone sentenced in the last ten years was to be sent for their allotted punishment, but there was an element of mercy: 'if the men are elderly and have sentences dating back farther than ten years, they can be employed in work not far removed from penal labour, cleaning public baths and sewers, or repairing streets and highways, the usual employment for men of this type'.[25]

One area of particular concern was a number of major civic building projects which had either been abandoned, were delayed, or were of dubious quality, all at great public expense. Nicomedia had two aqueducts abandoned before completion, after spending 3,318,000 and 200,000 sesterces respectively. Nicaea spent more than ten million on a theatre which suffered from subsidence and had not been finished – Pliny noting that several prominent men had promised to add embellishments to the basic structure, but that nothing had been done. The same city was making little headway at great cost on a gymnasium intended to replace an earlier one destroyed by fire. At Claudiopolis there was limited progress on a bath, and the legate's concern was more for the funding of the project. The building at Prusa which was the grounds for the attacks on Dio Chrysostom had also stalled, as the orator wanted the project, and presumably its costs, to be taken over by the authorities. Magistrates and local aristocrats were expected to be generous in funding public works. They competed for prestige, while cities vied with each other to possess the grandest monuments. Like some politicians today, more than a few of these men had more interest in gaining the credit for announcing a grand project than in the arduous task of seeing it through to completion.

Trajan's replies generally returned the matter to Pliny, saying that each case could best be assessed on the spot and trusting in his legate's good judgement. Thus the *princeps* left the fate of the theatre at Nicaea in his hands, to repair or demolish and start again from scratch as was most practical, and only insisted that all the promised embellishments would be provided by the donors once the main building was complete. The Nicaeans were advised to be realistic in their plans for the gymnasium – something the 'Little Greeks' (*Graeculi* in Latin) dearly loved, which made the emperor fear that their plans were over-ambitious. Pliny was to look into the planned baths at Claudiopolis, but was once again assured that there was no need to send an architect from Rome or one of the military provinces since there must be capable men in the province. Trajan told him to ensure that Nicomedia finally got the aqueduct needed to give it a water supply, and was more concerned about the waste of so much money, telling Pliny to find out who was to blame.[26]

Pliny was willing to forward on requests from community leaders concerning new projects, for instance when Prusa asked permission to build public baths to replace the existing building, which was old and in poor repair. Such projects would not normally have required imperial approval, and the request reflects the recent spate of scandals and failures in public construction in the province. In this case, it was planned to use money set aside for another purpose, the free distribution of olive oil to citizens of the city, on the building, which would be fitting for the 'prestige of the city' and the 'splendour of your leadership'. Trajan told Pliny to let them go ahead as long as the funds were there and the cost would not overstrain Prusa's finances or require the introduction of new taxes.[27]

In other cases, Pliny appears to have come up with the idea rather than receiving petitions from the locals. For instance he felt Sinope needed a water supply, and so suggested that an aqueduct be built. Once again, Trajan's approval was ready, but conditional on the city being able to afford the project – we may recall the anger prompted when Pontius Pilate employed Temple funds for a similar work at Jerusalem. At Amastris Pliny found one of the main streets built on a grand scale, except that an open sewer ran along it, and proposed sealing this off to remove the stench and improve public health. He assured the *princeps* that the work was affordable and received the usual permission on this basis. His grandest design was for a canal to connect a lake near Nicomedia with the sea to make transporting heavy goods much easier, a work 'worthy of your immortal name and glory and likely to combine utility with magnificence'. Suitably impressed, this was the aforementioned exception where Trajan allowed Pliny to summon a military engineer from Moesia. Both men emphasised the need for careful and precise planning to make something of this sort succeed and understood that mistakes in calculation might do considerable damage, even draining the lake.[28]

Designs involving the control of large quantities of water were by their nature complex. A long inscription from Africa records the experiences of a similar specialist, in this case a recalled veteran soldier, sent to supervise the construction of an aqueduct, involving tunnelling through some high ground. Nothing proved straightforward for this man, Nonius Datus. Before he arrived he was attacked by bandits and 'escaped naked and wounded'. The project was already under way, and the locals had decided to begin the tunnel at opposite sides of the mountain. Measurement revealed that the combined length of the two tunnels was wider than the mountain, so that one or both had deviated from a straight path and there was no chance of them joining up. The mood of despair among the locals made it likely that the enterprise would be abandoned – at least so the military engineer claimed in his own account. Through careful survey, close supervision and using a labour force drawn from naval units and auxiliaries, who were encouraged to compete with each other as they worked, Datus was able to finish the tunnel.[29]

A better water supply improved the life of the inhabitants of the city it supplied, even if much went to the houses of the wealthy and to meet the high demands of public bath houses. Whoever had supplied amenities of this sort wanted the praise and gratitude of the population. The characteristic high arches of Roman aqueducts were not always necessary, but raised the structure to dominate the landscape and remind people of the benefaction. Pliny and Trajan show a concern for the welfare of the provincials, with regard to both the infrastructure and the status of such unfortunate groups as babies exposed by parents too poor to keep them and raised as slaves. The legate also recommended forming a fire brigade at Nicomedia, which had suffered from a serious conflagration that destroyed private houses and some public buildings. This seems to have been later than the blaze that badly damaged its gymnasium, suggesting that fires were a common problem, as they were in most ancient cities. Yet Trajan felt the proposed cure might make the citizens worse off:

You may well have had the idea . . . to form a company of firemen at
Nicomedia . . . but we must remember that it is societies like these
which have been responsible for the political disturbances in your
province, particularly in towns. If people assemble for a common
purpose, whatever name we give them and for whatever reason, they
soon turn into a political club. It is better policy then to provide the
equipment necessary for dealing with fires, and to instruct property
owners to make use of it, calling on the help of the crowds which
collect if they find it necessary.[30]

In Rome Augustus had created the *vigiles*, a paramilitary night police
and fire service, moved in part by an attempted coup in 19 BC led by a
man who had raised his own force of firemen. There was a good deal
of truth in Trajan's claim that any organised band or association was
likely to become a political force – especially firemen, who needed
to be physically strong, but who were only employed occasionally.
The *vigiles* were under close imperial control, and were balanced
by the other units in Rome, which as well as being the largest city in
the world also contained the biggest force of soldiers and other uni-
formed men in one place – some 20,000 by the late second century
AD. A fire brigade in Nicomedia, even if it numbered no more than
a few hundred, would have represented formidable and unmatched
strength if it entered local politics. The provincial garrison was too
small and too scattered to have countered it on a routine basis.[31]

Trajan remained concerned about the problem, hence instructing
Pliny to make sure that equipment was readily available, but that
was as far as he wished to go. The Roman administration was reluctant to play a direct role in local affairs by organising services like
this and controlling them, feared letting local leaders do this, and so
followed the usual practice of allowing the population to deal with it
on an informal, non-institutional basis. This is unlikely to have been
the most efficient way to deal with outbreaks of fire, although we
should note that the Romans did not suppress an existing fire brigade
– Nicomedia and the other cities had never possessed such forces at
any time in their history, and it was the Roman outsider Pliny who

raised the idea. Trajan could claim, at least from his perspective, that on balance it was better that this remain the case.

The *princeps* alludes to the political infighting and violence in the recent past of these cities, problems fuelled by the constant competition within communities for dominance and between the major cities for status. As we saw in the last chapter, such rivalry was commonplace in many parts of the empire. In this case it had not led to inter-communal violence, let alone resistance to Roman rule, and instead intensified aristocratic struggles within cities. So many grand projects, overreaching themselves and failing, gave the opportunity of announcing new plans to surpass rivals and of blaming them for past problems. Some of these struggles may have produced rioting or worse, and this is suggested by the speeches of Dio Chrysostom. In one he defends himself against charges of hoarding stocks of grain during a shortage, and speaks of a mob attacking his house. Dio was one of the wealthier men of the region, able – at least when he enjoyed imperial favour – to give largesse to more than one city. Such men were courted for their benefactions, but could then be blamed if they did not do enough to earn the honours and praise given by each place.[32]

Once again the small size of the provincial garrison meant that the resources to deal with rioting simply did not exist. Some cities employed professional policemen/watchmen, but these forces were not allowed to grow too big for the same reason that fire brigades were banned, so the only counter to a mob was all too often another mob. The escorts accompanying governors and other Roman officials offered protection against robbers of the sort who had attacked Nonius Datus, but not against larger-scale threats, so that the presence of these authorities could not suppress disturbances by force. While serving as proconsul in Africa, the future emperor Vespasian was pelted with turnips by an angry crowd. Governors had to rely for protection on the distant threat of the empire's overwhelming force. Even when they were accompanied by larger numbers of troops, these would still be outnumbered by the population of any substantial city. Turning the soldiers loose on crowds usually worked, but if the protestors were numerous or included organised groups willing to use violence, then success was not assured and might make the situation worse, as it did in Jerusalem in AD 66. The Gospel accounts of the trial of Jesus depicting Pilate as reluctant to refuse demands made by the crowd reflect a reality faced by many Roman governors, who knew that the force backing them relied as much on bluff as on actual strength.[33]

EVIL MEN

According to the legal expert Ulpian:

> It is right for a competent and conscientious governor to see to it that the province of which he has charge is peaceful and quiet. He will achieve this without difficulty if he carefully ensures that evil men are expelled, and hunts them out. He should hunt out sacrilegious persons, brigands, kidnappers, and thieves, and punish each one according to his crime, and he should also bring force against those who harbour them, since a criminal cannot escape detection for long without their help.[34]

The passage ties in with Fronto's recruitment of Julius Senex for his experience in hunting bandits, as well as stating quite openly the Roman assumption that people living near the scene of a crime were expected to help the authorities or be held responsible for protecting the criminals.

Modern scholars routinely describe banditry as endemic within the Roman Empire, and occasionally extend this to the entire ancient world. They tend to depict the imperial authorities as incapable of eradicating it, perhaps even of keeping it under control.

Some go further and see the *princeps* and his representatives as unconcerned about such things unless it threatened their persons, other people of importance, or the workings of administration and taxation. It was simply a reality of life, accepted by everyone as inevitable. Laws tended to rank death or abduction by bandits along-side natural disasters such as fire, storm or flood – what would now be termed 'acts of God' – when it came to liability for damages.[35]

One of Pliny's earlier letters mentions the disappearance of an equestrian friend while journeying in northern Italy. The man's son was searching for him, but Pliny was pessimistic about his chances, remembering Metilius Crispus, a young man from Comum who had vanished some years earlier. Pliny had secured him a commission as a centurion in a legion and given him 40,000 sesterces to equip himself in the style appropriate for an officer, but on the way to join the army he vanished; 'whether he was killed by his slaves or along with them, no one knows: at any rate, neither Crispus nor any of them were ever seen again'. Some slaves understandably tried to escape from a life of servitude – in Bithynia Pliny discovered two who had tried to hide by enlisting in the army, something only open to the freeborn. Loyal slaves offered protection on a journey, but the chance to disappear in some quiet spot gave them more chance of escape than at home, especially if they worked together. It is reveal-ing that the slave-owning Pliny considered that being murdered by one's own slaves was as likely as murder at the hands of bandits. Roman law decreed the execution of an entire slave household when even one killed or tried to kill his master – something Nero enforced, even though many senators felt it cruel to punish the innocent along with the guilty. Runaway slaves, like army deserters, were seen as likely to turn to banditry.[36]

Some tombstones list armed robbers as the cause of death, for in-stance one found in Upper Moesia dedicated to 'Scerviaedus Sitaes, age thirty, killed by bandits' and set up by his son and daughter-in-law, who had either married young or erected the monument sometime later. Although these are only a tiny fraction of the surviving me-morials from the Roman period – the vast majority do not say how the subject died – some are poignant, for instance of husbands and wives killed together, and a little girl killed and robbed of her jew-ellery. St Paul spoke of all that he had endured on his evangelical journeys, including 'perils of robbers' alongside such other dangers

as 'perils of waters', and attacks from Jews and Gentiles provoked by
his preaching. Nonius Datus and his party were robbed and stripped,
but escaped with their lives, so not all attackers were determined to
kill, although it seems that many were. The former slave-turned-
Stoic philosopher Epictetus noted that the wise traveller did not
venture alone along a road where armed robbers were said to operate, and instead 'waits to journey with an ambassador, a governor's
assistant, or a governor, so that he may travel along safely', shielded
by his escort. Fronto clearly expected banditry to be a problem in his
province requiring special attention, and governors were praised for
curbing violent crime.[37]

The resources at their disposal were limited, such policing being
just one of the tasks required of small and scattered garrisons. The
'picked soldiers' mentioned earlier were *beneficiarii*, experienced
and literate men posted as individuals, often in towns or villages
along the major roads. Their main concern was regulating traffic,
but they could play a role in dealing with crime. There were also
small outposts of other soldiers (*stationarii*), placed where it was felt
necessary. Centurions known as 'regional officers' (*regionarii*) were
placed in charge of some districts, and we know from Egypt that
people went to them seeking help after they suffered from theft or
violence. The effectiveness of such individual officers and detachments of soldiers can only have varied with their ability and the local
situation, and even more depending on how thinly they covered
the province. A character in Apuleius' second-century AD novel *The
Golden Ass* complains of gangs of youths roaming the streets at night
in a Thessalian city, free to do what they liked, robbing and killing,
because the 'governor's troops are too far away to relieve the town
of this slaughter'.[38]

Later in the same story, a rich young man appears at the camp of
a band of desperadoes holding prisoner his fiancée and pretends to
be a famous bandit called Haemus. He tells them that he had been
very successful until a raid on an inn, where by chance a procurator, his wife, slaves and escort of soldiers were spending the night.
Disturbed by the noise, 'the wife ran into the room and stirred up

the whole place with repeated shouts, calling the soldiers and her servants by name and even trying to rouse the entire neighbourhood to help. Only because everyone was terrified and stayed hidden out of fear for themselves did it come about that we got away scot-free'. Afterwards the procurator's wife appeals to Caesar, who acts. '. . . Caesar banned the guild (*collegium*) of Haemus the robber, and it disappeared forthwith: such is the power of even a nod from a great prince. Then, when my entire band had been hunted out, cornered, and cut down by regiments of soldiers (*vexillationum militarium*), I alone got away', disguised as a woman and riding on a donkey to get past the patrolling soldiers.[39]

Bandits and pirates offered a rich vein for storytellers, and so we should never forget that this is fiction – indeed presented as a fiction within the novel itself. Yet, in spite of strong elements of mysticism and fantasy – the narrator of the tale is a human turned by magic into an ass – much of the detail does seem to reflect life in the empire and in northern Greece at this time. By chance, an inscription actually tells us that around AD 176 – so roughly at the time Apuleius wrote the novel – several vexillations or detachments drawn from legions in Moesia were sent by the emperor to this region to deal with a band of Thracian brigands. The appearance of a force of well-trained legionaries would have drastically increased the strength and capacity of the otherwise tiny garrison of a peaceful public province. While it is interesting that in the story – we have no idea what prompted the actual intervention – this is supposed to have occurred only because the procurator was involved, and he and his wife's pleas were listened to by the emperor, we should not push this too far. People of influence – especially his own senior officials, senators and the wealthy, particularly if they were Roman citizens – were more likely to receive help when it was requested in this respect as with everything else. That does not mean that action would only be taken in such circumstances. Much depended on the inclinations of the provincial governor.[40]

The Roman army was thinly spread, and there were simply not enough soldiers to police, administer and defend every part of this vast empire, and individuals and communities were left to take measures for their own defence. Travellers often armed themselves and tried to travel in groups for safety. Shepherds were used to protecting flocks from animals and human robbers alike, as were other herdsmen. The owners of big estates or their overseers were able to muster their workers to drive off or chase attackers. In *The Golden Ass*, a party of innocent travellers were advised to be prepared to defend themselves from packs of wolves roaming the country, but equipped themselves so well and moved in such good order that

> ... the workers on an estate which we happened to pass assumed from our numbers that we were a band of robbers, and being worried about their possessions and extremely frightened, they set dogs on us. These were mad, enormous creatures, fiercer than any wolf or bear, and they had been carefully trained for guard duty. ... Suddenly this great danger was followed by even worse trouble. From the rooftops and hill nearby the farmers furiously began to hurl rocks down on us . . .[41]

There is plentiful evidence from the Greek-speaking provinces, and especially Asia, for magistrates called *eirênarchai* or peace officers, 'who are in charge of public discipline and correcting behaviour'. Although, like most magistracies, these were the preserve of the wealthy, they do seem to have been expected to be active. The famous orator – and noted hypochondriac – Aelius Aristides took great care to avoid being nominated for such a post in a city where an official had not long since been killed by bandits. More junior were *paraphylakes*, who may well have been professionals rather than wealthy aristocrats taking on the senior post for a while. A couple of sculptures, including a tombstone from Prusa, portray these officers mounted, backed by constables who are shown armed and in uniform. The relief from Prusa has them carrying small round shields, clubs and short swords. Another from Ephesus shows them with bigger, oval shields, much like the ones used by many auxiliaries. Such men were sometimes called *diôgmitai* or 'chasers', and we have no figures for their numbers, but it would more likely be a question of tens than hundreds, given the imperial authorities' suspicion of associations. There is no real evidence for police forces in the western provinces and we can only assume that some vaguely similar arrangements were followed there.[42]

Watch-towers were common in the frontier areas, and there were systems of such towers in other parts of the empire, especially along important roads. Only the foundations survive archaeologically, making it difficult to reconstruct their design and, except when there is a convenient inscription, their purpose. The best evidence comes from Egypt, where the Romans inherited and built on a well-established system of policing probably unmatched elsewhere in the empire. It is clear from documents on papyrus or pottery *ostraka* that both soldiers and civilians were employed on these towers, depending on where they were. Civilians volunteered or were conscripted to man the high platforms or *skopeloi*, which could provide warning of bandits, cattle rustlers or raiders. A text found at the military-run quarry of Mons Claudianus was written by a decurion, a junior officer commanding a troop of some thirty or so horsemen, and neatly combines the need to ensure proper manning of towers with action on a recent, and perhaps criminal, act:

Herennius Antoninus, decurion, to Amatios, greeting. Since the son of Balaneus who is in the watchtower is a boy, speak to the *dekanos* (*a civilian official*) so that he may place a young man in his stead; for I also have sent orders to him about him. And send me the civilian who set fire to the reeds near the new *praesidium*. Farewell.[43]

Towers – in this case little more than solid stone platforms, perhaps rigged up with some form of canopy as protection against the sun – were placed all along the roads leading to the Red Sea ports, and the army regulated movement along these routes. There and in other controlled regions, archaeologists have found many pottery fragments which acted as passes – for instance 'Let pass Asklepiades', or often not bothering with names, so just 'four men and twenty donkeys', or 'one woman and two children'. These were only valid for a set time period, and allowed soldiers to levy tolls on people passing along the road, but at the same time helped to prevent unauthorised access in an area where bandits sometimes preyed on travellers.[44]

A few soldiers or civilians on a watch-tower could not prevent an attack by robbers. All they could do was give warning, allowing travellers to flee and seek shelter, and raise the alarm to summon a larger force, assuming one existed. Manning so many towers was expensive in manpower, hence the use of civilians as well as soldiers. At the very least the towers, which by their nature were highly visible, helped to create an impression that the area was being watched – much like closed-circuit television cameras in town centres – and in this way deter criminals, or at least encourage them to move to a less well-observed area. In Egypt, and no doubt elsewhere, the army co-operated with local civilians to make areas more secure. Usually this was to protect trade, official communication or movement of resources needed by the state or the army, and so was not primarily altruistic. Yet it did also serve to protect others.[45]

'Endemic' is a loose term. It is clear that, in spite of the boasts of successive emperors, the Romans were never able to make the lands entirely free of bandits or the seas free of pirates. No state has ever managed to eradicate violent crime altogether, so it should not surprise us that the Romans were no exception. In the modern world dealing with crime is a never-ending struggle, not a battle that can be won for ever. Bandits and armed robbers willing to kill and kidnap appear in many different sources dealing with many Roman provinces throughout the history of the empire. They clearly occupied a place in people's imagination and were also seen as a real threat, most of all to travellers, but much of the evidence for them is too vague to quantify.

The concept of the 'Social Bandit', developed by the distinguished modern historian Eric Hobsbawm in a highly influential study of bandits in more recent times, has been imported to the ancient world, but has not proved helpful. The Social Bandit is supposed to

...erge from peasant societies oppressed by landlords and governments, but prey only on the oppressors; they 'remain within peasant
society, and are considered by their people as heroes . . . and in any
case as men to be admired, helped and supported'. Their appearance
was thus inevitable if the social and economic conditions were right,
and some would see the Roman Empire as fitting the model very
well, with privileged and wealthy aristocrats acting hand-in-glove
with the imperial authorities, all of them owners of great rural
estates worked by slaves or peasantry.

That picture is crude, arguable in many respects, and in addition
others have pointed out the weakness of Hobsbawm's thesis. Most
of his evidence came from folk tales about characters like Robin
Hood, with the assumption that these must be based on some reality,
which mainly shows that even serious scholars can have their romantic moments, in this case shaped by Hobsbawm's Marxist ideology.
Close analysis of more recent periods of history tends to suggest far
more predatory robbers preying on the peasants, fear being the main
reason why they are 'helped and supported'. For the Roman period
the model of the Social Bandit is even harder to maintain. If there
were any of these 'Robin Hoods' in reality, then they were exceptionally rare, and even the poor feared and hated bandits. In fiction
the heroes may impersonate bandits and pirates, but genuine bandits
and pirates are not depicted with sympathy – unlike Hollywood's
long-standing obsession with outlaws, criminals and gangsters. The
physician Galen described how on a journey he and his companions
'saw the skeleton of a bandit lying on rising ground by the roadside.
He had been killed by a traveller repelling his attack. None of the
local inhabitants would bury him, but in their hatred of him were
glad enough to see his body consumed by birds.'[46]

In the last chapter we saw that the evidence suggests that continued resistance by politically motivated bandits became extremely
rare as time passed, and may never have occurred in some provinces.
Similar caution is sensible before seeing serious violent crime such
as banditry as commonplace. Pliny could cite the single example of
the disappearance of Crispus and suspected that the same thing had

happened to the equestrian. He did not appear to see such incide
as common – after all, he and many of his correspondents travelleu
over wide areas and only these two vanished. St Paul and the other
early Christian missionaries covered large swathes of the eastern
Mediterranean in safety and were not killed by robbers.

One scholar made a good analogy between the risk of ancient
travellers falling prey to bandits and that of the modern motorist
or passenger being involved in a road accident. For both the danger
is genuine and can be readily imagined as happening to them. In
spite of this it is very rare, and the fear of it rarely deters them from
travelling. The overwhelming majority of car journeys do not end
in an accident, let alone one resulting in serious or fatal injury. In
the same way, only a tiny minority of travellers would have brushes
with armed robbers and some would escape, while just a handful of
householders or guests at an inn would experience a break-in.[47]

There is no doubt that armed robbers existed and posed a threat
to the wider population, even in the settled provinces far from the
frontiers. The authorities, whether at the level of the governor and
his officials or local magistrates in cities and other communities, actively sought to deal with the problem, but resources were limited
and it was more a matter of control than eradication. Bringing in
more manpower, by deploying detachments of troops or raising
local militias, could do more in the short term. There are plenty of
accounts of famous bandits being captured and executed, often in
imaginatively gruesome fashion in the arena as a public display of revenge and warning to others. Yet concentrating on dealing with the
problem in one region might do no more than force the criminals to
shift their activities somewhere else. On the other hand, breakdown
in government and society in general – whether because of civil war,
the great epidemics of the second century AD or local famine and
disaster – was likely to increase the frequency and scale of banditry
as more and more desperate men turned to crime.

Too often scholars have painted far too bleak a picture of Roman
provinces where banditry was inevitably present and widespread.
It existed, as it had existed before the Romans arrived, and would

reappear when the empire collapsed. It is doubtful that it was routinely any worse under Roman rule, and it is a mistake to see the emperors and their representatives as unconcerned. Propaganda exaggerated the scale of their success in making sea and land safe, but this was not wholly false. In some ways the very prosperity and stability that came under the Principate created new opportunities. People and goods travelled in vastly greater numbers, far more frequently and over greater distances than ever before, so that there were more potential victims for predatory criminals. Yet this commerce and movement of population continued at a very high level, especially in the first and second centuries AD, and was not significantly curbed, let alone stopped, by pirates and bandits. This was just one major difference between life in these countries before and under Roman rule.

LIFE UNDER ROMAN RULE

'Although often provoked by you, the only use we have made of our rights as victors has been to impose on you the necessary costs of maintaining peace; for you cannot secure tranquillity among nations without armies, nor maintain armies without pay, nor provide pay without taxes: everything else we have in common. You often command our legions; you rule this and other provinces . . . You enjoy the advantages of the good emperors equally with us . . . In like manner endure the extravagance or greed of your rulers. There will be vices as long as there are men, but these vices are not perpetual and they are compensated for by the coming of better times.' – *Tacitus' version of the speech made by the legate Cerialis to the Treveri and Lingones, early second century* AD.[1]

'CIVILISATION' AND 'ENSLAVEMENT'

Pliny's letters and Trajan's replies depict the government of the empire as benevolent and respectful of local law and tradition, wishing to ensure not only stable rule and peace, but also the welfare of the provincial population. The tone is mirrored in the actions and words of other emperors and their representatives and clearly presents the official view. This was how emperors and governors wished to be seen, and it may even be how some genuinely saw themselves. Outward and formal respect tied the empire together, reconciling senators to being ruled by an emperor, and provincial elites to living under Roman rule. Similar language – usually far more overblown in its enthusiasm – was used by provincials to praise their rulers. Rome's dominance rested on its overwhelming military might, but even this could be incorporated in the praise of emperors, since the army now served to protect the civilized world.[2]

Not only was rebellion rare, it is hard even to find open expression of resentment at the dominance of Rome. Plutarch and Dio Chrysostom both railed at contemporary Greeks for failing to run their own affairs and too readily calling on the Romans to intervene. Their anger was directed at the communities who were unable to regulate themselves and did not truly use the freedom granted to them by the imperial power. Neither man ever tried to rally opinion against Rome, although bad governors and bad emperors were criticised – the latter only after their death. Concern with traditional culture, whether it was rabbis trying to make sense of their religion after the destruction of the Temple, or Greeks revelling in writing about the glories of their pre-Roman past, was not a rejection of imperial rule. The fact of Roman dominance was accepted, but this was not because the empire ruled with so light a hand and through such a tiny body of administrators that it rarely intruded into people's consciousness, let alone their lives.[3]

No one living in the provinces was unaware of Roman rule. Much day-to-day administration was left to local communities, but everyone knew that the governor possessed greater authority than the highest local magistrate or council, that allied kings reigned only with the approval of Rome, and that over governors and monarchs and everyone else stood the power of the emperor. In Matthew's Gospel, when Jesus was asked whether it 'is lawful to give tribute unto Caesar or not?' he asked them to bring him a silver coin. 'And saith he unto them, Whose is this image and superscription? They say unto him, Caesar's. Then saith he unto them, Render therefore unto Caesar the things which are Caesar's; and unto God the things which are God's.' Taxes went to the emperor, and his head or other image was on all gold and silver coinage, as well as most of the bronze currency. Even in the most remote rural areas some use was made of hard coin – not least because some taxes were paid in money rather than in kind. Strictly speaking, these taxes went to the Roman state rather than to the emperor, but such fine distinctions understandably meant little to the people forced to pay them.[4]

The geographer Strabo told a story to illustrate the poverty of the tiny Greek island of Gyaros. In 29 BC he was on board a ship which anchored off the coast and could see a fishing village.

> When we sailed away we took on board one of the fishermen, who had been chosen to go from there to Caesar (Augustus) as ambassa- dor (Caesar was at Corinth, on his way to celebrate the Triumph after the victory at Actium). While on the voyage he told enquirers that he had been sent as ambassador to request a reduction in their trib- ute; for, as he said, they were paying one hundred and fifty drachmas when they could only with difficulty pay one hundred.

The tax of the entire island was substantially less than the annual salary of a Roman legionary, and less than the value of a milk cow recorded in an almost contemporary papyrus document from Egypt. Even so this had to be paid in coin, which meant that the fishermen needed to sell some of their catch for money and not simply use it for their own consumption or in barter for other goods.[5]

We do not know whether the ambassador managed to gain an audience from Augustus or from someone with delegated authority, so cannot say whether the fishermen's request was granted. What is striking is the belief that the representative of even so obscure and poor a community could go and wait his turn to be heard by the highest authority and hope for a favourable answer. Hadrian trav- elled almost as widely as Augustus, and 'once, when a woman made a request of him as he passed by on a journey, he at first said to her, "I haven't time," but afterwards, when she cried out, "Cease, then, being emperor," he turned about and granted her a hearing'. There was a widespread and deeply rooted expectation that rulers, whether kings or emperors, should be willing to listen and should also be the source of generous benefaction.[6]

Most emperors rarely chose to travel to the provinces, especially the more distant ones, whatever their wealth and military impor- tance. In the first century AD, only Augustus and Vespasian visited Syria while they were emperor – and in the case of the latter this was because he was proclaimed as ruler while he was in the east suppressing the Jewish rebellion. Thus the chance to see the emperor in person was granted to few, for it was usually only the wealthy who could afford to travel to Italy and hope to be received. Yet if the rulers themselves were distant figures, their names and images were everywhere. Apart from coins, there were milestones on roads, inscriptions on virtually every public building from bath houses to bridges and aqueducts, and statues, busts, sculptures and paintings. Arrian, a native of Nicomedia but a Roman citizen and senator, was sent by Hadrian to govern Cappadocia as legate. Part of his responsibilities included inspecting the garrisons and ports on the Black Sea coast, checking on the state of their defences and preparedness. At one, he also noticed that a statue of the emperor was poorly executed, and so ordered a better one to replace it.[7]

Portraits were idealised, and it might well have proved difficult to recognise the real person from them. Augustus' image remained eternally youthful, while Claudius' statues concealed his infirmity. Statues of the same emperor were not all identical, and it is clear that a succession of standard, approved representations were copied just as they were on coin dies. They were recognisably depictions of the current emperor or a predecessor, and at least some people were aware of the details on them. Hadrian was the first to sport a beard, a neater version of the full beards of Greek philosophers, and so encouraged a trend for more men to grow facial hair. The hairstyles shown in images of the women of the imperial household were similarly copied throughout the empire by ladies eager to be fashionable.

Most official documents were dated by the number of years of tribunician power of the current emperor – a system created by Augustus. In this way an emperor's name appeared in many contexts, particularly on inscriptions recording an event or the construction or repair of some project. His titles, or at least some of them, were also often included. A very long inscription from the city of Oenoanda in Lycia records the festival of Greek culture and sports set up and paid for by the local aristocrat Demosthenes. It begins by quoting a letter from Hadrian giving his approval for the project. He is 'the emperor Caesar Trajan Hadrian Augustus, son of the divine Trajan Parthicus and grandson of the divine Nerva Germanicus, Pontifex Maximus, in the eighth year of his tribunician power, consul for the third time'. Praise of the emperor and images of him reappeared time and again during the festival. Many of the western provinces adopted the Roman calendar, imposing a new structure on their year. In the Greek east existing systems continued, but still showed the presence of Rome and the emperor. In Egypt they used a system of dating based on the number of years in the reign of the current ruler or rulers, as they had done under the pharaohs, and the names of emperors slotted into this scheme just as seamlessly as the Macedonian dynasty of the Ptolemies had done. In 9 BC all the cities in Asia adopted a suggestion by a proconsul of the province to modify their calendars so that the year now began on Augustus' birthday, 23 September, which became the first day of a month called Caesar.[8]

Rome and its emperor infiltrated every aspect of public life until it was hard to imagine a world where this was not the case. New cities were founded by them, or old ones refounded – Hadrian's arch at Athens declared on one side 'This is Athens, the former city of Theseus' and on the other 'This is the city of Hadrian, not of Theseus'. Some cities were named Augusta, Caesarea or Sebaste to honour the *princeps*. All had monuments to emperors and made regular sacrifices for his health and success, while important communities had shrines or major temples to the cult of Rome and the emperor. These cities were also linked by the immense road network, and those best placed to exploit the transport infrastructure benefited from it.[9]

The Romans felt comfortable with the city as an institution, a central place with magistrates and other administrative machinery to administer the lands around it. Where such communities did not exist, they encouraged them to develop or created them. In Julius Caesar's day there were many towns or *oppida* in Gaul, usually sited on hills and defended by walls. Under Augustus and his successors these settlements were abandoned in favour of new towns and cities built on the plains in Roman style. At the beginning most of the buildings were made of timber, including the vital forum and basilicas for public business. Over time brick and stone replaced wood, and tiles replaced thatch, and more monuments and amenities were added, such as temples, bath houses, theatres, amphitheatres and occasionally the great circuses designed for chariot races. The pace of change varied, and not all communities could afford such grandeur. There were also regional innovations, such as a dual-purpose theatre cum amphitheatre much favoured in Gaul.[10]

Some new cities were colonies of discharged veterans given farms as a reward. A *colonia* was populated initially by citizens, obeyed Roman law, and they all operated under the same constitutional arrangements which reflected on a smaller scale those of the republic itself. Julius Caesar and Augustus between them settled several hundred thousand former soldiers in these new foundations. Some still preserved the military role of the early colonies, and all were meant to be models of proper city life and to be grand in appearance. Within a decade of its creation, the colony at Camulodunum had a theatre and the great Temple of Claudius, as well as a forum, basilica and meeting house for its council. In the western provinces, favoured communities were granted the status of *municipium* and each given a constitution set down in Latin and based on principles of Roman law, but their inhabitants were not expected to be Roman citizens. Senior magistrates in such towns were granted the franchise at the end of their year of office.[11]

In some provinces, especially in the Hellenic world, cities were already common and here there were far fewer new foundations. There were some colonies, but it was not necessary to give municipal status to other settlements because these already had constitutions and laws of their own. Yet even in the Greek east the city-state was not universal. Egypt was overwhelmingly a land of villages rather than cities, and the Romans did not change this. Galatia and the uplands of what is now Anatolia had scarcely any communities organised in this way, and instead were centred around walled strongholds. The Galatians were descended from three Gallic tribes who had migrated to Asia Minor in the third century BC, and had spent much of the time since then raiding their neighbours, extorting money from them by threatening to raid, and hiring themselves out as mercenary soldiers to the kings of the wider region. They remained powerful even after their defeat at the hands of Manlius Vulso in 189 BC. Much like their kindred in Gaul they did not live in cities, and so the Romans founded these, creating one each as capitals for the three tribes, and so preserving their names. The same practice was followed in Gaul and Britain, giving tribal groups an administrative centre. In most cases it is hard to tell how far the regions drawn up in this way reflected the actual boundaries of the tribes before conquest. In Galatia it looks as if the largest of the tribes, the Trocmi, lost territory, and probably administrative convenience was always the main factor. Egypt already possessed one of the most sophisticated bureaucracies in the ancient world, so there was no sense in changing its basic organisation.[12]

For Greeks and Romans alike, cities were essential for civilisation, but the Roman preference for cities was far more practical than ideological. The new cities in Gaul and Galatia were placed for ease of access and not defence. These communities were meant to offer their inhabitants, and especially the aristocracy, greater comfort and opportunities to compete for prestige in the form of magistracies and priesthoods, and to settle their disputes in the courts rather than by raiding each other. Cnaeus Julius Agricola governed Britain for an unusually long term of more than seven years, a post which provides the main theme of the biography later written by his son-in-law Tacitus. According to him:

> In order that a population scattered and uncivilised, and proportionately ready for war, might be habituated by comfort to peace and quiet, he would exhort individuals, assist communities, to erect temples, market-places, houses: he praised the energetic, rebuked the indolent, and the rivalry for his compliments took the place of coercion. Moreover he began to train the sons of chieftains in a liberal education . . . As a result, the nation which used to reject the Latin language began to aspire to rhetoric: further, the wearing of our dress became a distinction, and the toga was seen everywhere.[13]

This passage comes early on and is attributed to his second winter in the province, for the summers were filled by military operations, but it is fair to see it as characteristic of his entire term as legate, and also reflective of the actions of other legates. Tacitus, ever the cynic and inclined to take a gloomy view of Roman society in contrast with the simpler and superior morality of tribal nations, explained this policy as thoroughly manipulative: 'And little by little the Britons went astray into alluring vices: to the promenade, the bath, the well-appointed dinner table. The simple natives gave the name of "culture" to this factor of their enslavement.'[14]

The aristocrats gained most from urbanisation, but others also benefited if they lived in or near these new communities and so had access to their comforts. Many accepted this as a reasonable price for the loss of independence and subjection to Roman taxation. Yet it did not always work. The attempts to develop towns and cities in Germany east of the Rhine were swept away by Arminius' victory in AD 9. Nor were thriving cities in themselves essential to imposing peace on a region. In Gaul the aristocracy of many areas engaged in urban life, but still spent a good deal of their time in the countryside, and did not cut themselves off from rural life. Few cities in Britain could ever match those of Gaul, let alone other provinces, and many remained small and never acquired the grander monuments so admired elsewhere. Perhaps even more than in Gaul, the focus of society in much of Britain remained essentially rural. This did not mean that these areas were any less peaceful or integrated into the empire than the regions where cities were more numerous and grander.[15]

From a Roman point of view, cities were also administratively convenient centres, capable of controlling and policing the lands around them, assessing and collecting tax and dealing with many legal disputes. Governors and their tiny staffs were simply incapable of undertaking all this work. Other administrative structures, villages, collections of villages, or tribal groups, were also employed, but on the whole cities were preferred, since they were easily reached by road, river or sea, contained archives and were governed by familiar institutions. From the towns and cities of a province, places could be selected for the governor to hold assizes at set times each year, and those who lived elsewhere knew where to travel in order to bring a case before him. During these sessions cities would be crowded with plaintiffs, others seeking favours or audience, and plenty more people wanting to watch, as well as merchants and traders of all kinds, entertainers, pimps, prostitutes and pickpockets all eager to relieve people of their money. These were big events in the year and they were held in an environment where symbols of Rome and its emperors were concentrated – as well as having a Roman official at the centre of everything.[16]

From the very beginning, Rome exploited her provinces for resources and money. Revenue from the empire made it possible to maintain an expensive professional army. It also permitted the grandiose rebuilding of Rome, and many of the monuments, roads and amenities granted as largesse to Italy and the provinces. Tacitus claims that Agricola considered the practicalities of sending an expedition to Ireland, but concluded that the revenue raised by its conquest would not cover the cost of the legion and auxiliary units that would be required as a garrison. Strabo and Appian both claim that the poverty of peoples beyond the frontiers deterred emperors from expanding the empire, even when rulers came to Rome begging to become allies.[17]

Rome gained openly and unashamedly from her empire, and even if the Romans were also keen to talk about the advantages their rule brought, they never pretended that the desire to bring order to a chaotic world was their primary motive. Sadly, there is a good deal about the taxation system and even more about the economy of the Roman Empire which we simply do not understand, and this makes it very hard to judge its impact on the lives of people living in the provinces. It has been argued that the need to pay imperial taxes stimulated agriculture in many areas, creating a surplus which was either given in produce to the authorities or sold to provide the cash to pay them. As an idea, this makes a good deal of sense, but caution is needed for we do not always understand the agricultural system of a region well enough to trace the changes following annexation by Rome. Environmental archaeology has shown that there was widespread deforestation to permit farming in Iron Age Britain before the Roman conquest. We can only guess whether rising population, the markets opened by the presence of the empire on the other side of the Channel, political changes among the tribes or some other factor lay behind this. In other parts of the empire, communities were accustomed to paying tax or tribute to other powers, and in Egypt the Romans inherited the mechanisms used by the Ptolemies to exploit their territory.[18]

If the burdens imposed by direct and indirect taxation under the empire were heavy, they were not so heavy that the provinces were ruined. An angry Tiberius once told his governors that he wanted them 'to shear his sheep, not skin them'. The aim was a steady flow of revenue year after year, not to drain a region of everything of value in the shortest time possible. Sometimes governors, procurators or other officials went too far, usually to line their own pockets rather than increase revenue to the state, and provoked rebellion. Yet even a scholar who has consciously tried to emphasise the cost of Roman rule on conquered peoples expressed surprise at how rare such revolts were. Like so many other things, levels of tax depended on the circumstances in which a community had come under Roman rule. The burden was not even or equal, but varied considerably, not just between but within provinces. In some areas formal tax was an innovation, although the majority may well have been obliged in the past to give some of their produce to overlords. Under the Romans the system was often different, but it may not always have been heavier and, even when it was, within a generation or two it became the normal state of affairs.[19]

There were other changes to economic life apart from taxation, as so much of the world came under the authority of the emperor. This meant that wealthy men were far more confident that the right of property would be respected than they had been when the world consisted of so many distinct and often hostile states. Many bought estates in the provinces, for land was an honourable investment, but also considered a secure one, since it could not sink like a trading vessel and should yield a long-term profit. The environment of the empire favoured not simply Roman citizens, and especially the rich senators and equestrians, but provincials as well. Men acquired property far from their home, and many may never have seen the land, while happily drawing income from it. The greatest landowner of all was the emperor, for the imperial estates were immense, with property all over the empire, acquired during initial conquest or through confiscation from disgraced senators and other wealthy men.

Patterns of ownership varied, with estates sometimes concentrated or consisting of numerous smaller farms scattered across a region. A heavy reliance on slave labour for the bulk of work was rare outside Italy – and even there it was far from universal. In most cases plots of land were leased to free tenants, sometimes called *coloni*. Landlords were usually absentee, and the estates were run by their staffs, many of whom were freedmen or slaves. Often a bleak picture is painted of the lives of tenant farmers, based to a large degree on laws from the province of Africa banning them from leaving. Other evidence suggests that they were better off. In Asia it is clear that tenants passed their leases on to their sons, and some were able to build up considerable wealth, so that they were able to club together to pay for festivals. The impression is not of downtrodden serfs but of lively village life, with annual religious festivals celebrated with sacrifices and feasting. Small farmers owning their own land also existed, and were more or less common depending on the region, although inevitably they leave less trace in our sources than the big estates with their large central buildings, minor industrial activities and greater likelihood of setting up inscriptions.[20]

One of the greatest changes came from the creation of new markets for new goods. Many estates specialised in producing specific cash crops, often ones rarely grown in the region in earlier periods, and then only on a small scale for local use. Viticulture spread widely, and over time wines from Gaul and other regions became well established for export as well as local use. The demand for olive oil was also huge, for it was used not simply for cooking but also to anoint bathers and as fuel for the lamps found in such vast quantities all over the empire. The capacity to exploit such markets relied on ready access to transportation, ideally by water, for moving heavy goods over long distances. Long-distance trade by land and sea flourished under the Roman Empire, peaking in the first and second centuries AD, but still substantial afterwards. Areas became famous for particular things, such as the fine wool from the highlands of Asia Minor or fermented fish sauce from Spain, the famous – and pungent – *garum*. At the same time mineral resources were taken from the ground and used on a far larger scale than in the past. Examination of samples from the polar ice caps showed that pollution caused by industry was high in the Roman period, and especially in the first and second centuries AD, on a scale unmatched until the Industrial Revolution. Much of this came from state-owned mines, whether worked directly or through contractors. Whatever difficulties we face in understanding economic activity in the Roman period, we cannot doubt its sheer and unprecedented scale.[21]

Alongside commerce came the demands of the empire, with grain and other foodstuffs being transported to army garrisons on the frontiers and to supply Rome's population. Providing for soldiers and the inhabitants of Rome were priorities for the emperor, and so the sea routes to Italy from Sicily, then Egypt and also Africa and Spain were fostered, while in the provinces roads were built, canals dug and river navigation improved to reach the army on the frontiers. Most, although probably not all, of the goods involved came from taxes or imperial estates, but plenty of people profited as carriers. Other trade also piggybacked on these great shipments by land and sea. Long-distance transport of luxury goods, from spices to fine tableware and metalwork, is undisputed. There was also likely to have been far more bulk transport of staples than some scholars believe. It is quite clear that the roads through the mountains of Anatolia were intended for use by wheeled transport and not simply pedestrians and pack mules. Provincials were part of a much larger world, and goods from far away and of designs first created elsewhere were widely available to those able to afford them. Inevitably the better off were best placed to enjoy such things. Many agricultural workers produced crops on behalf of a landlord they never met for consumption by people in distant lands. Yet even the poorest sites usually show new styles of mundane objects, from tools to jewellery, so that even on a day-to-day basis the existence of the empire affected lives.[22]

SHEEP AND SHEPHERDS, ROMANS AND NATIVES

Tiberius did not want the provincials 'skinned', but his comments show his awareness that some of his representatives failed to follow his wishes, and echo the comment of the Pannonian rebel leader who said that the Romans sent 'wolves' to watch their flocks instead of 'dogs or shepherds'. The Principate made it a little easier for provincials to complain about the behaviour of a governor, since now they knew that they needed to reach the emperor instead of trying to find and persuade senators with sufficient influence to bring charges on their behalf. This still meant sending an embassy to Rome – or wherever else the emperor was at the time – and waiting in the hope of receiving an audience and gaining a favourable response. When Philo led a deputation of Alexandria's Jews to Rome and was ushered into the presence of Caligula, the emperor suddenly sprang up and left the room, forcing the delegates to chase after him before they were allowed to speak. Emperors of a more serious disposition did not behave in this way, but it could still take a long time for a plea to be heard. Anyone thought able to influence the emperor would be courted. Augustus' wife Livia spoke to him on behalf of provincial communities, while Josephus tells us that he and the other ambassadors from Judaea were aided by Nero's wife Poppaea.[23]

If accusations of misbehaviour by a governor were upheld, then Julius Caesar's *repetundae* law remained in force, especially in cases of extortion or corruption. Alternatively the charge could be one of *maiestas* – damaging the 'majesty' of the Republic or the emperor. Trials were no longer conducted in the public courts, where the composition of juries had proved so politically controversial. Instead they were dealt with by the Senate, or by the emperor in person, although only 'bad' emperors held such hearings and passed judgement privately. This did mean that senators were tried by their peers, who were just as inclined to be sympathetic as they had been under the Republic. Pliny was persuaded to undertake a prosecution even though this brought him back to Rome when he had obtained leave of absence from his treasury post. He was flattered because the Senate supported the request from the representatives of Baetica in Spain to choose him to act on their behalf as he had done in the past. The task was easier because the accused governor had died, 'which removed the most painful feature in this type of case – the downfall of a senator. I saw then that I should win the same gratitude for taking the case as if he were alive, but without incurring ill will.' Pliny's reluctance to have a hand in ending someone's career is all the more striking because he had no doubts about the man's guilt or the seriousness and cruelty of his crimes.[24]

There are thirty-five cases with known outcomes involving prosecutions for misbehaviour by governors or their staffs recorded from the period from Augustus to Trajan. Twenty-eight ended in the conviction of some or all of the accused, and only seven in acquittal. As in the past, convictions – and the most scandalous cases – were more likely to appear in our sources than charges that were dismissed. Five other cases are recorded, but we do not know their outcome. Charges tended to focus on the same sort of abuses familiar from Cicero's speeches. Tacitus claims that Agricola reformed the collection of grain and other tribute in kind by clamping down on the abuses of the officials involved. One trick was to make the Britons purchase the necessary grain from officials at an inflated price. Another was to demand that the food they owed be delivered to some distant garrison rather than ones close by, imposing heavy transport costs – unless they came to a private arrangement with an official. We have already encountered the imperial freedman who claimed to Augustus that he was extorting money from the Gauls for fictional extra months so that they would be too poor to rebel.[25]

Apart from the system of tax and levies, the favour of the governor was highly valued, and plenty of people were willing to pay to secure it, giving 'gifts' to him or those around him. Under the Principate it became routine for members of his staff and family to be prosecuted alongside a governor. Thus although the proconsul of Baetica was dead, there were people to prosecute, including friends who had accompanied him from Rome, associates from the province, and his wife – whom Pliny was sure was guilty even though he doubted that he could prove it. The prosecution began by making clear the crimes of the dead man, a task made simple because he had kept detailed accounts in his own hand of all the deals he had made for everything, including arranging the outcome of court cases. There was even a note to his mistress back in Rome – 'Hurray, hurray, I'm coming back to you a free man – now that I have sold most of the Baetici for 4,000,000 sesterces!' Some of the staff claimed that they had no choice but to follow the governor's orders – something Pliny did his best to prove was no defence against the law.[26]

Under the Republic, Verres could go into exile before the verdict was delivered, taking with him a good deal of his plunder. Under the Principate the range of punishments was wider, and some trials involved lesser charges solely concerned with regaining money extorted in the province. In this case, Pliny tells us that the property of the dead proconsul was assessed, and all that he had possessed before he went to Baetica kept separate and passed on to his daughter, who although named in the prosecution had been found wholly innocent. The rest was to be returned to the communities and individuals according to their claims for losses. Two of the governor's associates from the province were exiled for five years, and the commander of an auxiliary cohort was exiled from Italy for two years. The dead man's son-in-law was acquitted, as were several others – Pliny does not tell us what happened to the governor's wife so she was probably also acquitted – while a few more people of lesser importance were exiled. Apart from these punishments a man could suffer public disgrace (*infamia*) or be barred from holding higher office. Condemnation could end a man's career, but was not necessarily permanent, although some anticipated the penalty by suicide. Men exiled for a fixed period could resume their careers on their return, while others exiled permanently might be recalled when a new emperor took power.

Our sources contain more criticism of equestrian governors or procurators than senators, no doubt because it was easier to highlight the failings of men of lesser social status and poorer connections. There were also significantly more trials of former proconsuls than imperial legates. In part the greater wealth and more settled conditions of senatorial provinces made them easier to plunder. The presence in an imperial province of a procurator reporting directly to the *princeps*, and often of large garrisons with a senator in charge of each legion and another serving as tribune, made it harder for crimes to escape notice, unless all of these could be made complicit. Tacitus implies that abuses had occurred in Britain before Agricola took over, but places the blame at a lower level than the governors. He also held a procurator responsible for provoking Boudicca's rebellion, and does not tell us whether or not the man was punished. There are fewer details of the process in trials of equestrian governors and other officials.[27]

Provinces with sizeable garrisons were politically sensitive and closely watched. Over time, the *frumentarii*, soldiers responsible for collecting and supplying grain to the army, took on a wider intelligence role, and it was easier for emperors to keep an eye on what was happening in the major garrisons. Domitian recalled and executed a legate of Britain because the man had allowed a new pattern of spear to be named after him. This was seen as the cruelty of an overly suspicious and insecure *princeps*, much like Nero's instructions for several successful commanders, including the famous Corbulo, to take their own lives. Augustus came to power through civil war, as did Vespasian and his short-lived predecessors, and later Septimius Severus. A mistaken report of the death of Marcus Aurelius prompted the Syrian legate Avidius Cassius to declare himself as *princeps*. When he learned the truth it was too late to step back, but he does not appear to have attempted to fight with any energy against the widely respected Marcus Aurelius. Even so the emperor went to the province to confirm the loyalty of the east. Although Cassius and his son died, there were no widespread executions following this ghastly mistake.[28]

In AD 19 Tiberius' adopted son Germanicus held a wide command of the eastern provinces and chose to dismiss the legate of Syria, Cnaeus Calpurnius Piso. When Germanicus died amid rumours of poisoning, Piso not only celebrated the news at a feast, but went back to Syria and tried to resume command of the province, rallying some of the garrison and fighting skirmishes with troops loyal to his successor. He was defeated and later put on trial at Rome. His accusers, who included Tiberius' son Drusus, attacked him for his record as legate before he was replaced, as well as his later actions when he had started a brief civil war. Particular attention was paid to his attempts to win the loyalty of soldiers, by undermining discipline and pampering them. Commissions and promotions for centurions were bought or given to favourites, while experienced and strict officers were replaced. His wife Placina appeared at reviews, and was accused of ingratiating herself with the army. Her conduct may well have lain behind the attempt to ban governors' wives from accompanying them to their provinces.

Piso took his own life and was posthumously found guilty, and the Senate's decree recording this verdict was copied and posted up around the empire, so that the text has been found on an inscription from Spain, largely confirming Tacitus' account of the episode. The desire to publicise his misconduct was a reminder to all, and especially the army, of the loyalty they owed to the *princeps* and a clear message that any challenge to this would not go unpunished. It also demonstrated that even governors of provinces were bound by the laws and under the authority of the emperor. For all their pronouncements, there was far less certainty that emperors would act when the misconduct did not involve attempted subversion of the army or rebellion. Overall, governors of all kinds in the first and second centuries AD were probably better behaved than was typical under the Republic. Yet there were exceptions, occasionally of gross misconduct and more often of lesser peculation. As in all systems in any period of history, there are some individuals convinced that they can break the rules – and, even when regulation is tight, a minority who succeed and reinforce the confidence of the rest. Acceptance of gifts and the favouring of friends were common, no doubt justified on the 'everyone does it' basis common in many ages.[29]

As under the Republic, prosecutions of former governors were prompted by formal complaints from the provincial communities, usually via an embassy. The passage of time combined with the more settled conditions of the Principate meant that provincials were more aware of how to operate within the system. Pliny had already represented the Baetici in another similar case so they came to him again. He noted that people who should be grateful would quickly forget their obligation if the new request was denied, and felt obliged to act for them again to confirm the connection. The prosecution of several proconsuls of Bithynia in the years before Pliny's legateship suggests not only frequent misconduct by governors, but also a provincial population well aware of how to bring charges and get the cases brought to trial. If it is right to see minor giving and selling of favour as very common, then it is likely that most governors offered some fuel for charges, even if on the whole they had behaved well.[30]

Another big difference from the Republic was the even greater number of Romans living or active in the provinces, which also meant that there were more people of note to testify against a governor charged with maladministration. The colonisation programme during the civil war era and afterwards placed hundreds of thousands of citizens and their families all around the empire. Their descendants – in the case of the higher-ranking officers, already men of some education and wealth – could become men of substance. At the same time grants of Roman citizenship to provincials became more and more common. At least from the time of Claudius, auxiliary soldiers who served their twenty-five years and were honourably discharged were granted the franchise – a right extended to one wife and their children. At times non-citizen recruits were taken for the legions, for instance from Galatia, and granted citizenship immediately. Army veterans were not necessarily especially wealthy – one study based on evidence from Egyptian villages found it hard to distinguish them from their civilian and non-citizen neighbours. Yet they were numerous, especially in the areas of heavy recruitment such as Spain, Thrace, the Rhineland and parts of Syria.[31]

Less numerous, but individually and collectively more important, were the representatives of local elites who were granted citizenship on an individual basis – or in the case of magistrates in *municipia*, as a reward for public service. Such men were men of property and social standing in the first place, which was only increased by this additional honour. We should not underestimate their numbers. In the early first century AD Gades boasted no fewer than 500 residents who were not merely citizens, but *equites*. This status opened the prospect of a career in imperial service, usually beginning as commander of an auxiliary infantry cohort, then a spell as one of five equestrian tribunes in a legion, followed by command of an *ala* of auxiliary cavalry. Successful men went on to posts commanding the cohorts of the praetorian guard, the urban cohorts and *vigiles* in Rome. Some became procurators and the most successful governed equestrian provinces.[32]

Julius Caesar introduced several aristocrats from Cisalpine and Transalpine Gaul into the Senate, and this trend of promoting provincials continued under the Principate. Claudius made a long speech explaining his reasons for admitting men from the old 'long-haired' Gaul, but over time the presence of men born in the provinces ceased to require comment. Agricola was from Gaul – as perhaps was Tacitus. Arrian and Dio Cassius were both from Bithynia and Pontus. By the second century AD there were emperors like Trajan and Hadrian from Spain, and Septimius Severus from Africa. Hadrian was mocked for his 'provincial' Spanish accent, but no one questioned that he was truly Roman. Being born outside Italy did not necessarily make a man more sympathetic to the provincials. The proconsul of Baetica whose crimes were prosecuted by Pliny was from Africa.

Ironically enough, simultaneously with his governorship in Spain, the African province was being plundered by a proconsul born in Baetica, who was subsequently tried and found guilty. According to Pliny the Baetici jokingly quoted an old motto – 'I gave as bad as I received.'[33]

Yet the presence of families who produced equestrian officers and senators did mean that there were more and more provincials capable of bringing charges of misconduct against governors. It also played a central role in making provincial populations accept Roman rule. No more recent empire has matched the Romans' willingness and skill in absorbing others. Local elites were given the prospect of success, wealth and fame on a far grander scale as long as they integrated into the imperial system, with the most successful becoming senators, governors or even emperors. This required a willingness to learn Latin and to dress and act like a Roman – all the things Agricola encouraged the elite among the British tribes to do. Arminius, Florus, Sacrovir, Civilis and a few others followed this path only to reject it, but the vast majority embraced these opportunities and then competed with each other to succeed. It took longer for large numbers of men from the Hellenic east to follow this career path, a reflection of their greater attachment to domestic politics and also a slower spread of citizenship, but the elites of that area soon caught up. Religious restrictions prevented Jewish aristocrats from imperial service unless, like the Alexandrian Tiberius Alexander, they ceased to follow their faith, and this clearly hindered the absorption of the elite in Judaea and contributed to the rebellion under Nero.

Provincial elites benefited most from being part of the empire, and since they were the natural leaders of any revolt, this helped to keep control of the provinces. Men willing to serve in the army gained citizenship and so some status and protection under law. It is hard to know how easy it was for men of humbler birth to break into the ranks of the local aristocracies. Probably it was possible, if only for a handful. It looks as if many auxiliary centurions were local men, and not necessarily citizens during their service, but their pay was substantial and citizenship followed discharge if it was not gained during service. Over the generations a family might rise to equestrian rank and then even gain admission to the Senate. Paradoxically, a quicker route was open to slaves from all over the world. Wealthy freedmen were a topic for ridicule, but were often important figures in local communities, and their descendants faced no legal restrictions on their own careers. Pertinax was the son of a freedman, failed to get commissioned as a legionary centurion and became a schoolmaster instead, but later gained equestrian status, served in the equestrian commands, was admitted to the Senate for distinguished service, and went on to command legions, govern provinces, and in AD 193 become emperor – albeit being murdered after only three months.[34]

Until Caracalla extended citizenship to virtually the entire free population of the empire in AD 212 – by which time the legal advantages of the status were already being eroded – most provincials did not possess it, and even fewer were able to follow a career in imperial service. The better off, whether an existing privileged aristocracy or newcomers who joined or usurped them under Roman rule, gained much more from the empire than the bulk of the population. This did not mean that they were cut off from the rest of provincial society, although it could mean spending much of their lives elsewhere. Senators were obliged to own lands in Italy even if more of their wealth was invested in the provinces. Old bonds of obligation and service may well have changed and can rarely be traced, but this was not necessarily to the disadvantage of the less well off. On balance there was probably more chance of poorer provincials finding an influential patron as more and more equestrians and senators came from the provinces. Some areas did far better in this respect than others, with prosperity a major factor, since both equestrian and senatorial status required a man to possess considerable wealth. As far as we can tell Britain never produced any senators. It is impossible to say why, or whether this meant that its population was treated differently.

INSIDERS AND OUTSIDERS

Our evidence favours the well off over the poor, and urban over rural environments, even though the majority of people lived in the countryside and were in some way associated with working the land. Most distinctive styles of building and monuments occurred in cities, and by the later first and second centuries AD cities from all over the empire would look recognisably akin, very obviously part of the same broad culture. This imperial culture was neither purely Roman nor static, and grew under the influence of other ideas and societies. The strongest influence was Greek, but there were others and 'Greek' culture itself was a loose thing which changed as a result of coming under Roman rule. Fashions for clothes, food and drink, as well as a taste for bath houses, chariot-racing and gladiatorial games, spread throughout the empire, adding to rather than supplanting established institutions such as the *gymnasium*. Ideas travelled, so did literature and the arts, from formal portraiture to mosaics and wall paintings. Local variations in taste and material are small compared to the overwhelming similarities. The performing arts similarly spread, whether comedy or drama in Greek or Latin and, most common of all, mimes, mythological stories performed by dancers to musical and vocal accompaniment where the language and literacy did not matter so much. It is an intriguing thought that people living as far apart as the Tyne and the Euphrates may have watched the same stories and hummed the same tunes.

In the countryside the pace of change was slower, although as we have seen it was still considerable. The division between town and country can be artificial, for in some areas the two were closely connected and often physically close together, whereas elsewhere towns and cities were wide apart. In areas like Gaul and Britain the aristocracies did not transfer all their attentions to the towns, and remained an important presence in the countryside. The modern convention is to use the name 'villa' far more specifically than the Romans, as the term for a substantial country residence at the centre of a large estate. Even then the variation in size, scale and luxury is considerable. Some were essentially country houses in the more modern sense, built for comfort and to display wealth. These might still serve a practical function, but others were purely designed as centres for agriculture or pastoral activity, and some of them were not at all big. Rarely do we know who the owners were, and whether they were local or outsiders who had acquired the land.[35]

It took longer for new techniques of construction, new materials and styles of building to be adopted by the bulk of the rural population. This should not be exaggerated, as the use of timber and wattle and daub lasted for some time in many towns and cities, although traces of it do not always survive under later stone buildings. In Gaul it was several generations before tile roofs became common in villages and small farms. In Britain many people continued to build and live in roundhouses with thatched roofs just as their ancestors had done in the Iron Age and earlier. These were strong, often large and highly functional structures, and several joined together by a complex of walls serving as animal pens accommodated an extended family who farmed the land around them. The pattern was generally for numbers of them to be dotted short distances from each other rather than collected as a village, and unless excavated it is impossible to date such sites. Yet in spite of this continuity, finds show that the people living in roundhouses often had access to goods that were either very rare or unknown during the Iron Age. The occupants of these traditional houses may well have lived in equal or greater comfort than the inhabitants of the slum tenement blocks in the cities, albeit with less access to the amenities of urban life.[36]

Life in the ancient world could be a grim business. A bad harvest – or worse still, a succession of bad harvests – caused shortages which rapidly inflated the cost of staple foods. The free poor were at most risk, forced to do without or to place themselves in debt to buy enough to survive. Slaves were property and had a value, so that their owners were more likely to protect their investment and provide them with food even when times were hard – that is, assuming the owners were not themselves poor and forced to sell these extra mouths. Famine appears as a real threat in many provinces for much of the time, and some scholars would see the danger as universal. In this respect the Roman era did not differ from those before or after, so the danger was not peculiar to the empire.[37]

It took considerable effort and expenditure for the emperors to ensure that the population of Rome and the professional army did not go without, but other less significant groups were not so fortunate. Local magistrates and the wealthy – an overlapping group – did purchase stocks of food to be sold off cheaply or given to a city's population, and might be attacked by crowds if they failed to deliver. Urban populations, who possessed greater opportunities to protest, did better in such situations than scattered rural settlements, although these at least had better opportunities to forage. Under Augustus, Herod the Great paid for grain from the province of Egypt to be shipped to his kingdom when there was a shortage of food. Such an arrangement between an allied king and the equestrian governor of a province was surely not unprecedented, and it is likely that similar assistance came from one province to another. Yet transporting large quantities of grain was difficult, slow and expensive, even when some of the journey could be made by sea. The security created by the empire made such aid easier than in the past, and meant that most provinces were surrounded by other provinces or allied states. There were still severe limits to what could be achieved even when there was sufficient political will to deal with a problem, and the larger the scale of the famine or other natural disaster, then the greater the strain placed both on resources and good intentions.[38]

Some of the population teetered on the brink of starvation, and some families – and inevitably, even more women left on their own – were desperate enough to expose children on rubbish or dung heaps, letting anyone take them, even if they raised them as slaves. In Egypt some were given the name *Kopros* or 'dung' and a few did well enough to earn their freedom and turn this into a proud family name. It is very hard to know how common this was, but it did happen and was certainly something everyone could imagine. As we have seen, Pliny issued a legal ruling dealing with adults who had been exposed in this way as infants. Some people lived in desperate poverty even when they were in paid employment. In the first century BC Varro claimed that women working on the land in Liguria would take a break to give birth, before returning to their work rather than losing their meagre pay. The Roman senator found this both strange and alien, and obviously felt that it was unusual and so worth repeating. So much of our evidence is anecdotal, which makes it hard to generalise, but such tales remind us that we should not impose modern Western standards on the Roman past. Grinding poverty existed in Italy and the provinces, as it had in most areas before the empire, and as it has in much of human history, including the present day. There is no evidence to suggest that Roman rule forced a higher proportion of the population than before into this condition.[39]

Slaves had value as possessions, but no protection against punishment, execution or sexual abuse by owners. If for some life was tolerable, with eventual freedom and even prosperity possible, the frequency of laws dealing with runaway slaves shows that plenty of others would take any opportunity to escape. The free population were divided by legal status and wealth. Provincials might be compelled to assist with public works, whether serving the needs of the imperial post or acting as a labour force for a building project. These burdens were not fairly distributed and could be oppressive to communities and highly damaging to individuals, but such heavy demands were rare.

Unless condemned for a serious crime, the free population was not compelled to perform some of the most unpleasant work, such as toiling in the mines, where life was likely to be both hard and short. Such gruelling labour was left mainly to slaves and criminals, although there is good evidence that a surprising number of volunteers served because the pay was high. Some of these men were essential as experts, but others worked on many of the basic excavating and labouring jobs. Something of the conditions is hinted at by the extensive preserved mine shafts and galleries at one site in Jordan – the largest chamber measuring some 390 feet by 180 feet (120m by 55m) and up to 8 feet high (2.5m). Occupied before and after the Roman period, but used especially intensively then, to this day the surrounding landscape remains heavily polluted with a mixture of poisons produced by washing the ore and smelting.[40]

Most of the population of the empire did not live or work in such a harsh environment, and shared to some degree in the greater availability of goods and the comforts offered by the economy and society of imperial Rome. The picture is not straightforward. On balance residents of the cities were better placed to enjoy such things, but at the same time the urban environment also made it far easier for disease to spread. The open sewer Pliny found in the main street of Amastris was far from unique and was only covered after several generations of Roman rule. Even at their best, Roman systems of water supply, drainage and waste disposal were far from perfect, so that epidemics posed as big a danger as famine. Infant mortality rates were high, and life expectancy low – at least compared to prosperous and stable countries in more recent times, but again these are the exception to the broad sweep of human history. Yet some scholars have let caution make them too pessimistic, and it is hard to believe claims that life expectancy in the Roman era was as bad as in the early Neolithic.[41]

Provincials could be faced by arbitrary use and abuse of power by those who possessed it. In Apuleius' *The Golden Ass*, a Roman soldier tries to confiscate the donkey at the heart of the story, and when driven off returns with his comrades to take the animal by force. Some soldiers used the pretext of official requisitioning to pilfer what they wanted – note that John the Baptist asked soldiers to 'Do violence to no man, neither accuse any falsely; and be content with your wages.' If no higher authority was present and willing to act, then such demands could not be resisted. In the Gospels, the soldiers leading Jesus to execution compelled a bystander, Simon the Cyrenian, to carry the cross. Refusal of such a demand risked a severe beating and there was no certainty of recompense.[42]

Proof of status was not simple in an era without passports and where few carried formal documentation. At Philippi Paul and Silas were dragged before the magistrates of this Roman colony and accused of being trouble-makers. The author of Acts explains that they had cured a slave girl possessed by an evil spirit, whose owners had profited from her telling fortunes and were now angry at this loss of income and seized hold of the missionaries. A crowd gathered to support the accusations, whether from hatred of Jews or association with the girl's owners is not clear, but this encouraged the magistrates to take the matter seriously. Without a hearing, Paul and Silas were stripped, beaten and imprisoned. The next day the colony's magistrates sent orders to let them go, presumably because they had demonstrated their authority by inflicting punishment and also calmed the mob, so considered the matter closed. 'But Paul said unto them, they have beaten us openly uncondemned, being Romans, and have cast us into prison; now do they thrust us out privily?' Roman citizens were not supposed to be subject to arbitrary corporal punishment and imprisonment, and the discovery that the captives were of higher status than they had thought prompted the magistrates to come and release them in person.[43]

In Corinth another attempt was made to prosecute Paul and his party, this time before the tribunal of the proconsul of Achaea, who happened to be in the city conducting an assize. Paul's accusers were fellow Jews, and a crowd gathered, seizing him and taking him to the governor. The account in Acts is brief and lacks details, and it is uncertain whether this was done as part of a demonstration, forcing their way into the governor's presence or – which seems more likely – by formally requesting and being granted a hearing. Either way, the proconsul refused to listen to 'a question of words and names, and of your law' and declared that it was not a matter for his judgement. Paul was released and in the aftermath a crowd of Greeks beat up the leader of the synagogue in full sight of the proconsul's tribunal, who 'cared for none of those things'. This deliberate and humiliating attack on a Jewish leader suggests hostility between the Jewish and some of the Gentile community, the context of which is unclear.[44]

Later, Paul was arrested by some of the auxiliary soldiers garrisoning the Fortress of Antonia after a disturbance in the Temple in Jerusalem. The cohort commander ordered that he be bound and then interrogated during a flogging, so that more confidence could be placed in his answers. Before this began, Paul spoke to the centurion in charge, stating that he was a citizen, so not subject to such treatment. The commander was brought to the captive and in person asked whether Paul was in fact a Roman citizen. He accepted the prisoner's word, and from then on Paul was treated more gently and sent under escort to Felix, the equestrian governor of Judaea. Paul's confinement then and later was fairly comfortable, since not only was he a citizen, but also a man of some education and therefore perhaps either wealthy or with wealthy connections. It was claimed that Felix hoped to secure a payment in order to release him, but it failed to appear and so he remained a captive until Festus arrived as the new governor. Faced with charges made by some of the priests from Jerusalem, the latter gave him a hearing in the presence of Herod Agrippa II and his sister Berenice. During the course of this, Paul appealed to the emperor's judgement, so had to be sent to Rome, even though Festus was now willing to release him.[45]

The emperor as the ultimate court of appeal for citizens was an innovation of the Principate – note that Pliny sent the Christians who were Roman citizens to Trajan for his judgement. Paul and other prisoners were sent under the escort of a small detachment of troops commanded by a centurion of a *cohors Augusta*, an auxiliary unit which appears to have served as Herod Agrippa's bodyguard. They were not provided with official transport, and instead had to arrange for passage on any ship going in the right direction. The masters of these vessels were obliged to take them, but not compelled to deviate from their planned route for the convenience of the official passengers. The journey to Rome proved long and dangerous when the ship they were sailing in was wrecked, and after arrival it was several years before the emperor – by now Nero – chose to deal with the case. In Acts the narrative finishes before this, so that it is only later Church tradition which says that Paul was executed as part of the persecution begun when the emperor made Christians scapegoats for the great fire in Rome in AD 64.[46]

The episode highlights the slow, almost lethargic, pace of the empire's administration. This was not an urgent matter so far as the governors were concerned. Felix kept Paul under open arrest in the hope of profit and to keep happy the priests who had made the accusations against him. They were men of influence, with whom a governor needed to work, and so it was best not to antagonise them too much. His inertia cannot have pleased them, hence the fresh appeal on the matter to Festus when he arrived, but the priests will surely have had other favours or petitions for the procurator, so that his inaction in this case could be used to press for action on another matter. It was during the years of Paul's captivity in Caesarea that the attempt was made to have Nero declare the city to be Jewish, and it was also at this time that Josephus went as part of a delegation to Nero on behalf of some priests arrested by Felix. Paul's antagonists would also have needed to send representatives to Rome if they wished to argue their case in front of the emperor and, like Paul, these would have no choice save to wait until the *princeps* found the time and inclination to deal with the matter. In the event it took three to four years, and might well have taken even longer had Nero not embarked upon the mass execution of Christians in Rome.[47]

Action was a good deal swifter in the trial and execution of Jesus, who was not a Roman citizen, nor from a wealthy or well-connected family. His driving of the moneylenders from the Temple was a very public challenge to the authority of the priests in charge of the place – something which the Temple guards had failed to prevent. A group of these aristocratic priests felt threatened by this, as well as by his other actions and popularity, so decided to act. Only John's Gospel mentions the presence of Roman soldiers alongside the guards and followers of the priests when Jesus was arrested, but this suggests that the governor's approval was secured before action was taken. The prisoner was interrogated and by implication condemned by these senior priests, and then was taken to the Roman governor. In some circumstances the Sanhedrin, or high council, could execute for blasphemy and could arrange lynchings, but in this case they did not wish to take the responsibility, perhaps because they had not met in a proper way or wanted to pass the blame for a controversial act on to the Romans.[48]

Pontius Pilate had to work with the high-priestly Jerusalem aristocracy and relied on them to control the wider population. He was therefore obliged to listen to their concerns, just as after the crucifixion he was willing to grant the request of Joseph of Arimathaea – a rich man and a member of the Sanhedrin – to be given the body for burial. The accusations were backed by a crowd gathered and orchestrated by the priests involved, and the principal charge was Jesus' claim to be King of the Jews, and thus a challenge to the authority of Rome. As John's account puts it, 'If thou let this man go, thou art not Caesar's friend; whosoever maketh himself a king speaketh against Caesar.' Pilate could not be seen to ignore charges of this sort, especially when made by men of the wealth and education able to make a petition either to the legate of Syria or directly to Rome. The climate under Tiberius was a dangerous one, with the machinations of the praetorian prefect Sejanus, who disposed of many senators and wealthy equestrians as he tried to become the *princeps'* successor, and then his bloody fall which prompted a purge of his friends. It is no coincidence that the only inscription bearing Pilate's name records the construction in Caesarea of the Tiberieum – a building of some sort honouring the emperor.[49]

As with Paul's detention under Felix and Festus, the trial of Jesus was just one episode in a long and often difficult relationship between Pilate and the Jerusalem elite, who were in turn jockeying among themselves for influence and were not a united group. As governor he could not afford to alienate them entirely, but also needed to assert his power and try to play them off against each other so that they were less likely to unite against him. The Gospel accounts suggest little love was lost between them, and can be read as showing each group eager to make the other openly responsible for what was done. No more details are known than the vague Gospel references to the insurrection in the city and the *leistes* Barabbas, but this suggests some recent violence. Jerusalem had a large and volatile population, swollen at the time of Passover with visitors from all over the province and abroad for a festival commemorating release from servitude in Egypt. If there was a crowd calling for Jesus' execution, then in recent days there had also been a crowd acclaiming him, and he was known to have followers – who were not treated as open rebels and so suppressed with the usual prompt brutality shown by the Roman authorities. Pilate seems to have wanted it to be placed on record that both the senior priests and the people gathered outside his residence in the old Herodian palace demanded the execution of this man. He had no qualms about having the accused flogged and humiliated, while stating that he did not find evidence for a capital charge. In Luke's account he says, 'I will chastise him, and release him', a very Roman way of asserting his authority, by inflicting summary, though not fatal, punishment on a 'trouble-maker'.

This was prevented because key figures in the local elite and a chanting crowd, which could be taken as the will of the community, demanded that he go further. There is no evidence outside the Gospel accounts for a tradition of releasing a prisoner at the Passover, so we cannot say any more about how this worked or how long it was in force. Governors were expected to listen, and to listen most of all to men of wealth and high birth, the leaders of the provincial communities. The intervention of his wife offers an example of the frequently alleged influence of family and friends on a governor. Pilate ordered the execution of a man claimed to be a threat to Caesar, but ensured that he was shown to have been persuaded by the community and its leaders and not to have acted in an arbitrary fashion. The placard declaring the man he killed as 'The King of the Jews' in Latin, Greek and Aramaic was provocative to the Jewish leaders and the population as a whole, and was another assertion of the governor's power, reminding them that they could not control him and were subject to his power and judgement. It also made clear that this was a Roman official dealing with a threat to the emperor.[50]

The trial and crucifixion of Jesus is the most famous act by any Roman governor, even though it involved an equestrian prefect in charge of a minor province and can only be dated roughly to the early 30s AD. Nothing is known of Pilate apart from his term as prefect of Judaea, while his unnamed wife – without doubt the most famous governor's wife – only appears in Matthew's Gospel. Yet for all that, the way the events occurred, the pressures brought to bear on the governor and his assertion of his authority, fit with everything we know of Roman provincial government. It is also a useful illustration of the brutality that maintained the control of the provinces. Savage flogging followed by death by crucifixion – in most cases a longer, even more painful experience when the victims were not killed quickly by having their legs broken, but left to die slowly – was a common form of punishment, and many thousands perished in this way. No doubt the Sebasteni and Caesarean soldiers were particularly enthusiastic in the humiliation and scourging of Jesus, given their deep-seated hatred of the Jews – it can only have confirmed their view of the Jews as a perverse race, since now they had rejected their own king. Yet the willingness of the detachment who carried out the execution to sit and gamble while three men died slow deaths shows how casual and commonplace such violence was.[51]

Regardless of the genuine desire or pretensions of Roman administration to benevolence and care for the provincials, the rule of the emperor and empire was maintained by force, and it was the soldiers of the Roman army who were the agents of this.

THE ARMY AND THE FRONTIERS

'For their nation does not wait for the outbreak of war to give men their first lesson in arms ... On the contrary, as though they had been born with weapons in their hand, they never have a truce from training, never wait for emergencies to arise. Moreover, their peace manoeuvres are no less strenuous than veritable warfare; each soldier daily throws his energy into his drill, as though he were in action. Hence that perfect ease with which they sustain the shock of battle; no confusion breaks their customary formation, no panic paralyses, no fatigue exhausts them; and as their opponents cannot match these qualities, victory is the invariable and certain consequence.' – *Josephus, describing the Roman army, c.AD 80.*[1]

'A GREAT CIRCLE OF CAMPS'

The professional army created by Augustus was unlike anything yet seen in Europe, Africa and the Near East, for no other kingdom or state had ever maintained so many soldiers permanently under arms. At Augustus' death there were twenty-five legions – the three lost in AD 9 not having been replaced – with a theoretical strength of around 125,000 soldiers. Supported by a roughly similar number of auxiliaries, as well as naval flotillas, the praetorian guard and the other units stationed in Rome, there were perhaps a quarter of a million men under arms. Over time the total grew substantially, and in spite of the loss or disbanding of other legions, there were thirty in service at the start of the second century AD, and thirty-three under Septimius Severus at its end. Although the smaller units of the *auxilia* are harder to trace than the legions, it looks as if the increase in their numbers was even more substantial. By AD 200, the

nominal size of the army was at least 350,000 men, all sworn to serve
the emperor, and paid and promoted by him. It was not until the
French Revolution brought mass conscription that the army of any
European state surpassed this total, and even then few maintained so
many troops outside the grand mobilisations of wartime.[2]

The numbers are impressive, but then the Roman Empire was far
larger than any other ancient state – and indeed larger than the main
European powers until well into the modern era – and the size of its
army was small compared to the vast extent of territory conquered
and controlled by Rome. Estimates of the population of the ancient
world rely on guesswork, since the evidence is fragmentary and often
difficult to interpret. For instance, it is probably correct to assume
that the figures of more than four million Roman citizens registered
in censuses under Augustus include all adults, but it is not impossible
that this dealt only with men, which of course would at least double
the total, even before infants were included.

The commonest estimate for the overall population of the empire
under the Principate is some sixty million. This is almost certainly far
too low, based on pessimistic assumptions about life expectancy and
the maximum population able to be supported by agriculture over a
given area. Year by year archaeologists identify more and more settlements from the immediate pre-Roman and Roman periods, aided
by improvements in the techniques and technology of surveying. It
is early days, but over time this is likely to lead to higher figures for
populations in this period. Even if we accept sixty million as a working total, then by the end of the second century there were more
than 170 civilians for every soldier. The ratio was certainly higher
in the first century AD and probably throughout the period, since
not only is the population likely to have been considerably larger,
but the evidence suggests that most of the time army units were
substantially below their theoretical strength.[3]

At no stage was the army evenly distributed throughout the
empire, so that in fact the soldier-to-civilian ratio varied over time
and from region to region. Tacitus in his account of AD 23 gives a
convenient survey of the disposition of the legions at that time. The

'main strength' of eight legions was on the Rhine, while there were two each in the Danubian provinces of Pannonia and Moesia, backed by two more in neighbouring Dalmatia. Four were in Syria, three in the Spanish provinces, two in Egypt and two in Africa. This deployment reflected the main areas of military activity of Augustus' reign, with concentrations of troops in recently conquered territory such as Egypt, Spain and especially the Balkan provinces. The legions in the Rhineland stood ready to defend against attacks from the Germanic tribes or to advance if the emperor ever decided to renew the attempt at conquest. Tacitus notes that they were equally well placed to deal with trouble in Gaul, as they showed in the rebellion of Florus and Sacrovir. Deployments were not rigid. Later in the first century one legion in Upper Germany was moved west from the Rhineland for several decades, before once again being shifted back nearer the frontier. The strong army in Syria helped to control an area disturbed during the civil wars and the Parthian invasion in the last decades of the Republic.[4]

Priorities changed over time. The presence of two legions in Africa in AD 23 was short-lived, prompted by the struggle with Tacfarinas, a former auxiliary-turned-war leader who raided the settled province for several years. Before he was defeated the extra unit was withdrawn, and then for centuries the area was held by a single legion, *Legio III Augusta*, supported by auxiliaries. The Spanish Peninsula was also soon considered to be more secure, and its garrison was reduced to one legion, as eventually was the garrison of Egypt. Claudius sent four legions to conquer Britain, and three were considered necessary to occupy it from the end of the first century AD. Around the same time, units were shifted from the Rhine to the Danube, and the Rhineland garrison was halved to four legions, a pair in each of the two German provinces. There were ten legions in the Danubian provinces for most of the second century AD. Another marked increase was in the eastern provinces, where the total rose to eight legions in Cappadocia, Syria, Judaea and Arabia. At times provincial armies were reinforced by shifting troops from other provinces. There was no central reserve of legions, since the slow

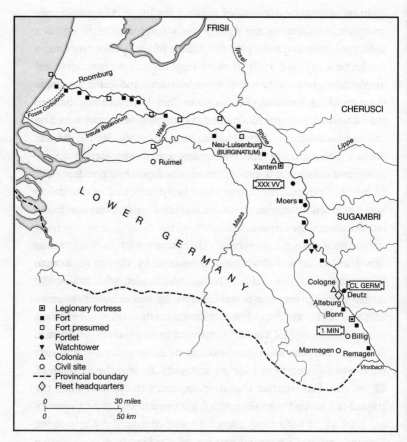

The Lower Rhine frontier

speed of movement made the idea impractical, which meant that units were deployed where it was thought that they were needed.[5]

Most of the army was on or near the frontiers of the empire. In the second century AD the orator Aelius Aristides claimed that the Romans 'did not neglect walls, but put these about your empire, not your city. And you erected them as far off as possible . . . just as a trench encircles an army camp.' A little earlier, Appian expressed a similar idea, saying that the Romans 'surround the empire with great armies and garrison the whole stretch of land and sea like a single stronghold'. A hundred years later another Greek author claimed that Augustus 'established a defensive system of forts' garrisoned by salaried professional soldiers 'to act as a barricade for the Roman Empire'. This scarcely reflected the decades of expansion under the first *princeps*, but is revealing of the ideals of the third century AD.[6]

Yet the Roman army was not structured to act as a static defensive force. Under Augustus, the bulk of the army spent the spring and summer under canvas, operating in the field on manoeuvres if not active campaigning. Then for the autumn and winter, in a way familiar to Caesar and Cicero and earlier generations of Roman commanders, it returned to *hiberna* or winter quarters. In settled, urbanised provinces, troops were sometimes billeted in cities as they had been under the Republic – something usually impossible to trace in the archaeological record. Otherwise they constructed fortified camps and timber buildings for accommodation. In Gaul, Caesar's legions rarely returned to the same place for successive winters. Under Augustus this became more common, especially along the Rhineland, so that the *hiberna* became more permanent and more solidly built, their basic design followed throughout the empire. Camps were sited to make best use of the emerging road system and transport of men and supplies by water. Unless the local situation changed dramatically, or the unit was transferred to another province, there was little point in shifting the site of a garrison and undergoing the cost and effort of creating a new camp. Over time, winter quarters turned into long-term bases, housing the unit's headquarters and records, workshops and other facilities. Even so, these bases were where the army lived when it was not required for active service or the many other tasks soldiers were called upon to perform, and were not places where it expected to fight, unless the situation was dire. Looking at a plan of such a camp it is the barracks, officers' houses, granaries and other buildings that dominate rather than the fortifications.[7]

A legion was designed as a force for fighting pitched battles. Its basic tactical unit was the cohort, with a paper strength of 480 men, and there were ten of these in each legion. At some point during the first century AD some legions increased their first cohort to number 800, and it is possible that the soldiers in this unit were taller or more experienced. A small cavalry force of 120 men acted as escorts for senior officers, as scouts, despatch riders, and could also serve as a formed unit. Otherwise all ten cohorts consisted of close-order infantrymen, protected by helmet, long shield and body armour – sometimes supplemented by greaves and articulated armour for the right arm. Offensive weapons consisted of the *pilum* – a heavy throwing javelin with an effective range of some fifteen yards – backed up by the well-balanced cut-and-thrust sword, the *gladius*, with a blade measuring between 20 and 24 inches. Even in defence, the classic tactic was to throw the *pilum* and follow this up with a charge sword in hand. As well as protecting the body from shoulder to knees, the heavy shield was designed to be used aggressively, punching an opponent with the dome-shaped metal boss to unbalance him and lay him open to the thrust of the sword.[8]

In support of the legions, the *auxilia* provided substantial numbers of well-mounted, disciplined cavalrymen – something often lacking under the Republic – as well as archers equipped with sophisticated composite bows. There were also slingers and other skirmishers, but the majority of auxiliary infantrymen fought in a style very similar to the close-order legionaries. They did not employ the *pilum* or carry the semi-cylindrical body shield – nor is there evidence for auxiliaries using the famous banded armour known today as *lorica segmentata*, but this was never universally worn by legionaries either. Instead auxiliaries had long, flat shields and carried a range of spears and javelins. They all wore helmets and a cuirass of mail or scale, so that it is a mistake to see them as 'light infantry' fighting in a drastically different way to their citizen counterparts. Josephus described both types of soldier as 'hoplites', and often it is difficult to tell them apart in his narrative – something all the more significant since he had actually fought against the Roman army. In AD 84, at the Battle of Mons Graupius against the Caledonian tribes, the Roman commander led his main attack with six auxiliary cohorts recruited from the Rhineland:

> . . . to bring things to the sword's point and to hand-to-hand fighting; a manoeuvre familiar to them from long service and embarrassing to the enemy, whose shields were small and swords too long; . . . Accordingly when the Batavi began to exchange blows hand to hand, to strike with the bosses of their shields, to stab in the face, and, after cutting down the enemy on the level, to push their line uphill . . . in their haste to snatch victory they left many behind them only half killed, or even unhurt.

To most opponents, legionary and auxiliary infantry were much alike as aggressive formed troops, well protected by armour, possessing a short-range missile capability and very dangerous at close quarters. Both types of soldier were well trained and highly disciplined.[9]

The *auxilia* provided the army with numerous good cavalry, useful missile troops and a strong supplement to legionary numbers, producing a well-balanced, flexible fighting force. There was no permanent command structure for auxiliary units above the level of the individual cavalry *ala* or infantry cohort, a tenth the size of a legion. This meant that the clear hierarchy of a legion made this an important division in any substantial field force. Roman doctrine emphasised the use of reserves in battle, and armies usually formed up in at least two, and more often three or more lines of units. Cavalry deployed on the flanks, sometimes with additional units in reserve, and the infantry in the centre. Auxiliary infantry were either placed on the flanks of the legions linking them to the cavalry, or made up

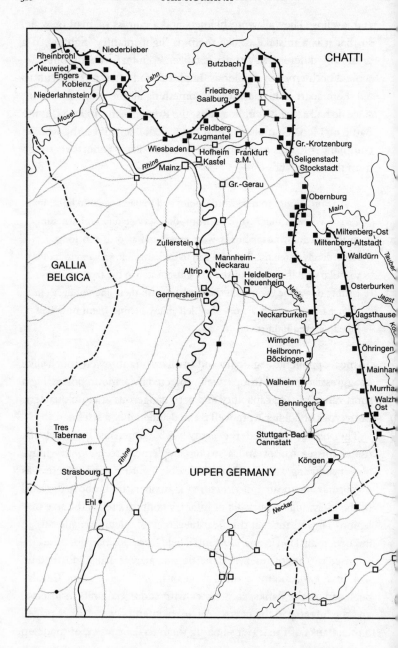

Niederbieber
Rheinbrohl
Neuwied
Engers
Koblenz
Niederlahnstein

Lahn

Mosel

Butzbach

CHATTI

Friedberg
Saalburg

Feldberg
Zugmantel
Wiesbaden
Hofheim
Kastel
Rhine
Mainz

Frankfurt
a.M.

Gr.-Krotzenburg

Seligenstadt
Stockstadt

Gr.-Gerau

Obernburg

Main

Miltenberg-Ost
Miltenberg-Altstadt

Zullerstein

Walldürn

Tauber

GALLIA
BELGICA

Mannheim-
Neckarau
Altrip

Heidelberg-
Neuenheim

Osterburken

Neckar

Jagst

Germersheim

Neckarburken

Jagsthausen

Ko

Wimpfen
Heilbronn-
Böckingen

Öhringen

Mainhar

Walheim

Murrha
Walzh
Ost

Benningen

Tres
Tabernae

Rhine

Stuttgart-Bad
Cannstatt

Köngen

Strasbourg

UPPER GERMANY

Ehl

Neckar

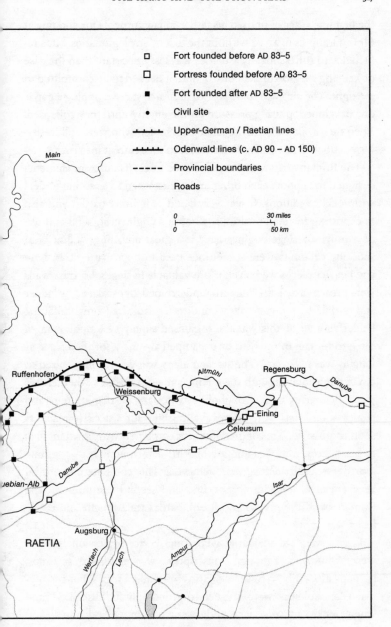

The Upper Rhine frontier

the first line. Tacitus praised his father-in-law Agricola for winning at Mons Graupius in AD 84 without the loss of any legionaries, but a reluctance to suffer citizen casualties was less important than the ease of keeping a legion under control until it needed to be committed to the fight. The aim was to be able to reinforce success or plug a gap if one developed, putting pressure on the enemy until they collapsed. Then the cavalry – ideally auxiliary horsemen who were still fresh – were launched in a controlled pursuit to turn retreat into rout.[10]

The Roman army was a sophisticated force, its different elements designed to support each other and accustomed to adapting to deal with local conditions. It was very good at fighting battles and also at capturing fortified positions, where its engineering skill and use of a range of siege engines gave it a great advantage. Light bolt-shooting catapults were sometimes used in open battle, but these and heavier pieces were even more valuable in sieges. Fortress walls were breached by battering ram, undermined, or escaladed by ladder and mobile siege tower, allowing direct assault by Roman infantry. Underlying all of this was the organised supply system allowing a force to remain in the field or encamped around a fortified place as long as was necessary. The Roman army was a force best suited to direct confrontation with the enemy's main strength – whether this was a field army or a stronghold – which meant that strategy and tactics at all levels were aggressive, pushing for a decisive result as soon as possible. This aggression was combined with a willingness to learn from mistakes and a stubborn determination to continue a struggle until victory was achieved. The combination proved very effective, and during the first and second centuries AD the Romans won the great majority of battles they fought and rarely lost a war.

Legionaries and auxiliaries were long-service professionals. Most were volunteers, although conscription was employed at times, perhaps especially to raise auxiliaries from allied tribes. For twenty-five years soldiers were subject to strict military discipline, and when not on active service underwent training as individuals and units for their wartime role. 'As though they had been born with weapons in their hand, they never have a truce from training, never wait for emergencies to arise. Moreover their peace manoeuvres are no less strenuous than veritable warfare. . . . Indeed it would not be wrong to describe their manoeuvres as bloodless combats and their combats as sanguinary manoeuvres.' That at least was the theory, but Josephus' account was too simplistic, and we have already seen that conflicting demands on soldiers' time and their employment as builders, administrators or policemen took them away from their parent units, reducing the latter's military readiness. The Roman army was not perfect, nor permanently kept at the highest state of preparedness for full-scale war, but even when other demands on its personnel left units weak, and lethargy and neglect undermined training, it only required effort and some little time to restore its efficiency. If the ideal condition of units could rarely be maintained for long, the average level of readiness remained high, supported by regulation and close imperial scrutiny.[11]

The army was probably the most heavily bureaucratic institution in the Roman world, in part because it was by far the greatest expense in the budget of the empire, and also because maintaining close control of it was important for every emperor. Record-keeping followed a soldier throughout his career. Thus on 24 February AD 103, the *cornicularius* or clerk of an auxiliary cohort made a copy of a document listing six new recruits, including 'C. Longinus Priscus, 22, scar on left eyebrow', and 'Caius Julius Maximus, 25, no distinguishing marks'.[12] Animals, especially cavalry mounts, were similarly entered in the books:

Marius Maximus to Valentinus

Received 16 March, AD 208

Enter in the records according to the regular procedure a horse, four years old, reddish, masked, without brands, approved by me; assign it to Julius Bassus, trooper of *cohors XX Palmyrenorum* under your command, at 125 denarii . . .[13]

Pay, promotions, postings and detached duties were all documented, up until the end of service. Thus we have discharges made early on medical grounds, such as 'Tryphon son of Dionysius, a weaver of the metropolis of Oxyrhynchus, suffering from cataract and impaired vision'. In unit rosters the Greek letter *theta* was used as shorthand for *thanatos* or 'death', equivalent to the DD or 'discharged dead' in the Royal Navy of Nelson's day, and in turn spawned the Latin slang word *thetatus*.[14]

Records were kept at unit level, while copies of some and summaries of others went to the administrative staff of the provincial legate. Inspecting the army and its bases in his province was an important part of his duties. Arrian, the Nicomedian-born Roman senator, served as legate of Cappadocia under Hadrian, and left an account of a tour of the garrisons on the eastern coast of the Black Sea. His *Periplus* was a literary essay, written in Greek, and twice mentions the fuller and more formal Latin report, which sadly does not survive. Even so it gives a sense of his activities: 'before midday we came to Apsaros, where five cohorts are stationed. I gave the army its pay and inspected its weapons, the walls, the trench, the sick, and the food supplies that were there'. At Phasis,

> ... the fort itself, in which 400 select troops are quartered, seemed to me, owing to the nature of its site, to be very secure, and to lie on the most convenient spot for the safety of those who sail this way. In addition, a double ditch as broad as the other. The wall used to be of earth, and wooden towers were set above it, now both it and the towers are made of baked brick. And its foundations are firm, and war engines are installed – and in short it is fully equipped to prevent any of the barbarians from even approaching it, let alone to protect its garrison there against the danger of a siege.

Like Pliny, Arrian looked to make further improvements, and in this case ordered a new ditch to be dug surrounding the civilian settlement outside the fort and protecting the harbour. Twice he mentions issuing pay to the garrisons – due three times a year – and talks about inspecting men, equipment and horses, as well as visiting the hospitals. There are few details of the exercises troops were required to perform. Arrian mentions getting a small detachment of cavalrymen to throw javelins, and another unit of horsemen to demonstrate leaping onto their horses – an important skill since the stirrup had not yet been invented.[15]

Some sense of the type of drills and exercises performed on such occasions comes from a long inscription from the base of *Legio III Augusta* at Lambaesis in Numidia. It records the speeches made by Hadrian after personally watching the army of the province going through its paces during his visit. His verdict was highly favourable – hence the desire to commemorate it – and in many ways his comments could have been made by a senior officer in many armies over the ages. Hadrian displays a close knowledge of the local situation, telling the *III Augusta* that he was aware that they were under-strength. He knew that:

. . . a cohort is away because, taking turns, one is sent every year to the staff of the Proconsul [of Africa]; that two years ago you gave a cohort and five men from each centuria to the fellow third legion, that many far-flung outposts keep you scattered, that twice within our memory you have not only changed fortresses but built new ones.

All of this would have excused some deficiencies in their performance, but no such excuses were necessary and he praised the legion, its officers and the care of the legate. During the exercise the legion deployed in battle order, marched, built a marching camp with stronger defences than was common, cared for its weapons and cooked meals as if on campaign. Auxiliary units were put through their paces in a similar way. Hadrian watched infantry archers shooting and cavalry manoeuvring, jumping obstacles and throwing javelins. There were constant admonitions on the value of rigorous training, salted with occasional, detailed criticism where he felt this was necessary. The men of a cavalry *ala* were warned against attacking or pursuing too boldly, for 'nothing must ever be done recklessly'. Hadrian felt that the cavalry of *III Augusta* had made some of the drills too difficult in the hope of impressing him, but praised their spirit. The *Ala I Pannoniorum* particularly impressed him. 'Had anything been lacking, I would note it; had anything stood out, I would mention it. You pleased throughout the whole manoeuvre.'[16]

No doubt an imperial visit encouraged a provincial army to put on as impressive a show as possible, especially if, like Hadrian, the *princeps* was well known for his deep interest in drills, skill at arms and equipment. There would be plenty of warning and time to prepare – just as the emperor was no doubt carefully briefed on the local situation so that he could demonstrate his concern for and knowledge of his soldiers. Exercises staged for the provincial legate would most likely be on a smaller scale, although still focused on essentially the same things – the javelin-throwing and vaulting into the saddle mentioned by Arrian find parallels in Hadrian's speeches at Lambaesis. We do not know how often a legate was expected to review the units under his command, whether this was just done on arrival in the province or was an annual event. Arrian's testimony suggests that written reports would be sent to the *princeps* giving a verdict on the state of each unit and their commanders – something likely to influence the latter's careers.[17]

It is clear that units regularly sent detailed strength returns to the provincial legate, while the culture of inspection meant that legions and auxiliaries alike did their best to prepare in advance. An early-second-century-AD writing tablet found at Carlisle in Britain gives a glimpse of a routine internal check:

> Docilis to Augurinus his prefect greetings. As you ordered, we have attached below all the names of lancers who are missing lances, either who did not have fighting lances, or who (did not have) the smaller *subarmales* [probably a type of jerkin worn with a cuirass] or who (did not have) regulation swords.

No reason is supplied for the missing items, so we cannot know whether they were lost on active service, through natural wear and tear, neglect or theft.[18]

The strength and condition of army units, their mounts and other equipment were matters of concern for any emperor. Military victories won by his legates were attributed to the *princeps*, even if he was far away when the action was fought, but conversely he would also be held responsible for any defeat. The governors of military provinces were expected to preserve the loyalty, readiness and efficiency of the army under their command. To aid them in this task, the army's bureaucracy kept them in regular contact with individual units and commanders. The records generated in these exchanges were clearly held in central archives – some surviving documents show signs of being kept up-to-date and many refer to copies. In the early years most legates appear to have based their headquarters and these archives in a legionary base, but as time passed dedicated facilities were constructed for them. In the late first century AD, a palace and fort with barracks were built at Londinium for the legate of Britain. Although the legate spent much of his time on the road to hold assizes or perform his military role, these centres became a form of provincial capitals and acted as administrative centres for an army stationed there.[19]

It is harder to know how much information routinely passed from the provincial headquarters to Rome. Legates reported to the emperor on many issues, and no doubt the state of the provincial army featured in this, but it is less clear how much detail was included unless specific requests for information were made. Some things were centrally recorded at Rome. From Claudius onwards, all auxiliaries gained citizenship when honourably discharged. These additions to the census of Roman citizens were documented at Rome – the soldier being given a bronze copy of the text confirming the grant. In AD 6 Augustus established the *aerarium militare* or Military Treasury to deal with army pay and the bounty or land given to demobilised legionaries. At the very least this meant some collation of soldiers' entitlements, even if much of the administration of salaries was carried out by the unit itself.

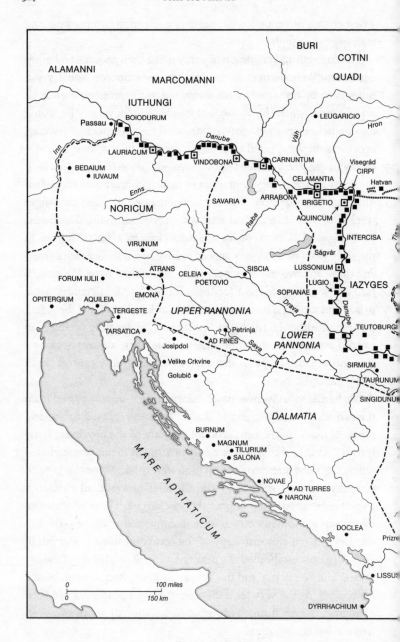

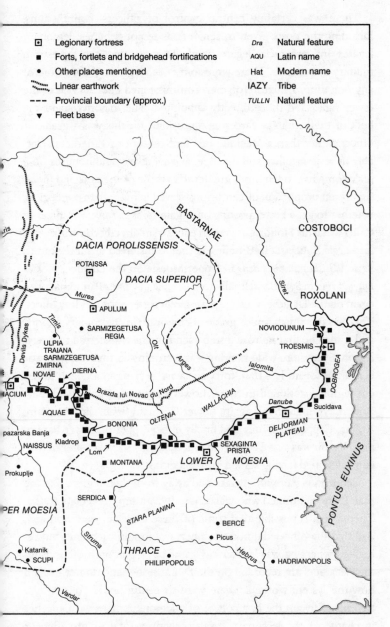

The Danubian frontier

There was certainly central control of officers' commissions, including the posts given to senators as senior tribunes, legionary legates and provincial legates, and the more than 500 equestrian military commands. There were some 1,800 legionary centurions at any one time, a mixture of men commissioned after service in the lower ranks and those directly appointed. The majority spent the bulk of their military career as centurions, for this was a grade of officer rather than a specific rank, and centurions varied considerably in responsibility and prestige, as well as pay and bonuses on a scale some five to ten times greater than those of the rank and file. A significant proportion of centurions served in more than one legion, whether to get a better posting or to gain steps in rank. For instance Caius Octavius Honoratus was an equestrian directly commissioned into *Legio II Augusta* in Britain. He then transferred in succession to *Legio VII Claudia pia fidelis* in Upper Moesia on the Danube, to *XVI Flavia firma* in Syria, and finally to *X Gemina* in Upper Pannonia, once again on the Danube, finishing as *princeps posterior* of its fifth cohort. This was the fourth senior grade of centurion in an ordinary cohort, and it may be that he rose a step each time he transferred to a new legion. Even more wide-ranging was Petronius Fortunatus, who was centurion for no less than forty-six years, serving in a dozen different legions, stationed in Syria, Lower Germany, Upper Pannonia, Britain, Numidia, Syria again, Lower Germany again, Britain again, Arabia, Cappadocia, Italy and finally either Upper or Lower Pannonia. His son was also a centurion, but died only six years after he was commissioned having served in two legions.[20]

Centurions were often stationed away from their legion, like the man Pliny mentioned who was sent to Byzantium to regulate traffic. Therefore it is possible that some of these transfers were nominal, and that the officer did not actually travel to join each unit, but remained where he was and simply gained a step in promotion. Both men's careers are recorded on their tombstones and do not explain how the system worked. There were six centurions in cohorts two to ten and five in the first cohort of a legion, perhaps with another in charge of the legionary cavalry, giving a total of fifty-nine or sixty per legion. Our evidence does not suggest that this total was ever exceeded, or that there were serving centurions unattached to a legion. In some cases men transferred between legions stationed in the same province, but others, like Honoratus and Fortunatus, were posted from one end of the empire to the other. Unit records report the addition of officers appointed from outside, noting that it was by order of the provincial governor. Yet it is hard to believe that governors of different provinces arranged transfers on their own authority, and such careers strongly suggest a central administration to keep track of vacancies and appointments.[21]

We do not know how this worked, and it is unlikely that an emperor hand-picked every centurion or equestrian officer in the army and kept a close eye on their careers. Appointments at all levels were determined as much or more by patronage than the talent of the individual involved. Pliny once wrote to the legate of a military province asking on behalf of an equestrian friend for a commission, probably as junior tribune in a legion. 'Your command of a large army gives you a plentiful source of benefits to confer and secondly, your tenure has been long enough for you to have provided for your own friends. Turn to mine – they are not many.' The recommendation of a governor to commission or promote someone, whether on the basis of his own observations or the urging of a friend, stood a good chance of being confirmed by the *princeps*, as long as the governor was in favour and had not made too many requests. Such matters were dealt with by those responsible for imperial correspondence, the *ab epistulis*. An extension of an aristocrat's household and secretariat, for much of the first century AD this office was supervised by an imperial freedman. Afterwards the post was given to an equestrian procurator.[22]

The loyalty of the army was the ultimate guarantor of an emperor's power. A sign of rebellion was to tear down the *imagines*, the images of the *princeps* and his family kept with the standards (which had caused such uproar when Pilate had them brought into Jerusalem). No emperor would let a provincial governor make himself too popular with the army in his province, and especially its officers.

This was one of the main charges against Calpurnius Piso, the legate of Syria dismissed by Germanicus in AD 19. According to Tacitus, Piso's tenure as governor saw a concerted effort to win over his soldiers, with his wife helping by attending troop reviews and exercises:

> . . . by bounties and bribery, by attentions to the humblest private, by dismissals of the veteran centurions and the stricter tribunes, whom he replaced by dependants of his own or by men of the worst character, by permitting indolence in the camp, licence in the towns, and in the country a vagrant and riotous soldiery, he carried corruption to such a pitch that in the language of the rabble he was known as the Father of the Legions (*parens legionum*).[23]

The Senate's decree condemning Piso talked of his illegal attempt to resume command of Syria, leading to a brief civil war. Soldiers who opposed him were executed,

> . . . many without hearing their cases, without consulting his staff, and by crucifying not only foreigners but also a centurion, a Roman citizen; he had destroyed the military discipline established by the divine Augustus and maintained by Tiberius Caesar Augustus, not only by allowing soldiers not to obey in the traditional manner those in command of them, but also by giving donatives in his own name from the *fiscus* [treasury] of our Princeps, a deed which, he was pleased to see, led to some soldiers being called 'Pisonians', others 'Caesarians', and by going on to confer distinctions on those who, after usurping such a name, had shown him obedience . . .[24]

In AD 14 mutinous legionaries of the Rhine army wanted to proclaim Germanicus emperor in place of Tiberius, an offer he refused. There were abortive risings by provincial legates against Claudius and Domitian. The legate of Britain executed by the latter for permitting a new design of lance to be named after him was seen as trying to ingratiate himself with the troops. Officers, and especially centurions, were the key to controlling the legions. The emperor was the ultimate source of patronage and the arbiter of careers, and he could not afford to let anyone else gain too much influence over these. Senators needed to be permitted a share of favours to pass on to their clients, but no one senator – still less a family or other closely linked group – could be permitted to decide on too high a proportion of promotions and appointments, especially for the garrison of a particular province.[25]

The office of the *ab epistulis* issued commissions and kept records tracking appointments in their archives. This meant that those working in this office, and especially the man in charge, were able to influence decisions and could be lobbied to grant favours. The poet Statius describes a freedman serving in this role under Domitian as recommending men for commissions as centurion or equestrian tribune. In addition to this office and its archives, there were the *frumentarii* or 'grain men', originally formed to supervise the supply of food to the army. Legionaries seconded from their units to the legate's staff, these men became couriers travelling back and forth to Rome, carrying despatches, but also able to report on events and conditions in each province. At any one time as many as half of them would be stationed at Rome waiting to be sent out, and over time their role grew. In later years, especially by the third century AD, they gained a grim reputation as imperial spies, concerned with any hint of disloyalty on the part of governors or other officers, but from the start they offered another source of information to the emperor and his advisors.[26]

THE OTHER SIDE OF THE HILL

Emperors relied on maintaining a monopoly of military power. Senatorial legates were necessary to lead the armies and govern provinces, but each of these men could become a rival if backed by the legions placed under his command. Thus the army posed a potential threat as well as being the basis of their rule – a situation the Emperor Tiberius described as 'holding the wolf by the ears'.

Augustus established the army at a size convenient for his needs both to secure his dominance and to win him military glory from expansion. Maintaining the army was expensive, the burden growing as it increased in size in the years to come. More legions were unnecessary to secure the emperor's position against internal rivals, and indeed presented greater opportunity for over-ambitious provincial governors to challenge him. A partial exception to this was the enlargement of the praetorians and other units stationed in or near Rome, although it was not until the reign of Septimius Severus that these became equivalent in numbers to a provincial army.[27]

Over time, more legions and auxiliary troops were raised in spite of the cost. Military pay changed less. Domitian increased the annual salary of a legionary from the 225 denarii introduced by Julius Caesar to 300. This was far from lavish, but was supplemented by periodic bonuses or donatives, issued to mark special occasions such as the accession of an emperor. Septimius Severus, victor in a civil war and nervous of losing his troops' support, increased both salary and bonuses. Allegedly his death-bed advice to his sons and successors was to 'indulge the soldiers and despise everyone else'.[28]

As we have seen, by far the greatest part of this highly expensive army was stationed on or near the frontiers of the empire, and it is clearly important to understand why this was done. In recent decades an intense scholarly debate has raged over the role of the army and the nature of Rome's frontiers. Although fruitful in many ways, all too often it has polarised and oversimplified the issue, so that the army's role is depicted as either offensive or defensive rather than varying over time and sometimes combining aspects of both. Much like the discussion of Roman imperialism, there has been a regrettable tendency to focus exclusively on Roman aims, ideology, methods and resources and to ignore those of their neighbours. It is well worth considering the wider world before we look at the function of the Roman army.[29]

Rome faced no foreign power capable of matching her strength. By far the largest and most sophisticated neighbour was Parthia, ruled by the Arsacid dynasty of once nomadic aristocrats who had seized much of the old Seleucid Empire. Early contact with Rome in the first century BC was diplomatic, and marked by the Romans' usual bullish disdain for foreigners. Then came Crassus' unprovoked attack, his subsequent defeat at Carrhae and the looming threat of Parthian invasion of the Roman east that preoccupied Cicero and later became a reality in 41–40 BC. Syria was overrun and Parthian allies invaded Asia and were installed in power in Judaea. Although they were ejected from all these areas a few years later, Mark Antony's counter-attack through Armenia ended in disaster.[30]

Civil wars distracted both sides during this period, and throughout its existence the Parthian monarchy was rocked by bloody power struggles between members of the royal house. Their empire was divided into lesser kingdoms and satrapies, each of these local rulers a powerful figure and potential backer of rivals. The Surenas – probably a title rather than a name – defeated Crassus, only to be executed a few months later by a king who did not wish a subordinate to win too much glory. Parthian armies consisted of a core of royal troops, but relied heavily on contingents provided by the lesser kings and rulers. Some of these troops were more or less full-time soldiers, and many more were called upon to serve in times of war out of obligation to the nobility. The Surenas is said to have taken 10,000 horsemen with him when he went on campaign or travelled on official business.[31]

We hear little of Parthian foot soldiers in our sources, even though it is likely that there were significant numbers of these. Some were archers or other skirmishers. There is no impression of significant numbers of close-order infantry able to match legionaries or auxiliaries in close combat. The main strength of every Parthian army was its cavalry. A minority – perhaps around 10 per cent – were cataphracts, with horse and rider both heavily armoured. These carried bows, but their principal tactic was a charge – delivered at a trot, given this weight of armour – using a long, two-handed lance called a *contus*. Horse archers were in contrast highly mobile, wore little or no protective armour and instead relied on speed to avoid enemy missiles. Carrying a powerful recurved composite bow – so called because when unstrung the bow bends back in the opposite direction – they concentrated less on accuracy than on deluging the enemy with clouds of arrows. Only when their opponents were weakened by casualties and demoralised would horse archers try to charge home and ride them down. The heavy and light cavalry worked best when closely co-ordinated, the cataphracts waiting for the right moment before launching their attack. All the while Parthian drummers pounded kettledrums to intimidate the enemy.

Well led and in open country, a Parthian army was highly formidable, as Carrhae had shown. Crassus and Mark Antony both discovered that it was very difficult to retreat from this mobile enemy, the latter only escaping with heavy casualties. When Antony did win a victory he failed to inflict decisive losses on the Parthians because their cavalry scattered and fled at speed. Yet clear victories were possible. His legate Ventidius twice beat the Parthians by luring the cataphracts into rash attacks against strong hilltop positions before his legionaries had been sufficiently worn down by archery. Many encounters between Roman and Parthian armies ended as standoffs, each side waiting for the other to make a mistake. Although difficult to defeat, the Parthians often struggled to win. With their soldiers mainly non-professionals, there was a limit to how long a Parthian army could remain in the field before contingents dispersed to their homes. Supply was another problem, made worse by the need to feed and care for so many horses. Rudimentary knowledge of siegecraft and the difficulty of keeping an army in one place for any length of time meant that it was difficult for them to capture or starve into submission fortified towns or cities.[32]

Under Augustus the Euphrates was confirmed as the effective boundary between the Roman and Parthian empires. It did not represent a natural cultural or ethnic boundary. Many people spoke Aramaic on both sides of the border, and there were substantial Greek communities living under Parthian rule – after Antioch and Alexandria, Seleucia was probably the largest Greek city in the world. There were also large numbers of Jews in Babylonia, who maintained links with the wider Jewish community and, until its destruction, travelled to worship at the Temple in Jerusalem. Trade between Rome and Parthia was always common, the border never closed, even if people passing across it were usually aware of when they had crossed it. Kingdoms such as Commagene, Osrhoene and Armenia lay between the two empires and had long-standing connections to communities in both. Although the Seleucids and before them the Persians had at times controlled territory as far as the Mediterranean coast, this wider region was no more a natural unit than the realm of the Parthian king or the eastern provinces of Rome. Occasionally Roman sources represent the Parthians as laying claim to the lands of these old empires, but there is little sign of deep ambition to seize them.[33]

The Parthians knew that the Roman Empire was large and very strong. Rome itself was so distant that it was unreachable by any Parthian army, but the Parthian king's heartland in the valleys of the Euphrates and Tigris were within the reach of Roman armies. The Romans made it very clear that they did not consider the Parthians as their equals. No Roman emperor ever met a Parthian king in person, or acknowledged him as his peer. A long succession of Parthian kings' sons went to Rome as hostages and were educated in the imperial household, while numerous challengers for the throne, along with their followers, were accepted into the empire. There was no similar traffic in the other direction. Many Parthian kings had a tenuous hold on power, a situation the Romans exploited through supporting and sheltering potential rivals. The border with Rome was also not the only threat faced by the king, for there was the ever-present risk of internal rebellion, while frontiers to the north and east faced dangerous and aggressive peoples. In the north-east, the nomadic Alans troubled both Parthia and the Roman provinces over a long period. By comparison it was far easier to maintain peace through negotiation and treaty with the Roman Empire.

The Alans periodically threatened Cappadocia, and were just one of the numerous peoples the Romans faced along their borders. Like the Parthians they were famous for their cavalry, some of them heavily armoured and lance-armed like the cataphracts and others skirmishers. Although they used composite bows, they were seen as less effective archers, and their armies lacked the discipline and organisation of the Parthians, but remained dangerous and were vigorous raiders. They were a Sarmatian people, and other similar groups lived around the Black Sea and along parts of Rome's Danubian frontier.[34]

Other European peoples relied mainly on warriors who fought on foot, with only small numbers, often noblemen, fighting from horseback. There were many different tribes, clans and kingdoms living near the frontiers of the empire, such as Dacians on the Danube, Germanic peoples on the Danube and on the Rhine, and the Britons. For all their differences in language and culture, they shared a common lack of political unity. Even tribes seen as a distinct group by the Romans were often divided into factions supporting different leaders. Competition within tribes was frequently violent, and hostility to neighbours common. Men like Sulpicius Galba and Julius Caesar would have noticed only minor differences between the tribal societies they had encountered and the ones living outside the empire in the first and second centuries AD.

Chieftains, kings and princes alike kept a following of full-time warriors in their household. Tacitus says that it was common for restless German warriors whose tribes were at peace to go and take service in the following or *comitatus* of leaders of another people, and talks of how chieftains rewarded their bravest warriors with gold, weapons or the gift of a horse. These household warriors or *comites* displayed and maintained a man's power, and their numbers and fame were a visible sign of his status. Effectively professional warriors, they were well equipped by the standards of the tribes, skilled with their weapons and highly motivated. Tacitus says that chieftains vied to prove their prowess to their followers, while the warriors would be shamed if they did not match their courage. Augustus formed a special bodyguard of German tribesmen because they were famed for their loyalty. Disbanded after AD 9, it was reformed under his successors. The bond between chieftain and household warriors was often as strong among other tribal peoples. They were the pick of a tribal army, but they were relatively few in number. A range of sources give the impression that even a king rarely mustered more than a few hundred warriors in his *comitatus*.[35]

Many tribes were capable of forming large armies, but the bulk of these consisted of free men able to provide themselves with weapons and willing or obliged to gather. These were farmers and herdsmen rather than dedicated warriors, which is not to say that they were unskilled. In such warlike cultures, most men grew up accustomed to weapons and the possibility of violence. Yet their equipment was likely to be basic. Few would have body armour, fewer still helmets. Swords were likely to be the preserve of the noblemen and their *comites*, and even among these armour was probably relatively rare. The majority would rely on spears or javelins and have only a shield for protection. Some might use slings or bows, but these longer-range missiles were no more than support for the mass of warriors fighting in close order. The contrast with the Roman army is marked, where the rank-and-file legionaries and auxiliaries wore armour and helmet, carried a shield, and each wielded a well-made sword. This was the equipment only a chieftain or leading warrior could match.

Large tribal armies were slow-moving and clumsy. It took some time for them to muster, and it was no coincidence that Roman armies ravaging tribal lands were usually faced with an enemy army only after they had begun to withdraw back to the frontier. Command and control was rudimentary, especially since there might well be several leaders rather than a single overall commander. Supply was left to individual warriors – or often their wives and families, who followed them when the army gathered – and this meant that after a couple of weeks they would have consumed the food they had brought and be forced to disperse. Tacitus singled out the Chatti as unique among the Germanic peoples for having an organised system to feed their warriors, and obeying commanders and submitting to a measure of discipline. 'Other Germans may be seen going to battle, but the Chatti go to war.'[36]

It was not a system suited to prolonged warfare or to large-scale attacks over long distances. Big armies gathered to defend their own territory against attackers or sometimes to challenge neighbours for dominance in short campaigns in spring or summer. Some inter-tribal conflicts led to the break-up or displacement of a group, but most activity was smaller-scale and likely to consist of the raiding common in so much of the ancient world. The *comitatus* of a chieftain were ideally suited to this, and successful expeditions gave the leader a chance to reward followers. Several chieftains might combine to gather a larger band, bolstered by volunteers from the wider community drawn by the prospect of adventure and loot. Aggressive raiding created hatred and sparked reprisal raids from the victims, but if it was sufficiently successful it deterred others. As we have seen, Caesar tells us that the tribes tried to create a strip of depopulated land around their own territory to display their strength and warn off aggressors.[37]

Sometimes charismatic and successful leaders emerged, able to unite their own tribe and even persuade or force others into confederation. Arminius of the Cherusci and Maroboduus of the Marcomani were examples of this, each uniting other tribes for a while. The former based his rule on defying Rome, the latter on avoiding conflict with the empire and seeking Roman recognition. The armies they led were larger and more tightly controlled than the usual tribal forces. Their warriors were also better equipped – Tacitus claimed that they had a plentiful supply of Roman equipment and adopted Roman-style tactics. Velleius Paterculus credits Maroboduus with an army of 'seventy thousand infantry and four thousand cavalry' which he was 'steadily preparing by exercising it in constant wars against his neighbours'. He and Arminius were exceptionally successful, and in time they became rivals, the resultant conflict leaving Maroboduus fatally weakened. Soon afterwards he was driven out by another challenger and ended his life in comfortable exile within the empire. Arminius was murdered by chieftains who resented the dominance of one man, and in neither area did a similarly strong leader appear for several centuries. The power of such warlords was precarious and rarely outlived them.[38]

In Julius Caesar's day Burebista united the Dacians and created a formidable kingdom, but this crumbled when he died around the same time as the Roman dictator. It was not until more than a century had passed that a similarly strong king emerged. This was Decebalus, whose rule extended beyond his own people to include neighbouring Sarmatians and Germanic groups like the Bastarnae. Dacia was heavily fortified during these years, with forts and walled towns defended by stone ramparts employing a mixture of local, Gallic and Hellenistic techniques, eventually combined with Roman engineering supplied by deserters and the experts loaned to the king as part of his treaty with Domitian. More deserters served him as soldiers, adding to the large number of men kept permanently under arms. Decebalus proved a dangerous opponent who invaded and plundered the Danubian provinces, inflicting several serious defeats on the Romans. Yet leaders of such power were rare, and most of the time along the frontiers in Europe and North Africa even the important tribal leaders wielded authority that was far smaller in scale and had far more modest forces under their command.[39]

ATTACK AND DEFENCE

Under Augustus poets sang of *imperium sine fine* – power without limit or end – and this dream lived on for centuries. To expand Rome's power was felt to be an admirable thing by emperors and aristocrats alike, although, as in earlier periods, this could be achieved without annexing territory. Yet it was not the only or even the first priority of his successors, nor was it generally felt to be an urgent and immediate need. Some emperors ordered or led aggressive wars and sought the glory of new conquests. Occasionally this sprang from a personal desire for fame or a longing to match the achievements of the great conquerors of the past, both Roman generals and Alexander of Macedon. More often the quest for personal glory came from the need felt by insecure rulers and ones without any past military achievements to prove themselves. Yet emperors who failed to expand were not automatically unpopular or condemned for this reason alone, as long as it was felt that Roman military might and dominance remained unimpaired. Modern scholars often present expansion and defence as mutually exclusive, but this is artificial. Rome's *imperium* could only increase if the Romans preserved what they already had, which meant that control of existing provinces was always at least as important. Allied states needed to be kept within Rome's sphere, and the Romans could not afford to let these or the directly governed provinces be destabilised by rebellion or attacks from outside. Augustus' reign saw as much consolidation as conquest.[40]

The Roman Empire at his death had borders stretching for thousands of miles across all three of the known continents in the world. Beyond lived a vast array of different societies and groups, some large, some small, but never united, so that it was very rare even for a few neighbours to act in concert. Rome did not face one or more rival great powers whose interests inevitably conflicted with its own, nor any potential opponent capable of matching her economic and military resources, still less with any realistic hope of crippling or destroying the empire. This may not always have been apparent to all their neighbours, aware only of the imperial province nearest to them. Under Augustus, the warriors of Queen Candace of Ethiopia attacked the Roman province of Egypt at least twice. The first Roman counter-attack achieved little, but after a second, deeper invasion the queen was willing to negotiate for peace. When her ambassadors were told by the prefect of Egypt that they must go to Caesar Augustus, they protested that they did not know 'who Caesar was or where they should have to go to find him', and were given an escort to the emperor, who happened to be on the island of Samos when they reached him.[41]

No one equalled Rome's strength, but then no one ever faced the full might of the empire for there were always other wars – or the fear of other wars – elsewhere. After AD 9 Arminius faced eight out of the twenty-five remaining legions. He was unable to stop them from marching through the tribes' lands, destroying farms and killing or seizing cattle, and then returning to their bases on the Rhine. They in turn were unable to break his and his allies' determination to fight on, and eventually Tiberius called a halt to major attacks east of the Rhine. Most of the Roman troops remained in place on the west bank of the river, but their commander, his adopted son Germanicus, was soon sent to Syria and the eastern frontier, the latest in a succession of imperial princes despatched to negotiate with the Parthians.

In spite of the enthusiasm of poets, Augustus did not attempt to conquer the Parthians, and avoided major military confrontation with them. Instead he negotiated, but these talks always occurred alongside a display of Roman might. Armies were massed and marched to the borders of the empire, led by the *princeps* or a member of his family, so that diplomacy rode on the back of the threat of force. The lost eagles were returned and installed in the Temple of Mars Ultor, and a triumphal arch built to celebrate the submission of the Parthians. Augustus presented Parthia – and for that matter India and Britain on the basis of embassies sent to him – as part of Rome's *imperium*.[42]

This pattern of diplomacy backed by the threat of force was repeated under Tiberius and for most of the first century AD, save that after Germanicus such negotiations were usually handled by a legate rather than a member of the imperial family. Only under Nero did these peaceful relations break down, when the Parthian King Vologases I intervened in Armenia and placed his brother on the throne. This led to a war fought by substantial forces on both sides, but the focus remained on Armenia. The Romans did not launch an invasion deep into Parthia's heartland, nor did the Parthians make a serious effort to overrun the Roman provinces. An early Roman advantage was lost, when the legate of Cappadocia was defeated and surrendered, but then regained, allowing them to negotiate from a position of more strength. The result was a compromise, with the newly installed king travelling to Rome to accept his crown from Nero. If this was partly a sham, since the Romans had not chosen the man but been forced to accept him, the willingness to submit to this ceremony was a public demonstration of respect for Rome's supremacy.

Throughout the first century AD the balance of power favoured

Rome. Most Parthian kings were not sufficiently confident in their own position to risk confrontation with their powerful neighbour. A war with Rome was likely to be difficult, and ran the chance of serious defeat which might well destroy a ruler's credibility. Their fears were reinforced by the Roman skill at harbouring and exploiting exiled members of the royal family. There was a consistent desire to retain influence in Armenia, ideally by having a relative as king, but ambition did not stretch much beyond this – or if it did, was restrained by respect for Roman power. During the civil war following the death of Nero, the Parthian monarch did not attempt to exploit Roman weakness, but pledged himself to peace and even offered Vespasian troops to support his bid to become *princeps*. This was declined, but it did make it easier to transfer some of the forces in the eastern provinces further west to fight in the civil war.[43]

Throughout the first century AD the Romans maintained substantial garrisons in the eastern provinces, with legions in Syria, and later Cappadocia as well as Judaea after AD 70. These units and their auxiliaries were not solely concerned with defence and deterrence of the perceived Parthian threat. As we have seen, the Syrian army made a succession of interventions in Judaea, and was also employed to enforce Rome's will with allied kingdoms, annexing several of them. Nero's war against the Parthians was essentially another example of this, fought to keep Armenia as an ally within Rome's sphere of influence. Vologases I's intervention was part of his wider efforts to gain control of several kingdoms in the area. According to Tacitus, Armenia was 'once the property of his ancestors' and now in the hands of a usurper. His actions were not intended to provoke Rome, and at first he was conciliatory, withdrawing his troops and giving hostages – Tacitus hints that this was a way of removing distrusted aristocrats – when threatened with the usual mixture of diplomacy backed by force. Only his unwillingness to see his brother stripped of his crown or installed by the Romans led to a renewal of open warfare, and in the end he compromised on the second point.[44]

The Romans had reasonable knowledge of Parthia, and there were frequent diplomatic exchanges, with Parthian embassies going to the provincial legates and to Rome. Centurions were the usual couriers for Roman letters and were able to negotiate and report back – a sign of the important roles given to this grade of officer. One of them happened to be at Vologases' court on another errand when the king was asked to hand over the hostages and so dealt with this matter as well. There were several moments of tension and posturing by both sides which did not lead to war, but it is hard to see any trace of a deep-seated Roman desire to conquer this rich and powerful neighbour, and instead the Augustan claim to be dominant was preserved. This was reinforced by a gradual increase in the size of the garrison in the east. Roman outposts were established further and further forward, and when Trajan annexed Arabia, it was just the latest allied kingdom to be taken under direct rule.[45]

In the second century AD both powers became more aggressive. Trajan's full-scale invasion marked a fundamental break with the cautious diplomacy of the past. While there may have been some provocation and pretext for this, the sources suggest that his main motivation was a quest for glory. The attempt to conquer failed amid widespread rebellion, and the new provinces were abandoned by Hadrian, although it is clear that Roman-backed allied rulers remained in power over a wide area. A generation later, an ambitious Parthian king began to recover some of this territory, perhaps encouraged by the reluctance of the elderly Antoninus Pius to authorise aggressive military action. In AD 161 the Parthians invaded Syria but after early successes were driven out, and in the Roman counter-offensive their capital of Ctesiphon was sacked for the second time. The Romans established some bases beyond the Euphrates and imposed peace on Parthia, but did not attempt wider annexation.

At the end of the century, Septimius Severus' legions took Ctesiphon again, in a war fought as much for glory and to secure the loyalty of the eastern armies as to deal with any perceived Parthian threat. He added a new province of Mesopotamia, claiming it would be a 'bulwark' for the eastern provinces, but Dio was sceptical of this boast. Two out of three wars were clearly caused by the aggression of Roman emperors, the other by the ambitions of a Parthian monarch – though obviously a ruler who was aware of past attacks by Rome. Between each of these conflicts were some four decades where the relationship returned to the pattern set in the previous century, with a peace that was always wary, sometimes uneasy or tense, but seen as being in the interest of both sides. Roman military superiority continued to grow, but was not so overwhelming that it prompted more frequent conflict, which suggests that the lure of conquest and expansion was not so strong that most emperors were unable to resist its siren call.[46]

Elsewhere, relations between the Roman Empire and its neighbours were complicated by the absence of strong central authority, each province bordering on the lands of many different communities and leaders. An emperor could not hope to keep track of all of these in the way that he could observe events in Parthia and gain a sense of the likely attitude of its king. Legates were better placed, aided by their headquarters staff with its record archive and accumulated experience, although no doubt it took time and diligence to become familiar with the local situation during their tenure. A glimpse of a report intended either for the garrison commander or the provincial legate – or both – may come from one of the Vindolanda tablets, dating to the end of the first century AD. Sadly only a fragment survives, which states that 'the Britons are unprotected by armour. There are very many cavalry. The cavalry do not use swords nor do the *Brittunculi* mount [or stay mounted?] to throw javelins.' The contemptuous diminutive 'little Britons' is not known from other sources, and may or may not reflect a widespread disdain for the locals.[47]

Given the slow pace of communications, emperors could not direct diplomatic and military activity in the provinces on a day-to day basis, so that legates were permitted a good deal of initiative and freedom of action. This was confined by their *mandata* and by the regular exchange of correspondence with the emperor. Often they acted and then sought approval in the knowledge that this was only likely if they had kept to the spirit of their orders. Even so, these men commanded armies numbering anywhere between 10,000 and

40,000 men, forces as big as or bigger than those of most governors under the Republic. A legate had usually served in his late teens or early twenties as the senior tribune in a legion, and then in his thirties commanded a legion. In the case of provinces with only one legion in garrison, this post was combined with that of provincial legate. Bigger provinces would be granted a decade later, to men in their early forties, and the prized and prestigious commands of Britain, Lower Pannonia and Syria, which held the largest armies, tended to go to men who had already governed an ordinary military province. Service on the staff of a relative or friend provided some men with additional experience of government and campaigning. All in all, the legates of the Principate had on average only a little more military experience than the governors of the Republic. They were selected by the emperor, who took account of talent and experience, but was also swayed by an individual's family and connections, and especially his perceived loyalty.[48]

Augustus left much of the army grouped together and ready to carry out major offensive operations if necessary. This was most marked on the Rhine, where even after AD 16 there were several bases where two legions as well as auxiliaries were stationed. Two of the legions in Spain were similarly brigaded together, and it is likely that the practice was also followed elsewhere. Such strong concentrations of troops, very much in the tradition of *hiberna* for an army waiting to resume mobile warfare, became less common by the later first century AD. The last two-legion camp was closed by Domitian, who moved the garrisons to separate locations. In this case his motive was fear after a legate of Upper Germany had used the accumulated savings in such a base to fund a rebellion against him. Although this may have been a factor in the earlier dispersal of these big garrisons, it is more probable that they were moved because the troops were of better use elsewhere.[49]

Major offensive operations, let alone attempts at conquest, had to be ordered by the emperor, who also retained control of the military resources of the empire. Only he could transfer legions, auxiliaries or detachments from one province to another, or authorise the recruitment of regular troops. New legions were usually formed in Italy under direct imperial supervision, while auxiliary units were naturally raised in the provinces. Thus the emperor decided upon the current priorities and shifted men and supplies accordingly. No doubt there was some inertia in the system, units remaining where they were even when the original reason had gone, but the deployment was not rigid. Units were redeployed, and over time the size of the army grew to meet new commitments.

Conquest was rare and always ordered by the *princeps*. Large-scale invasion of the provinces was similarly rare, if only because of the political disunity of neighbouring peoples. Occasionally one leader or tribe grew more powerful, or several banded together to create big armies capable of acting aggressively. Strong leaders like Decebalus had this potential, and if war resulted it was likely to be large-scale, but the unity they created also made it easier to observe and negotiate with them. In the long run they could not match Rome's greater strength and resources any more than the Parthians. Power struggles within and between peoples living outside the empire are almost invisible to us, occurring beyond the range and interest of our literary sources, all written within the empire. Archaeology can detect breaks in settlement pattern or major shifts in material culture, but such changes can be explained in more than one way. Academic fashion has turned against interpretations based on widespread migrations of peoples, who supplanted others and sometimes created a ripple effect that set several tribes on the move. If women are mentioned as accompanying tribal armies, they are dismissed as just the politically significant wives and daughters of kings and chieftains. As so often, the pendulum of opinion has swung too far. It is wrong to think of vast, unending waves of 'barbarians' washing against the frontiers of the empire, fleeing from enemies and desperate for new land. Yet sometimes large numbers of people did move over considerable distances and did seek admission to the empire or attempt to occupy land controlled by the Romans.[50]

Much of the activity on the frontiers was relatively small in scale, and even in the periods when we have detailed narrative sources, these pay less attention to the fringes of the empire than to the politics of Rome and the imperial court. We hear of the occasional major operations and wars, but only rarely of anything else. A memorial inscription recording the career of the senator Tiberius Plautius Silvanus Aelinaus tells us about some of the events during his term as legate of Moesia under Nero:

> ... he brought over more than a hundred thousand of the peoples from across the Danube to pay tribute, along with their wives, children and chieftains or kings; he put down an incipient movement of the Sarmatians, although he had sent a considerable portion of its army to take part in the invasion of Armenia; kings hitherto unknown or hostile to the Roman people he brought over to the river bank under his protection to pay homage to the Roman standards; to the kings of the Bastarnae and Roxolani he returned their sons, to the king of the Dacians his brothers, captured or carried off from the enemy; from them he received hostages, by which achievements he both assured the peaceful conditions of the province and advanced it, having removed the king of the Scyths from his siege of Chersonesus beyond the Dnieper.[51]

Vespasian awarded triumphal honours to Plautius Silvanus for his term in Moesia, praising his conduct. No doubt the text presents his record in the most favourable light, but his activities are interesting. It is unclear whether or not his army actually fought anyone, but they certainly crossed beyond the Danube and the threat of force backed up the intensive diplomatic activity. The balance of power between the peoples and leaders outside the empire was redrawn by his actions, making some of them return hostages they had taken while others gave them to the Romans. Ceremonies where foreign leaders made public acknowledgement of their submission to Rome in front of a governor and his paraded soldiers were a long-established feature of Roman imperialism. The number of tribesmen and their families brought across the river and settled within the province may be exaggerated, although in the circumstances it is at least possible that an accurate count was made.

All in all, most of what this imperial legate did is reminiscent of the actions of Julius Caesar in Gaul – with the difference that the former did not use his interventions as a basis for overrunning and occupying great swathes of new territory. From the latter days of Augustus, the borders of the empire settled down, only shifting occasionally. Such changes are significant and need to be understood, but just as important are the workings of the frontiers in general, where so much of the army was stationed.

GARRISONS AND RAIDS

'Besides these battles, many others less worthy of mention were fought in various parts of Gaul, which it would be superfluous to describe, both because their results led to nothing worthwhile, and because it is not fitting to spin out a history with insignificant details.'
– *Ammianus Marcellinus, late fourth century* AD.[1]

'CLANDESTINE CROSSINGS'

In AD 17 Tacfarinas and his followers began to raid the province of Africa. He was one of the Musulamii, a people living on the fringe of the province in land that today straddles the Algerian and Tunisian border. They were one of several tribes mentioned in our sources, along with broader groups such as Numidians, Moors and Gaetulians, but the impression is that Greek and Roman observers did not understand the relationship between them with any clarity, let alone appreciate their social and political structure. Very little is known about Tacfarinas, save that he had served in the *auxilia* and then deserted. It is possible that, like Arminius, he was from an aristocratic family and led a contingent of his people in Roman service until he became disillusioned and turned against his former allies. He does not appear to have gained citizenship or other honours, which in itself could be a cause of anger. On the other hand he may have served in the ranks and deserted because of some injustice, slight, misdemeanour or a growing resentment of Roman occupation. Whatever his background, Tacfarinas was a formidable soldier and talented leader, and early successes drew more and more men to join him. Tacitus dismisses his first followers as outcasts, and perhaps some of them were, but he admits that

Tacfarinas swiftly became the acknowledged war leader of the entire Musulamii.[2]

Several campaigns had been fought in the area during the reign of Augustus, the most recent concluded in AD 6. Since then the Romans had begun surveying the area and organising it for taxation, marking out regions using boundary stones, and had constructed roads through tribal territory. Perhaps this fuelled resentment, but it was the early phase of conquest when resistance and rebellion were common in many regions. The Romans may also have interfered with or tried to restrict existing patterns of raiding and warfare, for most of the victims of Tacfarinas and his men were locals rather than Roman settlers or other representatives of the imperial power. Plunder and glory drew men to him as much as any cause, and soon he allied with Mazippa, a Moorish leader. Later they were joined by another group, the Cinithii, and Tacitus says that this was through compulsion, giving them the choice of either being subject to raids or taking part in them. Tacfarinas aimed at creating a solid power base, and some of his men were organised into formal units, equipped and trained on the Roman model. These were kept as a reserve in camp while the Moors and others roved in raiding bands spreading 'fire, slaughter and terror'.[3]

Early successes led to over-confidence, and when the Roman governor mustered his army and advanced, Tacfarinas was willing to meet him in open battle. The Roman proconsul – Africa was still a senatorial province at this date – had *Legio III Augusta*, at least two *alae* of cavalry and some cohorts of auxiliary infantry. Numbers heavily favoured his opponents but, as so often in the past, the confidence, discipline and organisation of the well-equipped Romans were decisive. Tacfarinas' army was routed, and the Roman proconsul awarded the insignia of a triumph.

Tacfarinas' prestige had taken a blow, but he and many of his men escaped and were determined to continue the fight. In AD 18 he began to raid again, at first on a small scale, with little bands moving too quickly to be caught. Once again success helped him to draw followers to him. The attacks became larger, and entire villages were overrun and plundered. Encouraged by this, Tacfarinas risked attacking a more dangerous target and blockaded a cohort garrisoning a position near the River Pagyda. The place cannot be identified, and it is not clear whether the 'Roman cohort' was detached from the legion or was an auxiliary unit. Their commander, an experienced officer named Decrius, responded to the threat with the confidence typical of the Roman army, and deployed his men in formation outside the rampart to meet the enemy in the open. His enthusiasm was not shared by his men, who broke and fled when the Numidians charged them. Perhaps Decrius was unpopular or new to the command and a stranger to his men, but they ignored him as he tried to rally them. He was wounded twice, losing an eye, but fought on until he was cut down.

The total Roman losses are unknown, but the new proconsul ordered the survivors of this rout to be decimated. One soldier in ten was chosen by lot and beaten to death by the others, whose wheat ration was replaced with barley – the food of slaves or animals – and who were made to camp apart from the rest of the army until they redeemed themselves. It was an archaic punishment, revived by several commanders including Antony and Augustus during the civil wars, and seen as stern even by Roman standards.* Tacitus claimed that the appalling punishment stiffened the morale of the rest of the army. A little later, the same force that had routed Decrius' men attacked another garrison, this time consisting of some 500 veterans – legionaries who had already served twenty years and remained with the colours for another five years performing lighter duties. Tacitus' account is vague, so it is uncertain whether they came out to fight in the open or defended the encampment, but either way the Numidians were put to flight. During the fighting a legionary named Marcus Helvius Rufus saved the life of another soldier and was decorated, subsequently being awarded the *corona civica*. He may not have been a veteran, so perhaps other soldiers were present.

---

* As an aside, it is worth emphasising that this meant the loss of 10 per cent, not the far greater losses implied by the frequent journalistic misuse of the term.

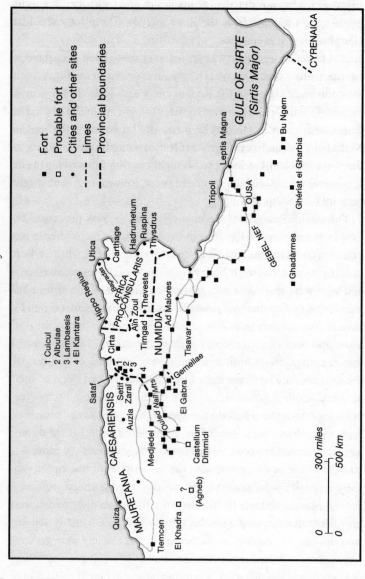

Roman North Africa

1 Cuicul
2 Albulae
3 Lambaesis
4 El Kantara

Legend:
- ■ Fort
- □ Probable fort
- ● Cities and other sites
- -- - Limes
- — — Provincial boundaries

GULF OF SIRTE (Sirtis Major)

CYRENAICA

Labels on map:
Utica, Carthage, Hadrumetum, Ruspina, Thysdrus, Leptis Magna, Bu Ngem, Ghériat el Gharbia, Tripoli, OUSA, GEBEL NEF, Ghadàrmes, AFRICA PROCONSULARIS, Aïn Zoul, Theveste, NUMIDIA, Timgad, Ad Maiores, Tisavar, Gemellae, Hippo Regius, Cirta, Setif, Auzia, Zarai, El Gabra, Ouled Naïl Mts, Medjedel, Castellum Dimmidi, SATAF, CAESARIENSIS, MAURETANIA, Quiza, Tlemcen, El Khadra, (Agneb)?

Scale:
0 — 300 miles
0 — 500 km

Then or later Helvius Rufus was also commissioned as a centurion, and eventually rose to become *primus pilus* and added Civica to his name. An inscription from Tivoli in Italy records his gift of a bath house to the community.[4]

This reverse persuaded Tacfarinas to avoid settlements protected by garrisons. Instead his men struck at the unprotected communities, and avoided any significant force of soldiers. Try as they might, the Romans were far too few to protect every settlement, and had to guess where best to place their garrisons. They chased the raiders, making long marches through difficult country, but were unable to catch them and inflict any serious damage on the fast-moving bands. This went on for several years, and once again success brought the war leader new problems, as he began to attack the more fertile country near the coast. The spoils were considerable, but needed to be gathered, transported and protected. Tacfarinas built a camp as a base for the plundering raids, where the booty was guarded as more was brought in. The Romans learned of this, and a force of auxiliaries backed by some of the fitter legionaries was put under the command of the governor's son and sent against them. They moved quickly and Tacfarinas did not receive sufficient warning to concentrate his men and carry away the plunder in time. The Numidians were badly beaten and scattered, and a second Roman proconsul was awarded the ornaments of a triumph.[5]

Yet once again Tacfarinas recovered and resumed his raiding. Tiberius wrote to the Senate advising them to choose a man of proven military ability as the next proconsul of Africa. It helped that the likely candidate, Quintus Junius Blaesus, was also the uncle of the praetorian prefect Sejanus. The emperor's suggestion was duly enacted by the Senate, and Blaesus given additional resources by the transfer of *Legio IX Hispana* from Pannonia to join the forces in Africa. At this point Tacfarinas attempted to negotiate, sending an embassy threatening 'unending war' unless he and his men were granted land. Tiberius was outraged at this 'arrogance' of a brigand presuming to dictate terms to Rome at the height of its power, and ordered Blaesus to press the war with vigour. Tacfarinas was excluded, but other leaders were offered an amnesty and many chose to surrender.[6]

Blaesus split his army into three mobile columns to advance from different directions and drive raiding bands onto a network of fortified outposts – an early version of the use of blockhouses in the later stages of the Second Anglo-Boer War. Several successes were scored as groups were caught or trapped. The proconsul then split his columns up into even smaller forces commanded by centurions, and continued to hound Tacfarinas and his allies throughout the summer. He kept his weary men in the field well after the end of the normal campaigning season. More fortified outposts were built, and the mobile forces, growing used to operating in desert conditions, kept chasing the enemy. Tacfarinas was pursued from one camp to another. He managed to evade capture, but his brother was taken, and at this point Blaesus called an end to active operations and withdrew the army to winter quarters. Victory was declared, a third Roman commander was awarded the ornaments of a triumph and in this case the additional, rare honour of being hailed as *imperator* by his men. Blaesus was permitted to keep the title, but did not get to celebrate a triumph when he returned home. *Legio IX Hispana* returned to the Danube around the same time.[7]

Tacfarinas claimed that the withdrawal of these troops was a sign that the Roman Empire was collapsing and had already begun to pull out of Africa altogether. For all the locals knew, this might be true, and once again he resumed raiding and every success won him more followers. In Mauretania the old king had died and was succeeded by his young son, who was equally staunch in his alliance with Rome but a good deal less popular. Dislike of the new ruler readily fed hostility to the Romans and enthusiasm for raiding and plunder, giving Tacfarinas new allies. Another who joined him was the king of the Garamantes, who provided warriors and a market for saleable booty. The attacks on the Roman province grew larger, culminating in the blockade of the town of Thubuscum on the frontier with Mauretania. Publius Cornelius Dolabella, the new proconsul and another man with considerable military experience, rushed to its relief and broke the siege. Several chieftains of the Musulamii were executed on suspicion of planning to join the war against Rome. Copying his predecessor, Dolabella split his army into four main columns and numerous roving detachments, bolstering their numbers with allies supplied by the king of Mauretania, men who were used to tracking and fighting in the desert.

In AD 24, the eighth year since he had begun his fight with Rome, Tacfarinas was finally cornered. Dolabella received a report that the war leader was camped at a place called Auzea, in wooded country where he felt himself secure. A special column was put together, carrying only essential equipment and supplies, and force-marched to the place. The Numidians were surprised, caught with their horses tethered or grazing, and were unable to escape or organise a defence. The frustrations of years of chasing such an elusive foe fired the Roman soldiers, who were ordered to take or kill Tacfarinas above all else. His son was captured, his bodyguard cut down, and after a fierce fight the leader was also killed. The defeat and death of this charismatic man finally brought the war to an end, although since victory had already been declared and Blaesus generously honoured, Tiberius refused to grant triumphal ornaments to Dolabella.[8]

GARRISONS, FORTS AND WALLS

The war with Tacfarinas is usually described as a rebellion, since the lands of the Musulamii were already part of the Roman province when it broke out, and it conforms to the common pattern of at least one major revolt within a generation or so of conquest. There is no evidence for a rising on a similar scale in the same area in the centuries to come, much as lowland Britain was peaceful after Boudicca. In the future, the greatest concentration of Roman troops would be in Mauretania Tingitana, after the annexation of the allied kingdom by Caligula. Otherwise, a comparatively small number of units and bases held a much larger geographical area. If there was trouble requiring active operations by the Roman army, then it seems mostly to have been on a small scale. Yet the region was not totally denuded of troops, and not only were bases established, but substantial systems of ditches and ramparts constructed as barriers to the movement of animals as much as people. These helped to channel seasonal movement by the pastoralists who formed the bulk of the population, directing them to areas where they could be monitored and taxed. The focus of the military presence shifted, the frontier advancing, and it was clearly considered worthwhile to have military outposts dotted across a wide area.[9]

The Roman provinces in Africa bordered on land that the empire did not control, large parts of it desert or semi-desert with little or no settled population. This border was long and open, even when the frontier was moved forward, and this meant that conflicts like the revolt of Tacfarinas also had much in common with campaigns fought on the frontiers, drawing in peoples who lived outside the empire. Tacitus describes the war at greater length than many conflicts involving larger armies, using these passages almost as punctuation to his main narrative tracing the increasingly despotic rule of Tiberius. Even though he is often vague on important details, especially of geography, his account still gives us a fascinating picture of a long-running struggle between the Roman army and a determined indigenous people whose principal mode of warfare was the raid. It shows the Romans adapting to the local situation, experimenting with different strategies, sometimes during the same year, and mixing mobile columns with fixed fortifications to put pressure on their opponents.

Such flexibility and the speed with which the local situation could change need to be borne in mind when looking at the Roman army on the frontiers, where so much of the evidence for its deployment comes from archaeology. In many cases this allows us to plot on a map lines of forts, fortresses and smaller installations such as fortlets and towers, but it is incredibly rare for any of these sites to be mentioned in our sources. Inscriptions tell us something about the garrisons of some bases, and excavation provides detail of the development of the sites and glimpses of the lives of the soldiers and civilians who lived in and around them. They tell us far less about what the garrisons were doing and why they were stationed there. It is a sobering thought that Hadrian's Wall is only mentioned some half-dozen times in Greek and Latin literature, even including Bede and others who wrote after the Roman period. The claim that it was built 'to separate the Romans from the barbarians' comes in a very late and often unreliable source, but is the only explicit statement about its purpose.[10]

Today Hadrian's Wall is a World Heritage Site, famous as one of the greatest monuments left by the Romans. Yet not only does it scarcely feature in our literary sources, it was also a highly unusual project, very different from the bulk of the imperial frontiers. Although there were other linear barriers, in the main constructed of earth, turf and timber rather than stone, these were rare and covered only a small proportion of the frontiers. If possible the Romans far preferred to employ the natural barrier of a river, most obviously on the Rhine and Danube, as well as smaller rivers such as the Main, and to some extent the Euphrates. Rivers encourage communication, fostering trade and cultural exchange, so that the peoples living on either side often have much in common, and this had led to an unfortunately persistent myth that rivers do not make good frontiers. In fact they provide clear boundaries and significant obstacles to any movement on a large scale. With few exceptions most army bases were on the Roman bank, and it seems that bridges across the rivers were not part of the system. Trajan's great bridge across the Danube was partly dismantled within decades of its construction even though it connected to the province of Dacia. There were no permanent bridges across the Rhine where it was the frontier after the early first century AD. Yet the rivers themselves were kept under close control, patrolled by flotillas of boats, and the army was fully capable of building a bridge when it needed one. One advantage of stationing garrisons close to a river was that bulky supplies such as grain could travel along it to keep them supplied.[11]

Yet there were not always suitable rivers in a convenient place, and so some frontiers lacked such a clear natural feature. In the later

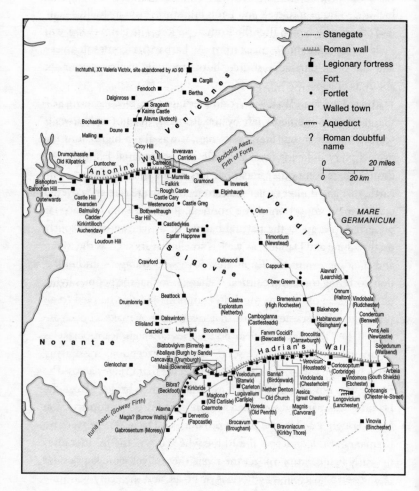

The frontier in Northern Britain and Hadrian's Wall

first and early second centuries AD, the Romans moved the frontier of Upper Germany and Raetia forward, creating a more direct link between the main lines of the Rhine and the Danube. It is improbable that this was simply due to the desire for a shorter frontage, and more likely connected with the need to control the peoples of the area and those living beyond them. In Britain the first organised frontier was in what is now southern Scotland, before this was abandoned and the army moved back to the line of the Stanegate road. Hadrian's Wall was constructed close to this, but almost as soon as it was finished it was decommissioned when a fresh advance was made and the Antonine Wall built on the line between the estuaries of the Rivers Forth and Clyde. This in turn was abandoned and Hadrian's Wall reoccupied, remaining in use until the end of Roman Britain over 200 years later. Apart from a few vague or ambiguous comments, none of our sources explain why these changes occurred, leaving us to look at the installations themselves and try to deduce their purpose.[12]

While emperors allocated resources to each area, and gave orders for any significant advance or withdrawal, the detailed implementation of these instructions was left to provincial governors, who then reported what they had done. Much had to be decided by the man on the spot, for this was a world almost wholly without maps as we would understand them. There were some drawn to scale and close to the modern ideal, such as the famous plan of the City of Rome, but these covered only a few areas. Ptolemy of Alexandria was one of several geographers to produce the data for a world map superimposed with a grid to show the true relationship between the continents, and was on the whole fairly accurate. His work was large-scale and it is hard to know how often such maps were actually made. More common were plans based on written itineraries, which focused on routes, indicating the main roads, the cities and towns on them and distances between them. There was no attempt to show the correct relationship between places and so the countryside in the gaps between towns and cities is shrunk or expanded for convenience. The best surviving example, the Peutinger Table, is compressed to fit the entire empire on one long scroll. Such plans were functional, for they did show the way to get from one place to another, and gave an indication of the distances of each stretch of the journey. They were not intended to guide off-road travel and were useless for this, but then no state official, officer in charge of any significant body of troops, or even an ordinary traveller would choose to avoid going by road on any long journey. They also failed to give reliable indication of the positions of provinces and other territories relative to one another.

The absence of detailed maps is seen by some historians as proof that there was little central strategic planning in the Roman Empire. This is part of a wider trend in scholarship to emphasise the primitiveness of the Romans, a reaction against some older studies – and the deeply entrenched popular view – that stressed the modernity of ancient Rome, seeing Romans in essence as 'just like us'. It is healthy to challenge existing wisdom, and often this is revealing. Studies of the frontiers that look at a modern map, declare lines based on natural features as the 'best' positions and then judge the Romans on how well they conformed to this are rightly dismissed. The Augustan attempt to create a province in Germany reaching to the Elbe was not the result of studying a map and seeing this as a shorter frontier line connecting to the Danube frontier than one based on the Rhine. We simply do not know how much sense Augustus and his advisers had of the geography of the region, especially before Roman armies reached it. Political geography – the divisions into peoples and the followers of particular leaders – was also far more important in Roman thinking than physical geography. It was peoples, rather than the land itself, that submitted to Rome, and it was peoples, whether allies or provincials, who needed to be controlled and defended. Information about them can be as readily expressed in words as in the diagrammatic form of a map or plan.[13]

Yet too much stress on the primitiveness of the Romans is unconvincing. Modern maps are very modern indeed – the Ordnance Survey in the United Kingdom began its major work when Britain was threatened with invasion by Revolutionary and Napoleonic

France, and much of the country was not covered until later in the nineteenth century. Other parts of Europe, let alone the wider world, were not accurately mapped until well into the twentieth century. It is a mistake to take all this for granted, just as it would be to wonder how anyone in the past navigated or made strategic decisions before the advent of GPS and satellite imaging. At a generous estimate, it is only in the last two centuries that statesmen and military leaders have had access to significantly more information about the wider world than was available to Roman emperors. Napoleon and Wellington often had to make do with poor and unreliable maps, so sent officers out to produce more accurate ones, even though this was inevitably a slow process. Armies on campaign need very detailed topographic information, and even now will supplement modern maps with direct observation.

Even if they had possessed the levels of information provided by modern maps, it would have made no sense for emperors to direct the small detail of the army's dispositions and operations on the frontiers, given the slow pace of communications. Provincial governors had a better chance of understanding the local situation, in particular in areas where the military presence was long established. There is clear evidence from several systems of towers built by the army on the frontiers that their positions were carefully surveyed and chosen, with each one placed so that it could be seen by a larger base, permitting signals to pass between them. The tower's field of observation was important, but secondary to this. On the rare occasions when a tower was built on a key point invisible to any larger garrison, a second tower was sited to act as relay station between the two. The Roman army's skill in understanding and working with topography is shown very well in the erection of these lines of towers, something that could only be done by people on the ground. Even the best map is unlikely to show areas prone to flooding or where line of sight is blocked by trees or other vegetation.[14]

Tacitus praised his father-in-law Agricola for his skill in choosing the sites of forts and providing them with well-stocked granaries, so that none of those he established were lost to enemy attack. The compliment was a conventional one, which in itself is an indication of how important an understanding of the ground was for Roman commanders. Defence was one consideration. The fort needed to offer security to its garrison and also allow them to perform the wider function requiring the troops to be there. Although a position on high ground offered advantages, it did not matter if the site chosen was not on the highest elevation. Until the development of effective cannon, being overlooked by hills outside of bowshot was not a significant disadvantage – something too often forgotten by archaeologists, whether discussing Roman military bases or Iron Age hillforts.[15]

Most forts appear designed to accommodate an entire unit, although there are exceptions, where the garrison appears to have consisted of detachments. Some caution is needed. Excavation is time-consuming and costly, and even an auxiliary fort presents a very large site, while legionary fortresses are more than ten times bigger. No legionary base has ever been fully excavated, and only a few forts have been substantially or wholly explored. The Roman army built these bases to a fairly standard pattern, so that many excavation plans represent guesswork, optimistically linking the finds from small sample trenches to form the expected layout of buildings. Understanding the location of forts and other military bases is difficult, since we tend to know very little about the local circumstances. The latter might well have changed over time but, unless such changes prevented the garrison from performing its most important roles, the fort could remain in the same place. The fort at Arbeia (modern South Shields on the Tyne) has been fully excavated and has revealed substantial changes in its design and, presumably, function. At one stage much of the fort was given over to twenty-two granaries, suggesting that it acted as a supply depot for a wide area.[16]

For all the Romans' skill at engineering and understanding of the landscape, there were doubtless plenty of cases where sites were poorly chosen, and sometimes excavation reveals drastic modification. The design of Hadrian's Wall was altered several times. Before it was completed the curtain wall was reduced in width from 10 feet to 5 and a half feet – small sections joined on to milecastles and some foundations had already been laid down to the original plan and can still be seen today. Also early on, the decision was made to place some forts actually on the line of the wall itself, and at Housesteads this meant building on top of a turret. Later, the northern gates of most milecastles were walled up, leaving just a narrow door allowing access to the front of the wall. Ideas changed, bases and fortifications were adapted. Recent excavation of the earliest frontier system in Scotland, and in particular the turrets and outposts on the Gask ridge, suggest that it was occupied for far longer than we assumed, perhaps for almost two decades, and in that time there are signs of rebuilding. The vast majority of Roman army bases have seen limited field work, especially employing modern techniques, and simply plotting them on a map and guessing at their function is unlikely to tell us anything useful.[17]

It is also wrong to think of the garrisons of auxiliary forts, let alone the much larger legionary fortresses, as spending the bulk of their time in residence, peering over the rampart at a hostile environment while nervously awaiting an enemy onslaught. Only in a few areas and for limited periods of time was this ever the case. When the army fought, it tended to do so in the open, confident in its superiority over the enemy – misplaced confidence in the case of Decrius, but usually valid. When campaigns occurred, much or all of the garrison joined other army units to operate in the field. When there was less prospect of major operations, then soldiers were drawn off to patrol, provide escorts, to build and to administrate elsewhere. One of the Vindolanda writing-tablets gives the current strength of *cohors I Tungrorum*, the double-sized or milliary auxiliary cohort which garrisoned the fort from around AD 92–97 and had a nominal strength of just over 800. On 18th May (year unknown) the unit mustered 752 of all ranks, including 6 centurions, but no fewer than 5 centurions and 456 soldiers were currently away from the garrison. The largest detachment consisting of 337 men and (probably) 2 centurions, were not too far away at Coria (modern Corbridge). The

remainder were in smaller groups, some in London, another 46 men
serving in the bodyguard of the provincial legate, so perhaps also
in London or escorting the governor elsewhere in the province. Of
those at Vindolanda, 31 were in the garrison's hospital and unfit for
duty, leaving 265 and a centurion available.[18]

Other surviving strength returns show a similar picture of widely
scattered units. On 31st December early in the second century AD,
the mixed cohort, *cohors I Hispanorum Veterana quingenaria* stationed on the Danube had 546 soldiers on its books, ' . . . including
6 centurions, 4 decurions; 119 cavalry; also including __ *duplicarii*,
3 *sesquiplicarii*, 1 infantry *duplicarius*, __ infantry *sesquiplicarii*', and
gained another fifty, including returning stragglers, in the first weeks
of the new year. Permanent reductions in strength were then recorded, such as men transferred to other units, and fatalities, with a
soldier killed by bandits and one or more drowned. Others remained
on the strength, but were currently detached, for instance collecting
grain and clothing from Gaul, or sent to get horses, and still more
attached to other posts, or serving various officials. One party were
'across the Danube on an expedition', others attached to a force of
scouts led by a centurion, and separate detachments guarding grain
ships, the grain supply, and draft animals, or fetching cattle from the
Haemus Mountains. Unlike the cohort at Vindolanda, most of the
centurions were with the main unit, although three out of four decurions – the commanders of the four *turmae* or troops of horsemen
– were absent.[19]

Legions tended to be based in the same place for long periods,
sometimes for several centuries. Auxiliary units also appear at the
same fort generation after generation, although in this case we
should be more cautious, as inscriptions attesting their presence but
separated by decades need not imply that the unit was based there
all the time. Even when units were in place for a long time, this may
mean no more than that the site acted as their depot. They were
administrative centres, the headquarters building or *principia* in each
base maintaining the unit's records. Legionary fortresses, and to a
lesser extent auxiliary forts, also housed workshops to manufacture

and maintain equipment. Some or all bases may also have played a role in training, for we do not really understand how the army trained recruits and whether this was done at unit level or collectively. Much of the time, perhaps especially in spring and summer, the bulk of a garrison was away from its base. Excavation shows substantial sections of the base of *Legio XX Valeria Victrix* at Deva (modern Chester) in Britain were abandoned in the second century AD, with buildings derelict, demolished or replaced with unusual structures. Some continued military presence is likely at all times, even if this was little more than sufficient manpower to maintain the site, keep the unit's paperwork in order, carry out minor duties, and care for the sick and injured. Presumably there was a point at which a base was fully abandoned and the unit moved elsewhere if there was no prospect of it ever returning and the site no longer performed any useful function.[20]

On the well-studied frontiers, especially in Britain and Germany and increasingly in the Danubian provinces as well, we can locate the legionary fortresses and most auxiliary forts as well as smaller installations such as fortlets and watch-towers. This is not the same thing as knowing where the bulk of their garrisons were and what they were doing. At times substantial detachments or vexillations were in another province, and it was even more common for smaller parties and individuals to be away. Service elsewhere in the same province was even more likely. This does not necessarily mean that a fort was empty save for an administrative rump of personnel. A fort built originally to accommodate a particular auxiliary unit could readily house another of the same or a different type. Legionaries could live in barrack blocks designed for auxiliaries and vice versa, although it would be difficult to station a cavalry unit in a fort without adequate stabling facilities, at least for any long period or over winter. There are plenty of hints of men from different units in or passing through other bases. None of this ought to have surprised us, but the great gaps in our evidence for the Roman army have encouraged scholars to piece each fragment together under the assumption that they were part of a simple neat reality. Instead the picture is of a far more dynamic, ever changing, often confusing situation, much like armies in more recent periods. It is worth noting that detachments rarely consisted of formal sub-units such as centuries or *turmae*, let alone the eight-man *contubernium* who shared a tent on campaign and a pair of rooms in barracks. Instead as many men as were felt necessary were placed under temporary command to fulfil a particular task.

Unit records tracked the movements of each soldier individually. For instance a first-century AD papyrus from Egypt records the detached service of the legionary Titus Flavius Celer: ' . . . left for the granary, 11 February, 80. Returned the same year, (*date lost*). Left with the river patrol (*month lost, 81*). Returned the same year, 24 May. Left (*destination lost*) 3 October, 81. Returned 20 February, 82. Left with grain convoy, 19 June, 83. Returned (*date lost*).'

Men were sent for as individuals by name. For example: 'Aponius Didymianus, decurion, to Iulianus the *curator*, greeting. Please send me quickly Atreides, cavalryman of the *turma* of Antoninus, when you receive the ostrakon from me, since the prefect has sent for him. Farewell.' And: 'Claudius Archibios to Aristoboulos his colleague greeting. I have sent Paprenis of the *turma* of Antoninus and Iulius Antoninus of the *turma* of Tullius to Aphis . . . in place of Aponius Petronianus and Iulius Apollinaris. I pray that you are well.'[21]

It was rare for the entire unit stationed at one base to be there, especially for such large formations as a legion. Smaller sites, such as fortlets and watch-towers, were more likely to have something like the garrison for which they were designed, if only because it was easier to abandon these when they were no longer needed. Yet even with these small installations, there is no need to assume that the men stationed there spent all their time in the tower or behind the ramparts of a fortlet, or even that they were occupied all the year round. As we have seen, systems of towers were common along roads as well as on the frontiers, and there is evidence from Egypt for civilians as well as soldiers manning them. This seems less likely when they formed part of a bigger frontier system, which means that the larger garrisons faced further calls on manpower to station men in these outposts.

The design of Hadrian's Wall shows that at times it was thought useful to concentrate a large number of troops along one fortified zone. It is not known for certain whether the wall itself had a parapet and walkway, allowing men to patrol along it, or whether it was simply a barrier like the stockades in Upper Germany and Raetia. Even when the design was changed and Hadrian's Wall made narrower, it was certainly wide enough to have a walkway, so this seems likely but cannot be proven. For every one of the eighty Roman miles of its length there was a milecastle, able to accommodate at most a few dozen men, and between them three turrets. There were fifteen forts, each designed for a single auxiliary unit, on the wall itself and several more, including Vindolanda, close behind or in front of it. A wide, steep-sided ditch, known today as the Vallum, lay to the south, sealing off a military zone. It looks as if this was not carefully maintained throughout the occupation of the wall, but even today it is a formidable obstacle along much of its length. In front of the wall was a narrower ditch – except in a few places where the rock proved too hard to clear or where nature provided a very steep slope or cliff. Between the ditch and the wall were rows of sharpened stakes, some mounted on beams or concealed in pits – the ancient equivalent of barbed wire.[22]

None of this was intended to be a barrier to the movement of the Roman army. Every milecastle had gates on its north and south sides, allowing passage through the wall, although in some cases these opened out onto slopes impractical for men on foot or horseback, let alone a vehicle. Little was lost when many of them were sealed. More important were the fort gateways, with at least one, and sometimes three, of the four double gateways in each fort lying to the north of the wall. There were also two other main crossing places which may have been partly intended for civilian traffic and which lay beyond the only crossing places of the Vallum. Whenever it wanted to, the army could muster one or more columns and march out beyond Hadrian's Wall. There were also permanent outposts, several of them forts capable of holding an entire auxiliary unit, maintained well in advance of the wall. In most respects these bases appear typical of the forts built elsewhere, with no hint of exceptional defences to suggest that the troops there faced a permanent and serious threat of attack. Diplomatic activity reached even further north. There is evidence for centurions sitting in on tribal councils on other frontiers. The Vindolanda tablets mention a *centurio regionarius* at Carlisle, a type of officer who appears elsewhere in the empire and probably mixed political and military responsibilities. Hoards of recently minted Roman silver coins from far in the north of what is now Scotland look very much like subsidies paid to chieftains to secure alliance.[23]

Negotiation and bribery were backed by the permanent threat and occasional use of major military intervention. The first Roman army to operate in a region may well have had little reliable information about the country or its peoples until it arrived there – just as Julius Caesar was able to discover little about Britain before he launched his first expedition to the island. Much would be discovered during campaigning, and even more if the army settled down in or near the territory. Most of the frontiers of the empire were occupied for a very long time. Some locals welcomed the Romans from the start, while others came to accept their presence as a reality and did their best to come to some mutual accommodation; both types were sources of information. This was reinforced by direct observation, and peaceful exchange and encounters. Quite a few bases and even more towers and fortlets lay near indigenous settlements. One inscription from Africa records the construction of a 'scouting outpost (*burgus speculatorius*)' which provided 'new protection for the safety of travellers', a rare case where a site was named for its function. Roman frontiers were not an 'Iron Curtain' intended to keep the two sides apart, so much as networks of bases, garrisons, mobile troops and individual officers and men designed to observe, control and dominate an area. The function was the same, whether the main line lay on a river or some artificial boundary.[24]

THE ANATOMY OF A RAID

Raiding was the most common form of warfare in the ancient world, and even some large-scale invasions were raids on a grand scale, where permanent conquest and occupation was not the aim and instead the attackers wanted to plunder or take captives. Prestige was also important, for if an army was able to march up and down at will in enemy territory it showed that the attacker was strong and the defender weak. Some would choose to fight a battle to avoid this humiliation, which was often precisely what a stronger attacker wanted them to do. Defeat in battle or the devastation of territory persuaded some peoples to seek peace, offering the attacker hostages, wealth and other prizes to obtain it. Even if this did not occur, and they waited for the invader to withdraw, their perceived weakness invited more attacks from the same enemy and from others. There were also consequences for domestic politics and power. A leader who failed to protect the community from being plundered lost reputation and became more vulnerable to challenges. The *Táin Bó Cuailnge*, an Irish epic written down by monks in the early medieval period, but with echoes of an earlier Iron Age world of old gods, heroes in chariots and head-hunting, includes this tactless conversation between a king and his queen:

'It struck me,' Ailill said, 'how much better off you are today than the day I married you.'

'I was well enough off without you,' Medb said.

'Then your wealth was something I didn't know or hear much about,' Ailill said.

'Except for your woman's things, and the neighbouring enemies making off with loot and plunder.'

After this the couple compare their possessions, and Queen Medb discovers that her husband is wealthier, but only because he owns a finer bull. She promptly musters an army and invades the neighbouring kingdom of Ulster to take the even better animal owned by its ruler. The poem, whose title translates as *The Cattle Raid of Cooley*, is at the heart of the Ulster Cycle and tells the story of this invasion motivated by plunder – here a very specific theft. In this respect it is not too different from the story of Troy, where the great war is prompted by wife-stealing. In the *Odyssey*, when the hero Odysseus visits the Underworld and is surprised to encounter the spirit of King Agamemnon, he asks, 'Most glorious son of Atreus, king of men, Agamemnon, what fate of pitiless death overcame you? Did Poseidon overcome you on board your ships, when he had roused a furious blast of cruel winds? Or did hostile men do you harm on land, while you were cutting off their cattle and fine flocks of sheep, or were fighting to win their city and their women?' A willingness to attack and plunder is taken for granted, which surely explains the 'hostile' reception.[25]

Many wars in the Greek and Roman world focused on plundering attacks, which might sometimes provoke a battle. Many Roman operations, for instance Germanicus' campaigns beyond the Rhine from AD 14 to AD 16, were raids on a vast scale. This makes it unfortunate that scholars tend to see major wars and raiding as clearly distinct and unrelated to each other. Often dubbed 'High Intensity' and 'Low Intensity' warfare, the former is the only one seen as important and of concern to emperors. It was also rare for much of the first and second centuries AD on most frontiers. One study of the Rhine frontier in this and later periods denies any large-scale threat, while repeatedly admitting that raids into the empire were common by comparison. These are dismissed as not a threat, which then leads to the claim that emperors created an artificial image of powerful and aggressive tribes beyond the frontier to serve their own needs to win military victories.[26]

It is true that a raid by a few dozen men – or a few hundred or even a few thousand – would not bring down the empire. It is equally true that the disposition of forts and fortifications in frontier areas were not on their own well designed to stop major invasions. Garrisons spread out along the whole line of a frontier would have permitted a strong enemy to concentrate overwhelming force at a single point and break through. Yet this ignores all the evidence for the mobility of garrisons. Frontier lines were not intended to stop major attacks, which would be met by a field force mustered from the troops in the area and any available reinforcements. Given the diplomatic activity and scouting beyond the frontier, in most circumstances it was expected that there would be sufficient warning to gather enough strength to meet and defeat the enemy in the open, perhaps even in advance of the frontier. Nor was raiding a matter of no concern; an indication of this is the common practice of scattering small detachments of troops in towers and fortlets – something that would have made it more difficult to gather a strong force for a large-scale campaign. Several inscriptions from the Danube record how the Emperor Commodus 'fortified the whole river bank with fortified posts [*burgis*] constructed from the ground, and also with garrisons [*praesidiis*] stationed at advantageous places against the clandestine crossings of robbers'.[27]

These robbers (*latrunculi*) came from the lands outside the empire across the river. Dismissing them as bandits and criminals rather than formal enemies helped to vilify them, although no doubt their likely victims did not need any encouragement in this respect. It also preserved the legal distinction between proper enemies in a formally declared war and those whose use of violence was irregular. That an emperor wanted it known that he had taken extensive measures to deal with such bands makes it very clear that the authorities did not ignore low-level raiding. The Roman army dealt with hostile raids and sometimes launched raids of its own, but rarely have scholars given any thought as to the nature of such plundering attacks. Although no single incident is recorded in great detail, it is possible to piece together a composite picture of the factors involved and how both sides acted, and much of this applies equally to bandits within the empire as well as ones coming from beyond the frontiers.

A good deal depended on the purpose of an attack. The most common motive was plunder. Cattle, sheep and other livestock could be consumed or taken home to augment the attackers' own herds or traded for profit. Some communities relied for their survival on supplementing what they could produce with food stolen from others. Tacitus noted that the Germans took great pride in their cattle, which meant that gaining more would be attractive as well as a blow to the prestige of the victim. Another form of livestock was human captives, especially ones suitable to be kept or sold as slaves. Then there were objects of value, ranging from money, jewellery and statues or vessels made of precious metals to clothing, material, tools, especially metal ones, and other practical items. Such things were useful and had the added prestige of having been won by strength. Another motive was to kill or capture people as proof of courage, perhaps confirming warrior status. Head-hunting was common in many Iron Age societies. The desire to kill was not incompatible with a desire to rob, but the dominant motive would influence the conduct of a raid. Alternatively, both might be secondary if the raid was first and foremost about making war on an enemy, whether that was Rome or its provincial and allied communities. In this case the objective was to inflict injury and humiliation on the target, with plunder a means to this end and to feed the attacking band.[28]

The leader planning to raid needed to recruit followers. A chieftain's household warriors were obliged to accompany him, and indeed expected the rewards brought through war. Depending on his importance, this meant a force of a few dozen up to 200 or 300. Other men from the tribe might be persuaded to join, depending on their attitude and obligations to the chieftain as well as an assessment of the chances of success. Accomplished raiders with a past record of winning plunder and glory were better placed to attract other warriors. Another option was alliance with other leaders who brought their own household warriors and anyone else willing to join. Warriors joining the *comites* of the aristocrats were likely to be less well equipped, probably on foot rather than horseback – except among nomadic or pastoral peoples like the Sarmatians and Numidians. Warfare was not the main occupation for these men, who were mainly farmers or herdsmen, which meant that they were only available for short periods and at certain times of year. Finally there

Above left **Augustus:** Augustus was the first emperor, or *princeps,* and the last and greatest conqueror in Rome's history. Apart from a few later additions, such as Britain and Dacia, the basic shape of the empire formed under his rule. Much of his reign was spent touring the provinces.

Above right **Trajan:** Trajan came to power with modest military experience, and this may well have encouraged him to expand the empire. In two wars, he conquered Dacia and turned it into a province. Later, he embarked on a major campaign against the Parthians, but most of the gains were lost in a spate of rebellions or abandoned by his successor, Hadrian.

Septimius Severus: Septimius Severus fought his way to the throne in a civil war with rival provincial governors from Britain and Syria. It was no coincidence that he subsequently launched attacks on Parthia and the Caledonian tribes of Northern Britain. While these may have been necessary to reassert Roman dominance on the frontiers, they were also a means of confirming the loyalty of the legions in each region.

South Shields reconstructed fort gateway: This reconstructed gateway at the Roman fort of South Shields near the mouth of the River Tyne was built in the late twentieth century. It is probable that it should be a storey higher. Roman gateways were intended to look impressive, but once again the towers barely project in front of the curtain wall.

Saalburg reconstructed fort: In the nineteenth century, the German Kaiser encouraged the grand reconstruction of much of a Roman auxiliary fort at the Saalburg. While archaeologists today would change some aspects of this, it gives a good impression of the sheer scale and grandeur of one of these army bases. Legionary fortresses were more than ten times bigger.

Cologne cavalry tombstone: The tombstone of Titus Flavius Bassus from Cologne shows the auxiliary cavalryman trampling an unarmoured and semi-naked barbarian. At least half of the Roman army consisted of non-citizens or auxiliaries who received Roman citizenship at the end of their twenty-five years of service. Bassus died at the age of forty-six, soon after being granted this honour and probably before he was formally discharged from the army.

Trajan's Column, rampart and severed heads: This scene from Trajan's Column shows a row of severed heads – some already decomposed – mounted on spears along the rampart of a Dacian fortress. Archaeology has shown that similar trophies were sometimes raised on the walls of Roman auxiliary forts. The security of frontiers relied on shows of force intended to intimidate potential enemies.

Hadrian's Wall milecastle: Hadrian's Wall is the largest monument left by the Roman army. Eighty Roman miles long, stretching from the Tyne to the Solway, there was a small outpost or milecastle like this one at intervals of close to a mile. This is milecastle 39, with the lake of Crag Lough in the background.

Hadrian's Wall milecastle gateway: Hadrian's Wall was subject to numerous changes of design. Here at milecastle 37, the gateway opened out on to a cliff. Although at first given proper gates in this arch, this was later sealed up, apart from a narrow door allowing access to the outside, probably to permit maintenance of the wall.

Trajan's Column, watchtowers: Most Roman frontiers did not have a continuous wall or rampart like Hadrian's Wall. Wherever possible frontier lines were placed on a major river, the bank lined with forts and smaller watchtowers and outposts in between. This scene from Trajan's Column shows a watchtower on the Danube. Beside it are what looks like piled hay or timber, probably a warning beacon.

Adamklissi metope of family in cart: At times large groups of people journeyed looking for new land, while seasonal movement of pastoralists and nomads occurred in other areas. Roman frontiers and tower systems helped to ensure that such movement was controlled and regulated by the empire. This metope from the Roman monument at Adamklissi in Romania shows a barbarian family travelling in a wagon.

Adamklissi metope of battle around cart: Successful raiders acquired plunder and needed to transport this home. Inevitably this slowed them down. Time and again, the Romans only intercepted raiding bands while they were plundering or as they withdrew, burdened with loot and captives. This metope from Adamklissi shows a Roman legionary fighting a warrior beside a cart carrying a woman and child.

Adamklissi metope of woman and child as captives: Several sculptures from Adamklissi show captives taken by the Romans, in this case including a woman holding a baby. Captives had considerable value as slaves, and some raiding outside and across the frontiers was fuelled by the profits from selling prisoners.

Caerwent third-century walls: In the third century AD, the *Pax Romana* was undermined by frequent civil wars and problems on the frontiers as garrisons were stripped of men to go off and fight in the power struggles within the empire. Many cities acquired walls for the first time or strengthened existing defences. The third- century walls at Caerwent have projecting towers, allowing men in them to shoot missiles into the flank of anyone attacking the curtain walls.

were cattle-rustlers, horse-thieves and bandits, for whom raiding was their main occupation. Some were on the fringes of the community, others preyed on its enemies. Such men might join in a larger raid, but also operated on their own, usually in small groups – larger bands either became chieftains and their followers or were hunted down by established chieftains as threats to the communities they ruled.[29]

One thing all types of potential raider had in common was a desire to stay alive. If there were ever bands for whom casualties were less important than killing the enemy, then they were exceptionally rare. Even when a raid was a means of waging war, it was not expected to win that war on its own, but help to wear the enemy down. The full-time warriors in an aristocrat's household were drawn from a small pool within the tribes, and such skilled men were hard to replace. Other men who volunteered for a raid did so for adventure, glory or profit and quite naturally wished to survive to enjoy these things, while full-time bandits acted for profit rather than in the hope of finding an heroic death. Raiders were highly motivated, since most had chosen to take part in the expedition, and many were skilful and ferocious fighters, but they were reluctant to take heavy casualties. In later eras much the same could be said of the Vikings or Apaches. The aim was to take the enemy by surprise, striking with overwhelming force, looting what they wanted and then escaping. It was never the intention to let the enemy gather in sufficient force and risk a battle on anything like even terms, for a costly victory – let alone a defeat – could cripple a band and discredit a leader.

Surprise was vital, which meant that time was always the key factor. Successful raiders needed to strike and escape before the defenders could gather in sufficient force to deal with them – something especially dangerous when the area was garrisoned by the Roman army. Once it was decided to mount an expedition, the first important decision was the choice of targets. If the raiders wanted livestock then they needed to know where these were likely to be, something often dependent on the season. Over winter, animals tended to be gathered in one small place rather than wandering to graze. They were likely to be at their fittest when brought down from summer pastures at the start of autumn, before they became thinner on winter feed. If the raiders wanted slaves then they needed to know where houses, farms, villages – and towns for very large raids – were located. The same was true if they wanted to steal things of value, adding temples and shrines to the list, although sometimes there might be a taboo against touching sacred sites.

Everything said about the Romans' lack of maps and precise geographical knowledge applies equally to peoples outside the empire. Fiction and cinema have fed a false image of raiders relying on chance, attacking whatever they happened to find – the Viking long ships gliding out of the mist, the Comanches appearing from nowhere out of the desert. The truth is very different. Raiders carried only enough food for a short time, and wandering around hoping to spot likely targets and then attack them was bound to take too long. More importantly, it increased the chance that they would be discovered and so gave the defenders the opportunity to hide, flee to fortified places of safety, and gather in strength to deal with the raiders. Unless the defenders were considered so weak that they were incapable of posing any threat, the raiders needed to have a good idea of where they were going and how to get there before they attacked, especially if they were coming by sea.

Settlements which had been raided in the past were known about, but over time these would be abandoned, yield less and less plunder or be fortified and become harder to take. In the fourth century AD we read of a Roman commander sending a tribune fluent in the native languages on a diplomatic mission to the tribes, but secretly tasked with discovering their intentions and also spying out the land. On another occasion the same general ordered some officers to capture one of the Alamanni and force the man to guide a Roman column raiding the tribal lands. This was a common method, but relied on finding someone willing and able to co-operate. Hannibal's army was once led astray by confusion over the pronunciation of a place name. In 53 BC a band of Germanic warriors responded to Julius Caesar's announcement that anyone who wished might plunder the territory of the Eburones. Two thousand of them crossed the Rhine and caught large numbers of Gauls fleeing from other attacks. Taking many cattle and captives, the Germans were quite content to act as freelance allies of the Romans in this way, until:

One of their prisoners said: 'Why do you pursue this miserable and slender booty, when you now have the chance of the utmost fortune? In three hours you may come to Atuatuca; in that spot the Roman army has concentrated all its stores; the garrison is so small that it cannot even man the walls, and no one dares step outside the entrenchments.' With this hope offered them, the Germans left in a secret place the plunder they had got and made for Atuatuca, using as guide the very man by whose information they had learnt the news.[30]

In this case the information was not entirely accurate. Although the Germans surprised the Romans and managed to cut up a detachment out foraging, as well as merchants plying their wares outside the rampart, the camp itself was too strongly defended for them to take. Abandoning the attack, they retrieved the plunder and captives they had already taken and retired across the Rhine to their homeland.

Caesar employed Roman merchants operating among the tribes as sources of information, and in the same way traders from outside the empire who worked in the provinces were a valuable source for tribal leaders. Tacitus notes that of all the Germanic tribes, the Hermunduri were uniquely 'loyal to Rome, and with them alone of Germans business is transacted not only on the riverbank, but far within the frontier in the most thriving colony of the province of Raetia [Augusta Vindelicum, modern Augsburg]. They cross the river everywhere without supervision.' In contrast other Germanic peoples were only permitted to cross at set places and use specific, closely monitored markets, making it harder for them to learn about the layout of the wider province. In the second century AD one tribe seen as more reliable was still banned from trading outside designated markets, because the Romans were afraid that others, similar in appearance but from hostile peoples, might infiltrate with them.[31]

Although difficult to date with any precision, several passages in

the Talmud clearly assume that raiding was a common risk, especially
to communities in Idumaea, bordering the Nabataean kingdom. For
instance, 'It is ordained that if gentiles come on the Sabbath upon
villages that are close to the border, the inhabitants issue forth fully
armed to meet them and return fully armed. [This law applies] even
in the case that they come only to loot straw and wood. If they fall
upon villages further in the interior, one may draw out armed only if
they attack with the intent to kill.' Other provisions concern watch-
towers and watchmen, who looked out for natural disasters such
as storms, but also wild animals and raiders. Jewish law required
slaves to convert to their master's faith, but 'if somebody bought a
slave from a gentile and he does not agree to circumcision, the new
master may attend to his persuasion for 12 months and if he remain
adamant he should be sold to a non-Jew. Rabbi Simon ben Elezar
said . . . in a town on the border he [the slave] should not be kept at
all, since he could pass on to his kinsmen matter he had heard.'[32]

Runaway slaves and army deserters carried information with
them which was very useful to potential attackers – one reason why
peace treaties at the end of wars often stipulated that these people
be returned along with captives taken by force. As with intelligence
gathered by the Romans, not everything told by traders, runaways
or spies was accurate. Several Germanic tribes came to believe that
Claudius had bound his provincial legates by strict instructions not
to cross the Rhine or mount any aggressive operations. As a result
they began to settle on land that was east of the river but previously
kept clear by the Roman army, and were forcibly evicted. In the
fourth century AD a major raid was prompted by the tales told by
auxiliaries recruited from beyond the frontier who had gone back
on leave. They repeated a rumour that the bulk of the Roman army
was about to march away to the east. Presented with such an opportunity, the tribes attacked, only to discover that it was wrong. In
AD 68 the Sarmatian Rhoxolani defeated two auxiliary cohorts. This
victory, and the realisation that much of the provincial army had
gone to fight in Rome's civil war, encouraged them to raid across the
Danube into Moesia. In this case their information was correct, but

the chance arrival of a Roman force coming from Syria, marching through the region on its way to take part in the struggle for the throne, led to their defeat.[33]

Once raiders had decided upon their targets, they needed to reach them quickly. If there was a river or sea in the way it had to be crossed, and the boats or rafts employed hidden and protected for use on the return trip. Maritime raiders tended to be reluctant to stray too far from their boats in case these were destroyed or the route back to them cut. Roman fortlets on the coast often overlooked landing places. The garrisons were too small to stop a major force from getting ashore, but were well placed to threaten the men left to guard the boats. Man-made boundaries like Hadrian's Wall or the German *limes* presented a different problem. Crossing these was possible for men on foot, especially with the aid of rope or ladders, but it would take time, particularly when it involved getting through obstacles like the stakes and other defences in front of Hadrian's Wall. It was much harder to get horses or other mounts across them without seizing control of a gateway, and these were guarded. The garrisons of towers, milecastles or other fortlets were small, so a strong band was likely to be able to overpower them. Yet this inevitably took time, risked casualties, and meant that an alarm might be raised. Frontier areas without rivers or other barriers were easier to cross. Towers, fortlets and patrolling garrisons increased the chance of detection, and careful use of ground or the cover of darkness was essential to avoid being seen.

None of the Roman frontiers were able to prevent every determined attacker from passing through them. They stopped some, and made it difficult for the rest while increasing the chance of spotting them and raising the alarm. In our sources, raiding bands were intercepted while they were plundering or as they returned home, but almost never on their way into a province. Attackers were able to choose when and where they crossed, while the Roman troops were spread widely, covering every possible approach. Thus even when bands did raid into the province, most of the garrisons of towers and fortlets would have been in the wrong place, watching and waiting for something that did not happen in their area. Overall numbers mattered far less in such circumstances than the forces able to react to an incursion. The quicker the alarm was raised, the better chance the defenders had to respond.

Advancing armies routinely burned settlements as they passed. Caesar once achieved surprise by not doing this, catching many of the tribe he was attacking while they were working the fields – they had not had warning to flee to fortified places. Larger raiding bands often acted in a similarly destructive way, aware that their sheer numbers made them visible so stealth was impractical. They also moved more slowly than smaller forces and, if composed of numerous disparate groups and individuals, were harder for their leaders to control. The alarm could be raised by the civilian communities as they approached. Cicero mentions the guards and watchmen at a temple in Sicily raising the townsfolk with their shouts when robbers attacked the precinct – in this case sent by Verres. In another incident at a different town, temple guards sounded a cow-horn to raise their neighbours, who grabbed arms and gathered to resist the attack. The Talmud mentions a villager put on guard and instructed to blow on a ram's horn trumpet to raise the alarm. There were also guard dogs, and the rabbis decreed that 'none shall raise a dog, unless he is kept on a chain except in a town adjoining the frontier, in which he is permitted to keep the dog unchained, but only at night time'.[34]

Watch-towers – whether in a village, as part of a grand villa, along a road or part of a system of military outposts – were all defensive in the sense that they offered an elevated platform from which to observe and spot potential attackers. Some towers built by the army were clearly intended to signal, with a beacon or raised flag to warn of danger or in some cases a semaphore system allowing a more detailed message. Even a simple alarm alerted anyone able to see the sign, whether civilians or the largest garrison post nearby. The most detailed means of passing on information was in a written message carried by a despatch rider. The presence of horses at fortlets is highly likely, and it may also have been common to have a cavalryman and his mount at some towers. Otherwise, this would mean the main garrison sending a rider to find out what the tower's men had seen and then riding back with the information. This is possible, given that, except at times of highest emergency, a garrison would take time to prepare a patrol or relief force to deal with the incursion. Response times were more likely to be measured in hours than minutes.

Part of a report of this nature survives from one of the outposts watching the routes down to Egypt's ports on the Red Sea. What we have is a copy, written on the fairly flat side of a used amphora. Such pieces of pottery or *ostraka* were a common and cheap alternative to papyrus, but in this case part of the amphora has broken off, taking with it a section of the text. The real report was no doubt written on more easily portable papyrus or a wooden writing tablet. It was written and sent by Antonius Celer, a cavalryman from the century of Proculus in *cohors II Ituraeorum equitata*, to Cassius Victor, centurion in the same auxiliary cohort, and describes an attack by 'sixty barbarians' on the outpost/way station at Patkoua. Its location is unknown, but it was one of a series of small outposts along the road, all of them provided with wells and protected by a square of high stone walls. Celer does not appear to have held any formal rank, and was an ordinary soldier appointed as acting commander of a garrison consisting of a dozen or so men. Civilian travellers sheltering in and around the fort were also involved, and were probably the main target of the attackers. A woman and two children were abducted, and one of the latter or another child was later found dead. The 'attack began at the tenth hour of the day and went on until the second hour of the night, and again around dawn the next day. Hermogenes, an infantryman of the century of Serenus, was killed.' At least two other soldiers were wounded, including 'Damanais, cavalryman from the century of Victor & Valerius Firm . . . and his horse . . . of the century of Proculus'. The report was sent along the road to the main garrison at the port of Myos Homos, and then circulated to all the outposts, commanded by prefects, centurions, decurions, *duplicarii*, *sesquiplicarii* and post commanders (presumably, like Celer without other formal rank).[35]

Other documents record the theft of animals from a quarry site run by the army in the Egyptian desert, while there are mentions in *ostraka* from North Africa of the sighting of groups of nomads. Information was recorded and circulated. In the case of the attack on Patkoua, all military stations in the area were warned of the presence of the 'barbarian' raiders. They were placed on their guard, able to warn travellers of the danger, while the larger garrisons prepared to chase the raiders. Forewarned, civilians hid or gathered together for mutual protection, ideally in buildings. Even a simple Iron Age farmstead with houses surrounded by animal pens gave its occupants a better chance than if they were caught in the open. Seeing them warned and ready, a handful of raiders might well decide to look elsewhere rather than take the risk of fighting. Surrounding ditches and animal pens made it much harder to take livestock or captives by stealth. The sturdily built house and work-buildings of a villa, defended by owners, families, workers and slaves armed with whatever was available, were capable of strong resistance, something shown well in the passage from Apuleius where the travellers were mistaken for bandits and set upon by dogs and bombarded by missiles. Sturdy doors and locks presented barriers to small groups of attackers even if they would not normally be considered as 'military' defences. Such things could be overcome, but risked casualties and delay. Large raiding bands were unlikely to be deterred, knowing that the bigger villas also yielded plenty worth stealing. Excavations at a villa site near Regensburg-Harting in the Rhineland showed that it was sacked in the early third century AD, and thirteen skeletons were dumped down a well. Several were dismembered and partly scalped – one of the rare instances of scalping in the European Iron Age.[36]

If it came to a fight then the raiders were likely to win, for they were more skilled in the use of violence and better equipped than most civilians. Small detachments of soldiers were also vulnerable, if able to put up much more of a struggle. The handful of men stationed in a watch-tower were incapable of prolonged resistance against a serious attack. Their protection relied on the reluctance of raiders to take the time and suffer the losses involved in killing them, balanced against the minimal plunder to be gained, apart from the soldiers' weapons. The fortlet at Patkoua held out against a long, if probably sporadic attack, even though its garrison was small.

Once the fighting was over, plundering the victims took time. When Caesar wanted to punish the Eburones in 53 BC, he was reluctant to give the task to his legions. The tribesmen lived in scattered houses and farms, hard to find for anyone who did not know the area well. 'These localities were known to the dwellers round about, and thus the matter required great care, not for protection of the army as a whole . . . but for the preservation of individual soldiers . . . For the passion for plunder was apt to draw many men too far afield.' Reluctant to risk his own men, Caesar 'sent messengers round to the neighbouring states and invited them all, in the hope of booty, to join him in pillaging the Eburones, so that he might hazard the lives of the Gauls among the woods rather than the soldiers of the legions'.[37]

Cattle, sheep or other livestock had to be gathered and then watched to prevent them from straying. Human captives had to be restrained and prevented from escaping. Hunting out hidden valuables required time and ingenuity. A few of the coin hoards found in the modern era were buried as offerings, but the majority were surely put in the ground to keep them safe by owners who never returned to retrieve them. The mutilation of the inhabitants of the villa at Regensburg-Harting may have been savagery for its own sake or torture intended to force them to reveal secrets. Warfare in the ancient world was extremely brutal, and war captives were routinely subjected to violence or murder and women to rape, with almost their only protection being their value for ransom or sale as slaves.

Although this was little consolation to the victims, raiders busy looting and celebrating were highly vulnerable. As Caesar noted, the search for plunder made men scatter – whether in broken country or the alleys of a town or village – and caused them to be careless and off their guard. In Britain two auxiliary cohorts were ambushed and wiped out by the Silures, who used the prospect of plunder to lure them into an ambush. Under Claudius 'a panic was caused to Upper Germany by an incursion of Chattan marauders. Thereupon, the legate Publius Pomponius sent the auxiliary Vagiones and Nemetes, supported by a cavalry *ala*, with instructions to head off the raiders, or, if they scattered, to envelop and surprise them.' The Roman troops 'separated into two columns; one of which, marching to the left, entrapped a newly-returned detachment of pillagers, who, after employing their booty in a debauch, were sleeping off the effects'.

In AD 366 Roman scouts located a band of Germanic raiders resting after plundering several villas. The Romans approached with care, sheltered from view by woodland and achieved complete surprise. Some of the warriors were drinking, some bathing, and others dyeing their hair red.[38]

Raiders inevitably returned home far more slowly than they attacked. Livestock had to be driven, human captives – some of them young or old, others unused to long journeys – had to be forced to keep going and kept under close guard. In the fourth century AD there is a grim account of the Persians hamstringing and abandoning captives too old or frail to keep up as their army returned from raiding the Roman provinces. Loot needed to be transported, and often it was heavy or bulky, which meant that it had to be carried by human porters, pack animals, or in carts. In recent years carts stuffed with plunder have been found where they sank into the mud of the River Rhine as Germanic raiders tried to get them home. The greater the success of a raid, the slower the band travelled. Wheeled transport restricted them to good going and often to known roads or tracks, making their route predictable. Carts, herds and captives also meant that rivers had to be crossed by bridge, at a good ford, or by the use of a lot of boats and rafts. Linear barriers – whether a ditch, stockade, curtain wall or a combination of these things – were far more formidable obstacles to an encumbered band of warriors trying to escape from the empire.[39]

Tacfarinas was caught by a Roman flying column when he built a camp to protect the plunder he had gathered. In the raid launched by the Chatti into Upper Germany, the second Roman force:

. . . who had taken the shorter route by the right, inflicted graver loss on the enemy, who met them and risked a set engagement. Laden with their spoils and honours, they returned to the heights of Taunus, where Pomponius was waiting with the legions, in the hopes that the Chatti, anxious for revenge, would afford him an opportunity for battle. They, however, afraid of being caught between the Romans on one side and their eternal enemies, the Cherusci, on the other, sent deputations to Rome with hostages, and *ornamenta triumphalia* were voted to Pomponius.[40]

Unless raiders did not go far into a province before retreating, then under normal circumstances it was very likely that they would be intercepted by elements of the Roman army. An altar from Hadrian's Wall was set up by 'Quintus Calpurnius Concessinius, prefect of cavalry, after slaughtering a band of Corionototae, fulfilled his vow to the god of the most efficacious power.' The Corionototae are otherwise unrecorded, and may well have been a small people, but the inscription, like the Patkoua *ostrakon*, offers a glimpse of small-scale skirmishing on the frontiers that was unlikely ever to be mentioned by our literary sources.[41]

FEAR, REPUTATION AND DOMINANCE

The establishment of systems of towers and fortlets became more common from the late first century AD, and was subsequently complemented in some places by linear barriers. All of this implies considerable dispersal of the units garrisoning the bigger forts. The bulk of the Roman army was deployed in frontier areas – or in mountainous or other difficult country inside the provinces – and significant numbers of soldiers were spread out in penny packets. Movement through these frontier areas and controlled zones like the roads to the Red Sea ports was restricted and regulated by the Roman army, which was also responsible for collecting tolls, taxes and other levies on the peoples on these routes. This financial role was important, but it cannot in itself justify the sheer scale of the military presence and the structures and bases built to assist it in its task. Controlling movement also made it harder for potential raiders to gain useful information about the provinces. None of the frontier systems were capable of stopping all attackers from crossing them, but no defensive system in history has been impregnable to all types of assault. The Roman frontier defences were worthwhile because they made it difficult for attackers to pass through, slowing them down and increasing the chances of detecting them, and then made it even more difficult for the band to escape.

Once the band was spotted, the army was in a position to keep it under observation while a force was gathered to meet and defeat it in the open. It was impossible to defend everywhere – something shown in the campaigns against Tacfarinas – and the great strength of the Roman army was its skill in battle. As with the early stages of a rebellion, there was a precarious balance between waiting to muster sufficient troops to be confident of victory and acting fast enough to catch the raiders. Yet a raid was only a success if the attackers managed to reach their homeland with their plunder and boast of their achievements. In this context it did not matter whether the raiders were caught and defeated on their way into a province or on their way out. The latter was always far more likely, as gathering plunder made the raiders slower and far easier to locate. If the province was well garrisoned, then the longer a band stayed, the more the odds inevitably shifted in the Romans' favour.

The same familiar pattern of raiding is visible throughout our entire period, and appears typical of the ancient world as a whole. If a neighbour appeared weak then plundering attacks were likely, each success encouraging the raids to grow more frequent and larger in scale. In contrast, every band that failed to break through, and still more each one intercepted and badly mauled or destroyed, deterred future attacks. There was no simple divide between full-scale war and minor raiding and skirmishing, for one led naturally to the other. The physical presence of the army and its forts, towers, and even more the long linear barriers was in itself a deterrent, much like the depopulated strips of lands around the territory of a Germanic tribe. Something like Hadrian's Wall was a very visible presence, running across the landscape. On some frontiers the army maintained a strip of depopulated land stretching for some distance – five and ten miles are both mentioned in treaties – employing a symbol of strength understood by the tribes.[42]

It was never a question solely of static defence and keeping enemies out of the settled provinces. Apart from the diplomatic activity beyond the frontiers, the army operated aggressively outside the empire. Pomponius, the legate of Upper Germany, hoped to draw the Chatti into a major battle in the aftermath of destroying their raiding bands. Instead the tribe negotiated for peace and accepted the terms imposed by Rome, because they were frightened of the Cherusci. The Romans backed one tribe or leader to fight another, and also launched raids of their own into tribal territory, burning, pillaging, killing or taking captives. This reinforced their reputation as overwhelmingly strong and determined enemies. The communities closest to the frontier were most exposed to Roman punishment, for they were easy to reach and the location of their settlements and the routes through their land well known. It was harder and riskier, but not impossible, for the Romans to reach deeper into the lands beyond the frontiers, and as a result leaders there were more likely to be cultivated by gifts and other forms of diplomacy.

The security of Rome's frontiers was based on dominating her neighbours, very much in keeping with the belief that peace came from Roman victory. Rome was to be feared, which meant that her might was paraded as a constant reminder of her strength, while attackers were dealt with ruthlessly and the communities believed to support them ravaged with fire and sword. Such methods were effective, but did little to win affection and instead reinforced old hatreds. This made it all the more likely that attacks would happen whenever the provinces were believed to be less well defended. The transfer of troops elsewhere, whether to fight against a rebellion, act on another frontier or take part in a civil war, was one sign of such weakness, as was inertia or inactivity on the part of garrisons. Newly arrived governors were expected to be slow to respond, and some emperors were believed to be cautious.[43]

On occasions large numbers of raiders crossed a frontier and defeated the forces gathered to meet them. Such a defeat, or the substantial reduction in the size of a provincial garrison when troops were posted away, left the defences weak, so that the usual restrictions on raiders ceased to apply and there was no need to escape as quickly as possible. The raiders had time to settle down, search out prime targets and plunder with a thoroughness normally denied bands who wished to escape before the Romans caught up with them. Such things happened several times in northern Britain and on the Danube in the latter first century AD, and again during the Marcomannic wars of Marcus Aurelius. In the last case the army was weakened by the dreadful plagues which had ravaged the empire and spread quickest of all in crowded cities and army bases.

Yet such major failures were rare. Large attacks were infrequent and in most cases punished severely by the Roman military response. The frontiers were maintained for generation after generation, and it is this that has sometimes led scholars to portray them not as defensive lines, but designed to regulate and tax the movement of people and animals. It is very likely that the frontier systems created and manned by so large a part of the Roman army did carry out this function, but the resulting revenue is unlikely to have met the expense involved. In a strange way the very success of the frontier systems in military terms has convinced some scholars that there were no serious threats facing them. The deployment of the army in frontier regions makes great sense when the problems posed by raiding are considered. They were very well designed to cope with it and were, on the whole, highly effective. This meant modifying the habits of an army designed for large-scale warfare, but the Romans adapted and adjusted to changing conditions. Only in the third century AD did large parts of the system come under strain.

BEYOND THE *PAX ROMANA*

'For Ireland, I believe, which lies between Britain and Spain and also commands the Gallic Sea, would unite, to their mutual advantage, the most effective portions of our Empire.

'That island, compared with Britain, is of smaller dimensions ... In regard to soil, climate, and the character and ways of life of its inhabitants, it is not markedly different from Britain; we are better informed, thanks to the trade of merchants, about the approaches to the island and its harbours.' – *Tacitus, end of the first century* AD.[1]

OUTSIDE

Rome aimed to dominate the peoples living beyond the frontiers through a combination of military force and diplomacy. Although boundary stones and other markers survive showing the clear demarcation of areas subject to different cities or communities within the provinces, between provinces and with allied kingdoms, there are none marking the external frontiers where the empire ended. As in the past, the Romans refused to see other peoples or rulers as their equals and did not grant them any rights. Rome's *imperium* did not and could not end at some fixed point. Even when the reality of Parthian power was undeniable, imperial ideology presented the Parthians as allies who had submitted to Rome's *imperium*. In that sense they were part of the empire, even though they were 'allowed' by the Romans to govern themselves. A boundary was entirely acceptable between land directly ruled by the Romans and an allied realm where other laws and a king's authority held sway.[2]

None of this meant that it was not clear where the boundaries of frontier provinces lay, or that travellers would not have known when they crossed into or left the empire. These zones were tightly controlled and regulated by the army, whether marked by the line of a river, a man-made physical barrier, or the presence of outposts of soldiers. Both the Romans and their neighbours clearly knew the extent of the strips of depopulated land kept in advance of some frontiers. At times tribesmen occupied parts of this territory, but this was never done in ignorance and was conscious defiance of the ban. Everyone living adjacent to the frontiers of the empire was well aware of the restrictions imposed by Rome, and of their one-sidedness. The Romans kept land free of settlers and restricted access to the provinces, but accepted no limits on their own actions, intervening whenever they chose far beyond the frontiers of the empire. Leaders and peoples had to judge the chances of their actions provoking a hostile Roman response, aware that the odds varied depending on the aggressiveness of legates and, most of all, the attitude and priorities of the *princeps*.

The empire's frontiers were never intended to be impermeable fortified lines, keeping the provincial population and the peoples outside wholly separate. Not only did the Romans intend their power to reach far in advance of the frontiers, but it was both expected and seen as desirable to permit people to cross into and leave the empire as long as this occurred under their control. On occasions this meant the admission of large groups, even entire tribes, for settlement on land within the provinces, for instance during Plautius Silvanus' tenure in Moesia. Massed immigration of this sort was rare, and on a day-to-day basis movement was smaller-scale and in most cases connected with commerce. Raiding and trading went hand in hand in the Roman period just as it did in the Viking era and much of human history. Peaceful commerce was always more common since, as with bandits, an area and an economy was only capable of supporting a limited number of raiders if it was not to become unstable, forcing its population to leave or turn to raiding – the situation in large swathes of Lusitania and Further Spain in the middle of the second century BC. Under the Principate, the strong military presence in frontier areas prevented such situations from developing. Attackers were deterred or dealt with, and on the rare occasions that the system broke down it was soon restored.

Frontier systems allowed the Romans to dominate these areas and control movement, only preventing it when it was seen as a threat. People, goods – and indeed ideas – passed in both directions across the empire's frontiers, but did so under official supervision. This was difficult, if not impossible, to evade, and bans on many tribesmen from crossing into the empire other than at designated market places do appear to have been enforced. In AD 70, during the revolt of Civilis in the Rhineland, the success of the rebels allowed their allies from the east bank of the river to cross freely. Tacitus says that the Tencteri were overjoyed, since they could now cross where they liked and no longer entered provincial communities 'unarmed and almost naked, under guard and paying a price for the privilege'. Now allied to the Roman colony at Cologne, the Tencteri's ambassadors tried to persuade the city to demolish its walls as a mark of friendship. Prudently the colonists refused to do this for the moment, and continued to insist that when the tribesmen came to the city on business, they should only do so during daylight hours and should not carry weapons.[3]

Rivers, mountain passes, roads and fortified lines all helped channel traders and other travellers to crossing places observed and controlled by military outposts. This allowed certain groups to be detained and either turned back or only permitted to go on to a particular market, while others were granted more freedom. All were recorded, as were their animals and their loads, and at set places they were made to pay a toll or levy to continue on their journey. The Tencteri had resented this burden, but had had to pay – and soon were faced with the return of the system after the collapse of the rebellion and restoration of normal provincial rule. On the roads leading through the Egyptian desert to the Red Sea ports, travellers were charged during their journey and again on arrival at the port, before being permitted to embark with their wares, their movements being tracked by the passes they were required to carry on

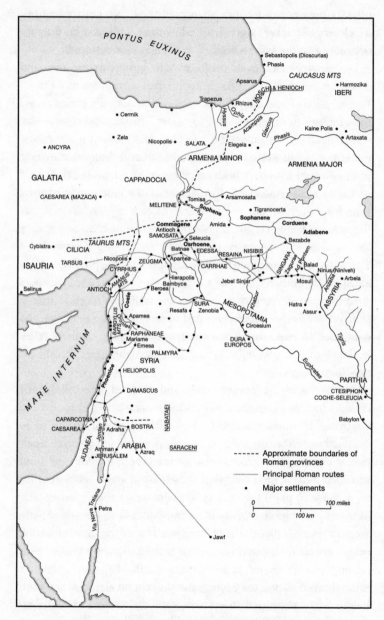

The frontier in the east and Parthia

their journey. The system was well established and clearly understood, so that hauliers and animal drivers were able to make a living
transporting people and goods, while others provided services along
the route. A pottery *ostrakon* records the leasing of a prostitute to a
military outpost or *praesidium*:

> . . . to Ptolema, very many greetings . . . I have let Procla to the prae-
> sidium of Maximianon for 60 drachmas with the quintana [a levy of
> a fifth on transactions and goods]. Please send her with the donkey
> driver who brings you this ostrakon. I have received the deposit of 12
> drachmas out of which I have paid the fare of 8 drachmas. Receive
> from the donkey driver [missing] drachmas. Give her the cloak. I shall
> give her the tunic. Do not do otherwise. Greetings.

The writer is presumably a pimp writing to his local agent, and the
hiring of a prostitute to go to a desert outpost is recorded on other
ostraka. Apart from the soldiers in garrison, travellers routinely
stopped to rest and draw water from the wells at these fortlets, so
there was a good chance of business. We do not know whether
women like Procla were hired by the army, by groups of soldiers
clubbing together or by someone else eager to profit from their activity. The toll for a prostitute passing along the road was higher than
that charged for a soldier's wife or other woman.[4]

The very presence of the Roman soldiers in such numbers in
the frontier zones created new demands and new markets. Trade
piggybacked on the state-run system for supplying the armies and
soon developed a momentum of its own. The sale and purchase of
food, drink and clothing all feature prominently in the correspondence from officers and soldiers in garrisons at opposite ends of the
empire. In areas like the Rhineland, such large concentrations of
troops and animals could not be maintained solely by the produce
of the surrounding area, and from early on these garrisons drew on
the resources of peoples beyond the frontier. Sometimes this took
the form of a levy on a tribe as part of their alliance with Rome,
for instance the cattle taken from the Frisii. More often farmers and

herdsmen realised that there was a great demand for their produce and that the Romans paid a good price, even after tolls and levies. Apart from grain and meat, the army required a constant supply of animal hides to make leather tents, saddles and harnesses for animals, belts, boots, clothing and shield covers.[5]

Merchants followed army units on campaign. In spite of the Augustan ban on marriage, many soldiers took 'wives' and raised families who followed them, so that almost as soon as a fort was built a civilian settlement grew up around it. If the base proved permanent, then these *canabae* grew and steadily became more organised, and many in time gained the formal status of a *vicus* – a settlement often covering a larger area than the fort itself. If the army moved on, then some former bases became towns in their own right or were established as colonies. All this meant that, apart from the soldiers and the slaves owned by the army, the establishment of the Roman army in a region greatly increased its population. On the heavily garrisoned Rhine and Danube, population density was higher in the frontier zones occupied by the army than inside the provinces.[6]

All these soldiers and civilians required staples and luxuries, some of which came from outside the empire. This traffic was too useful to be stopped, and may even have been essential to support the military and civil populations of the frontier zones, which meant accepting the risk that merchants passed on information of use to potential attackers, or that spies masqueraded as traders, was better than blocking all trade. The danger was reduced by restricting the access of certain groups, but even in this case the imperial authorities wanted the commerce to go on. Apart from foodstuffs and other goods, some communities may also have relied on labour from outside the empire, including the army, which recruited auxiliary soldiers from beyond the frontiers. It also looks as if the transhumant pastoralists on the frontier in North Africa had a symbiotic relationship with more settled communities. Each had goods to trade, while the pastoralists provided much-needed seasonal labour at harvest time. All benefited from the arrangement, so that over the course of a year some of these groups crossed into and left the directly governed

Roman provinces, their movements being channelled by the *fossatum* ditches and walls and supervised by the army.[7]

Raids were dramatic episodes in a wider context of peaceful exchange and movement across the frontiers, whether they attacked the provinces or were launched by the Romans as an assertion of power. In some areas raiding by either side was extremely rare, because of the inclinations of the peoples bordering the empire or the effectiveness of the Roman army's presence as a deterrent. As frontier lines remained in place for generations, there are signs that some communities outside the provinces adapted to supply the needs of the garrisons and civilian settlements, farming more intensively or mining natural resources. Yet the picture is not simple. In some areas few native settlements are known in the lands beyond the Roman frontier, and elsewhere the farms and villages that were occupied show scant signs of contact.[8]

TRADE AND TREATIES

Roman goods – in the sense of things produced within the empire – travelled a long way. Ports like Berenike and Myos Homos on the Red Sea coast of Egypt flourished primarily because of the trade with India and Sri Lanka, making use of the monsoon winds to undertake this great journey, and sometimes calling at ports on the southern Arabian coast. An anonymous first-century AD description lists the wares most in demand in one Indian port:

> . . . wine, principally Italian but also Laodicean and Arabian, copper, tin, and lead; coral and perdidot [a green gemstone]; all kinds of clothing with no adornment or of printed fabric; multi-coloured girdles, eighteen inches wide . . .; Roman money, gold and silver, which commands an exchange at some profit against the local currency . . . For the king there was imported in those times precious silverware, slave musicians, beautiful girls for concubinage, fine wine, expensive clothing with no adornment and choice unguent.[9]

The big profits came from sailing back west with the luxuries of the east, silks and cotton, gems, ivory, onyx and pearls, scents and spices – the Romans developed a great fondness for pepper. India was not a single state, but was divided into many kingdoms and there were marked regional and local differences. Kingdoms in the north tended to be bigger and had a monetised economy, and had had contact with Greek culture and settlers for a very long time, something greatly reinforced by the incursion of Alexander the Great in the fourth century BC. This pre-existing exchange and influence sometimes makes it difficult to know the source of Western influences on artworks. Far more Roman coins have appeared in hoards buried in southern India, where money was rarely used in commercial exchanges, and it looks as if a lot of the Roman gold and silver coins acquired by the locals were used as bullion rather than currency. In the first century AD Pliny the Elder expressed concern at the amount of money leaving the empire every year to purchase luxuries from the east. Such worries did nothing to reduce the scale of imports, and there is no good evidence that it had a seriously detrimental impact on the economic life of the empire. On the whole all parties benefited. Shifts in the balance of power in northern India created favourable conditions for the trade with Rome, and placed more emphasis on the sea lanes than the overland routes along the ancient Silk Road.[10]

Roman traders and their employees formed more or less permanent settlements in India and Sri Lanka, while there is evidence for Indian communities residing in the ports along the Red Sea coast. Plenty of Romans – both citizens and in the broader sense of inhabitants of the empire – went beyond the frontiers in search of profit, just as they had done under the Republic. In the early first century AD there was a sizeable community living in the heartland of King Maroboduus of the Marcomani, 'drawn from their respective homes and implanted on hostile soil first by the commercial privileges, then by the lure of increased profits, and finally forgetting their own country'. During Nero's reign a Roman equestrian journeyed overland from the Danube frontier to the Baltic, visiting trading posts and markets and bringing back considerable quantities of amber which was used as ornaments in a series of games celebrated in Rome. A tombstone found in Slovakia, well outside the empire, commemorates Quintus Atilius Primus, who served in *Legio XV Primigenia* as an interpreter and a centurion. After his time in the army he became a trader or businessman (*negotiator*) – helped no doubt by his ability with local languages – and lived among the Quadi, dying at the grand old age of eighty. Until the great wars during the reign of Marcus Aurelius, the Marcomani and Quadi enjoyed generally good relations with the Romans, and had ready access to many products from inside the empire. Excavation has revealed buildings constructed in Roman style and even including one or two small bath houses. Some were most likely the homes of men like Atilius, but others reflect an enthusiasm for some aspects of comfortable Roman living on the part of local leaders.[11]

Not everyone wanted the same things from the empire. The Greeks and Romans called the people of the Sahara the Garamantes, portraying them sometimes as raiders and enemies, telling fanciful stories of their strangeness, but also admitting that they had a capital, were ruled by one or more kings, and traded in semi-precious stones and other products. Archaeology presents a picture of stable communities of stone houses, as well as larger temples, public buildings and monumental tombs, although it also confirms their warlike prowess, with depictions of warriors on foot and horseback, and even in chariots. In this harsh environment, settlements could only exist around springs and oases, but the Garamantes created irrigation systems to permit them to farm over a wider area. Roman sources emphasise how far they lived from the fertile Mediterranean coast, with the geographer Ptolemy mentioning journeys of twenty and thirty days to reach their villages.[12]

There were several campaigns into Garamantian territory under Augustus, and some Garamantes allied with Tacfarinas, but on the whole major military operations by the Roman army were rare in this area. In spite of the distances involved, trade and other peaceful contact were commonplace – in AD 69, when the leaders of Oea recruited Garamantes to help them in their dispute with Lepcis

Magna, they clearly knew how to get in touch with their leaders. Coins are rare finds in Garamantian settlements, suggesting that money was not the basis for trade, which either relied on some alternative tokens of wealth or on barter. Domitian's reign saw a resurgence of conflict, ending in treaties imposed by the Romans. Later in his reign, a Roman representative accompanied the king of the Garamantes on a campaign against the Ethiopians, marching for four months until they reached Lake Chad.[13]

The long reach of the Garamantes added to the products they could offer from their own lands, such as gem stones, worked beads and salt. They also supplied exotic African animals for Roman entertainments, and talk of hunting the peoples to their south suggests that they were slavers. Some of their captives are likely to have toiled on Garamantian farms, but many went north to the markets of the Roman province. Ancient sources describe the Garamantians as dark-skinned, but saw them as distinct from the even darker Ethiopians, and it is probable that they resembled the mixed population of modern Berbers. Their activities as slave hunters provided the empire with many of the black slaves from sub-Saharan Africa occasionally mentioned in our sources. The Garamantes were traders and raiders, like so many of the peoples of the ancient world, with trade the most common form of contact, admittedly sometimes selling captives or spoils from raids. Here as elsewhere, the Romans aimed to maintain military dominance in the region, while engaging in mutually beneficial commerce.[14]

Evidence for Romans living or journeying outside the empire is rare and usually no more than a mention which does little to explain the background. On the other hand, vast quantities of objects from the Roman Empire are found in the lands outside it, for instance at sites in Scandinavia, the Baltic states and even Russia, apart from in Africa and the east. Trade to these parts of the world receives little or no mention in our sources, so the evidence is almost exclusively archaeological, which presents its own problems of interpretation. A lot of material, especially prestigious and expensive objects such as fine tableware or jewellery, comes from burials. Some tombs in

Russia combine goods from the empire with artefacts from the almost equally distant China of the Han dynasty. Roman-made weapons, especially swords, are also surprisingly common finds even at considerable distances from the frontier – in fact more Roman swords have been discovered from sites outside than inside the empire. One reason for this is the large-scale deposits of military equipment found in dozens of Danish bogs that were once lakes – with no fewer than 100 swords at one site. These were mainly Roman in pattern, most made within the empire and sometimes stamped with their makers' names or symbols of Roman power, combined with local copies.[15]

Tacitus mentions that before a battle some German tribes pledged the spoils of victory to the gods, sacrificing prisoners and all their equipment when they won. The deliberate throwing of weapons and other items – sometimes ritually broken beforehand – into lakes in Denmark reflects the same idea, and this practice, combined with local conditions which preserved the deposits, offers a far more detailed picture of the weaponry in use in these regions than can be gained solely from grave offerings. Most bog finds date to the third century AD, so a little later than our period, and the consensus is that they represent the spoils of a defeated enemy, most likely invaders from another tribe, dedicated to the gods in thanks for the victory. The bigger sites have been interpreted as containing equipment for 200 or 300 warriors, with between a fifth and a quarter wielding swords as well as spears and javelins. At Illerup Ådal in Denmark, a deposit of equipment from the early third century also contained reindeer-bone combs and other items from southern Norway or Sweden, and it looks as if the attackers had come from there to raid. This was the largest deposit at a site where several dedications were made over the course of successive generations.[16]

The combination of these ritual dedications and the environmental conditions which turned lakes into peat bogs and preserved many of the objects offers unusually spectacular finds for this region. Other areas outside the empire are less fortunate, and regions where it was not the tradition to bury corpses or ashes with grave goods yield far fewer, if any, Roman treasures. The distribution of Roman goods beyond the frontiers is not even, but this may reflect the cultural practices of the peoples involved or the extent of modern archaeological work in a country as much as it does real differences in access and taste. Under the Principate a lot of wine and other substances previously transported in *amphorae* were shipped in barrels, which are inherently less likely to leave any trace in the archaeological record, so we cannot hope to follow trade routes in the same way that we can for the Republican era. Objects placed in a grave were usually precious and thus prestigious, and tend to show few traces of heavy usage. In death as in life, possession of such things was a mark of status. In contrast, finds from settlements are more likely to comprise broken or lost items, and may have traces of modification and repair. Fragments of Roman pottery trampled into the floor of a house or the surface of a yard suggest its use in everyday life. In the past, archaeologists were drawn to the rich potential yields of graves, and it is only more recently that ordinary settlements are being investigated in greater detail.

With these caveats, there are discernible patterns in the types of goods leaving the empire. Prestigious items clearly were important and valued by the elites in many regions. In Europe in particular, the prominence of elaborate tableware for use in feasting, and especially communal drinking, hints at the importance of these things for the elite in many societies. Whether ceramic, silver, occasionally gold and more often bronze, highly decorated vessels to hold, pour and drink wine added to the grandeur of gatherings where a chieftain entertained lesser leaders and his household, displaying his wealth and generosity. Clusters of burials with such objects suggest established dynasties lasting for many generations. Weapons are another indication of the power and prominence of princes and chieftains. Graves containing military equipment show a gradation from a man armed only with one or more spears to ones of higher status, possessing a good sword or the spurs that indicate a horseman. The sheer quantity of swords found in bogs makes clear the substantial numbers of well-equipped warriors in the following of some leaders.

Coin hoards are another indication that some individuals came into the possession of considerable amounts of wealth, but how they used it is more complex. Tacitus claims that the tribes nearer the frontier made more use of money, and preferred the older silver coins. It certainly does look as if many people outside the empire valued coins which were purer in their silver content – something which over time declined as Roman coins were debased and became tokens rather than intrinsically valuable. Silver coins are most common and bronze coins of the sort used for small purchases are rare, suggesting that these were not used as an active currency. On the other hand, their lesser worth made bronze coins less likely to appear in a hoard, and practices must have varied from region to region and over time. Silver and gold coins made impressive gifts for a chief to present to a favoured follower, even if they were not actually used as money. There is evidence that the Germans used coins as bullion, to be melted down and made into other precious things. Yet this does not appear to be the case in Scotland, where a number of silver hoards have turned up. Since this region certainly did not have a monetised economy, it looks as if the coins were valued as portable wealth, to be accepted and given as conspicuous gifts rather than spent.[17]

In northern Britain funerary ritual did not require lavish grave goods, so the region has produced no splendid collections of prestigious objects to rival finds on the continent. Yet it is clear that considerable quantities of items from the Roman province of Britannia and from the wider empire reached what is now Scotland. They occur in so many settlements as to suggest that some access to these things was commonplace and not limited to a tiny elite. Samian pottery – vessels that were not cheap, but were not luxury items either inside the empire – was available, if not in the quantities or variety found on sites within the Roman province. This may reflect their cost in relation to local buying power, or local taste. There were also regional variations. The western coast and Isles were less populated and had access to fewer imports than the Lowlands. Wherever they are found, it is always much harder to say how these and other objects were used, and whether employing Roman tableware or brooches meant some adoption of Roman-style cooking or dress. Many items were repaired or turned into something else – for instance, the base of a large pot cut away to make a smaller, shallower vessel. Pieces of decorative pottery and fragments of glass bowls were reshaped into whorls, counters or beads. These were eagerly sought out by the inhabitants of Scotland, who were short of mineral resources, so that most work in copper and bronze came to rely on metal originally brought in from the empire. Recent excavations at a village site near Fienstedt in Germany have shown the stock-piling of scrap metal fragments from the provinces for reuse by local smiths.[18]

The usage of Roman material varied considerably, whether it was valued for – or in spite of – its association with Rome, and whether it was something rare and precious, something for everyday use, or simply a commodity to be turned into something else. In every case it must have reached the lands outside the empire in one of three ways, as a gift, through trade or through plunder, but only occasionally will this be suggested by the material itself or the context in which it was discovered. Two richly decorated silver cups found in a grave at Hoby in Denmark had the name Silius scratched on their bases, and were stamped with the name of their manufacturer, Cheirisophos. A senator named Caius Silius commanded a fleet which sailed around the coast to the Baltic during Augustus' reign, and a few years later under Tiberius was legate of Germania Superior, so that there is a good chance that the cups were his gift to a friendly leader. If so, it is a reminder that diplomatic activity stretched a very long way from the frontiers.[19]

Gifts, perhaps regular subsidies, were one way of gaining and keeping the goodwill of important leaders outside the empire and many of the prestigious objects found beyond the frontiers arrived in this way, just as they had done under the Republic. Usually they came from representatives of the empire, although as in the past it is likely that merchants wishing to operate in an area gave similar presents to win the favour of local leaders. Other expensive items were acquired through trade in return for hides, animals, slaves or whatever else was sought from the region. More mundane tableware, metalwork and other items are likely to have arrived through commerce, although we should not always assume that things that were commonplace within the empire did not gain a far greater value in regions where they were rare. At times there were restrictions on selling weapons across the frontiers, but this was probably not always the case, especially if they were going to allies, while smuggling is also possible.[20]

A sword was an important symbol as well as a weapon and marked a man out as a warrior. A good-quality Roman sword was especially valuable as well as very effective, and the quality of warriors' equipment as well as their numbers added to the prestige of a chieftain's *comitatus*. Greater availability of swords, as well as an increased supply of prestigious objects for feasting and displaying wealth, intensified competition among aristocrats far beyond the frontiers. With wealth a man could attract more followers and reward them generously. A chieftain who controlled access to goods from the empire grew rich and powerful, while those able to supply Roman traders with what they wanted attracted these to them and also profited. The slave-hunting practised by the Garamantes was probably prevalent in many areas beyond the frontiers. With expansion far less common, Roman warfare could not provide the numbers of newly enslaved captives to meet demands within the empire. The appeal of trading slaves for swords or luxuries from the empire gave an added incentive to warfare between the tribes. A Roman law code describes an episode when:

> A woman condemned, for a crime, to hard labour in the salt-works, was subsequently captured by bandits of an alien race; in the course of lawful trade she was sold, and by repurchase returned to her original condition. The purchase price had to be refunded from the Imperial Treasury to the centurion Cocceius Firmus.[21]

A centurion named Cocceius Firmus dedicated several altars in northern Britain, which makes it quite possible that the capture and sale of this woman occurred on the frontier of the province. In this case the 'bandits' had come from outside the empire, taken this woman captive on a raid into the province, and then subsequently they, or some third or fourth party, sold her to a buyer within the empire. It was a story no doubt repeated elsewhere, and even more common outside the empire.

Rich grave goods, especially in a long succession of burials in the same area, and large bands of well-equipped warriors raiding over long distances indicate the presence of powerful leaders, often in competition or direct conflict. Our literary sources show that the Romans supported friendly rulers with money, gifts, diplomatic and occasionally military aid. After his defeat at the hands of Arminius, Maroboduus' prestige was fatally damaged. The man who completed his downfall was encouraged and supported by Rome, in spite of the fact that Maroboduus had always tried to be a loyal ally and avoid conflict with the empire. Yet the Romans had invaded his territory in AD 6, and it is uncertain whether the memory of his perceived threat swayed them now to dispose of him or whether they acted from a pragmatic desire to back a winner. Arminius' brother Flavus had remained loyal to Rome, even naming his son Italicus. The boy was a citizen, educated at Rome, but was also a prince of his people. When some of the Cherusci appealed to Claudius, the young man was sent home and became the king of the tribe. Other Cheruscan leaders were less enthusiastic, although it is not clear whether they distrusted his Roman connections or simply backed rivals for power. In spite of Roman financial and moral support, Italicus was driven out, and only returned and regained power with the aid of warriors from another Germanic tribe, the Langobardi.[22]

Roman diplomacy was cynical and self-serving, and thus no different to the ambitions of leaders in the tribes outside the empire. Roman backing was not always enough on its own to raise up and maintain a ruler and there were other forces at play; the history of the Iron Age communities was surely no less dynamic simply because it was never written down. Tribes and leaders flourished and declined as they had done in the past, and the presence of the empire was merely one element influencing events – a major factor close to the frontiers, growing slowly less so with distance. There is a natural if misleading temptation to see the presence of artefacts from the empire as a sign of direct contact, even though many items may have passed through a succession of hands. Gifts, trade or plunder were the likely means of transferring these objects, even if none of the parties involved were Roman.

Excavated Germanic settlements show long-term, stable occupation. Over time the size and number of houses increased, and there are signs of greater social distinction, with one house and its compound rebuilt on a markedly grander scale than the others. Sites have been found specialising in stock-rearing and trading or in manufacture, both on a scale far greater than was needed for the local population, so intended for trade with outsiders. Commerce with the empire is probable, but so is exchange with other tribal communities. The ability to do this shows that the regions had a stable and secure environment, most likely created by force through the protection of well-established leaders and their *comites*. In Denmark there were chieftains capable of marshalling sufficient manpower and resources to construct a number of linear boundaries. Anchorages were protected by timber defences, while on land ditches, ramparts and stockades were built.[23]

The barrier at Olgerdiget stretches for eight miles, with multiple timber stockades – on average four rows of beams – and a ditch and earth wall for around two-thirds of its length. In some ways it resembles a miniature version of the Roman *limes* in Upper Germany, which has led to the suggestion that someone from Denmark served as an auxiliary and brought back ideas of frontier systems. Yet we should never underestimate human ingenuity, and the locals may have come up with the idea wholly independently – there are plenty of examples of long fences or earthworks in European prehistory, their function often unclear, while during the campaigns under Augustus and Tiberius the Romans were confronted with ramparts built by the tribes. The purpose of the line at Olgerdiget and others in Denmark does appear similar to that of the Roman frontiers, as a statement of power, an obstacle to raiders and a means of channelling movement towards set crossing places. It is another indication that life outside the empire was far from peaceful.[24]

CIVIL WAR AND PEACE

In AD 211 Septimius Severus died at Eboracum (York) in northern Britain, after spending several years campaigning against the Caledonian tribes. He was succeeded by his sons Caracalla and Geta, but his dying wish that they live in harmony failed to overcome their mutual loathing. Within less than a year Caracalla had murdered his brother and ruled alone, later launching a major offensive against the Parthians. In AD 217 one of his officers stabbed the emperor to death near Carrhae, the site of Crassus' great defeat in 53 BC, but now in Roman territory. The conspiracy was led by his praetorian prefect Macrinus, who persuaded the army to proclaim him emperor. It was the first time that a man who was not only from outside the imperial family but also from outside the senatorial class was raised to the imperial purple. His reign proved brief when other army units came out in support of a fourteen-year-old boy who was claimed to be Caracalla's illegitimate son and was in reality his nephew. These troops defeated Macrinus' men and he was killed in the aftermath of the fighting. Several short-lived and unsuccessful coups erupted in Syria during the next few years, but it was left to his own family to assassinate the young emperor and replace him with his cousin, Severus Alexander, in AD 222.[25]

Civil wars were an ever-present threat and a frequent reality throughout the remainder of the history of the empire, until its Western half vanished in AD 476. The middle decades of the third century were particularly disturbed, with dozens of emperors coming and going in rapid succession. Claudius Gothicus achieved the rare distinction of dying of natural causes, in this case an outbreak of plague, in AD 270, but all of the rest met violent ends. Decius was killed by the Goths in AD 251, and Valerian captured by the Sassanid Persians and died in captivity. All of the rest were killed by Roman rivals or took their own life when faced with defeat. Later, military strongmen like Diocletian and Constantine gave the empire spells of comparative stability, but the extent of this should not be exaggerated, and the former's retirement and latter's death were both followed by renewed violent power struggles and civil war. It is sobering to note that from AD 218 to 476 there were only three periods of ten years without a usurpation or full-scale civil war.

In the third, fourth and fifth centuries AD the willingness of Roman leaders and their armies to fight each other repeatedly shattered the *Pax Romana*. The Roman army and the Roman state wasted their strength in these internal struggles. These were not conflicts fought over issues and, even more than the civil wars of the Late Republic, were purely about power, ended only by the death of one of the rival leaders. Provinces were stripped of their garrisons to muster the armies needed to make a man emperor. When opponents faced each other with the same tactics, equipment, command structure and discipline, victory tended to go to the bigger army, so numbers were vital. Soldiers on the losing side were usually willing to take an oath of loyalty to the victor, but that ignores the losses suffered in any fighting and the catastrophic dislocation of the army's systems of recruitment, training, promotion and organisation.

Several things stand out in this period, including something which conspicuously did not happen. Internal dissension and civil war weakened the defences of the empire's frontiers, so that during the third century AD raiders crossed the Rhine and Danube, striking deep into the western provinces and reaching as far as Italy, Greece and Spain. In the east the Persians plundered widely in Syria, reaching Antioch in AD 253. Regions nearer the frontiers suffered even more heavily and were attacked again and again. With frontier armies depleted by the need to fight civil wars, the defensive systems were unable to cope. A few successes soon encouraged more and more raids, as chieftains and their followers returned home with glory and plunder. Some attacks were provoked by Roman leaders recruiting allies or persuading tribes to attack their rivals. The withdrawal of frontier garrisons may also have dislocated long-standing trading relations by removing the big market provided by the army and individual soldiers. Groups like the Goths become far more prominent in our sources in the third century, while new peoples like the Alamanni and Franks appear for the first time. None were politically united, and their behaviour looks no different from that of the tribes of earlier centuries. While Roman diplomacy and trade helped augment the power of favoured leaders outside the empire, there is no hint that this established broader and lasting control among the tribes, creating permanent confederations of tribes that posed a far greater threat than in the past. Men like Ariovistus, Maroboduus and Decebalus were still very rare, and the tribes were just as disunited and mutually hostile as they had been before. What had changed were the opportunities for attacking the Roman provinces and plundering their wealth.[26]

During the third century AD most towns and cities without walls acquired them, while those already fortified made their defences stronger. Raiders from outside the empire were a threat over a wide area, and in some regions banditry became far more common than in the past. With the collapse of the established frontier systems, attackers were no longer faced with the need to move fast and escape before Roman forces caught them, and instead were able to settle down and plunder more methodically. Sources from the third century AD make frequent mention of the danger posed by runaway slaves, deserters and captives aiding the raiders, leading them to settlements and hiding places. Some raiders were still intercepted and defeated, as usual on their way home. An inscription found at Augusta Vindelicum in Raetia commemorates such a victory:

In honour of the divine house, (and) to the blessed goddess Victoria because the barbarians of the race of the Semnones or Juthungi were slaughtered and routed on the eighth and seventh days before the Kalends of May [24–25 April] by soldiers of the province of Raetia, by soldiers from Germany, and by militia, after freeing many thousands of Italian prisoners, (and) in the realization of his vow, Marcus Simplicius Genialis, *vir perfectissimus*, acting in place of the governor,

with the same army, (and), with proper gratitude, erected and dedicated this altar on the third day before the Ides of September when
our emperor Postumus Augustus and Honoratianus were consuls
[AD 260].[27]

Emperors did not ignore the threat posed by peoples from outside
the empire. Many of them campaigned on the frontiers, or chased
down raiders plundering the provinces, but they were always more
concerned by Roman rivals. Whenever Roman dominance on the
frontiers was broken – as it had been under Marcus Aurelius – it
took years of hard campaigning and fresh victories to restore it.
From the third century AD onwards there were too many crises and
never enough time and continuity of leadership to re-establish the
dominance maintained for most of the Principate. Each time one
frontier became calm, trouble would flare on another, and military
resources were drawn off to cope with the new problem, weakening
the security elsewhere. The advanced *limes* connecting the Rhine and
Danube was abandoned, as was the province of Dacia, because there
were no longer the resources to garrison them. In the fifth century
AD core provinces in the west were lost one by one until nothing
was left. The process took a very long time, and until near the end
the empire was still larger and considerably more powerful than any
single opponent it faced. Civil wars weakened the strength of Rome
and undermined frontier systems, making the empire vulnerable, so
that it was gradually worn down by its enemies.

Yet conspicuous by their very absence from this period were
revolts and resistance to imperial rule in the provinces. When the
army and government turned against themselves and rival leaders
battled for power, there was no sudden upsurge of independence
movements within the provinces. No clearer proof could be given of
the degree of consent contributing to the success of provincial rule.
As far as we can tell, no province rebelled in the hope of throwing
off Roman rule, nor – at least until very late – did communities welcome foreign invaders. When provincial populations did rebel it was
as Romans, supporting a claimant to the imperial purple. Postumus,

mentioned in the inscription from Augsburg, was a Roman emperor, although he held power only in some of the western provinces including Gaul, the Germanies, Raetia and, for some of the time, Britain. Often referred to as the Gallic Emperors, he and his successors saw themselves as the legitimate rulers of the entire empire, but had not yet been able to bring the rest under their control. Around the same time Queen Zenobia of Palmyra led armies which occupied the Syrian provinces, Egypt and Asia Minor on behalf of her son. For all the trappings of this ancient oasis city, she and her son were Roman citizens as well as Palmyrene royalty and he was proclaimed as emperor of Rome and not as king. In neither case were these leaders aiming at carving out permanently independent realms of their own, nor were they leading ethnically based separatist movements. Their successes were meant to be stepping stones on the path to control of the entire Roman Empire.

When Roman power weakened, the subject peoples did not rush to throw off the imperialist yoke, and even in the fifth century AD there was a deep longing to be Roman. In part this was due to the sheer longevity of the empire, in which many generations had passed since conquest, and to the lack of any appealing alternative to Roman civilisation. Yet it also grew from the reality and the success of the Roman Peace. When the power of the empire weakened in the third century AD, frontier incursions became a lot more common, as did internal banditry. Like the empire itself, the *Pax Romana* decayed gradually rather than vanishing overnight. Maintaining it remained an ambition and a frequent boast of emperors for centuries, and some areas and some whole provinces were only rarely afflicted by civil war or reached by foreign raids. Life within the empire remained relatively safe and more prosperous than life outside, at least in much of the world – the difference between the empire and Parthia and Persia was always less marked. If life was less secure and comfortable than at the height of the Principate, the difference was one of degree, and as one generation followed another the slow decline was not obvious. People wanted to be Roman, and the Germanic tribes who carved up the Western Empire in the fifth century AD were desperate to share in the comforts and prosperity of Rome.

In the fifth century AD the Western Empire fell. The Eastern Empire survived, preserving the ideal of internal peace along with many other aspects of culture, custom, ideology and ambition. Greatly reduced in size and resources, especially after the Arab conquests in the seventh century, the Eastern Empire's influence was felt over a much smaller area than the united empire of the Principate. The world had changed.

CONCLUSION

PEACE AND WAR

The Romans were aggressive. Under the Republic they fought war after war, which over time allowed them to dominate an ever wider area. During concerted campaigning under Augustus and periodic wars of conquest under succeeding emperors, this process culminated in the creation of an empire encompassing by far the greater part of the known world. People after people and state after state suffered military defeat or accepted Roman domination because they realised that they could not match Rome's might.

There was no concerted, systematic plan to create this empire, which took centuries, but nor were the Romans secretive about what they were doing. Warfare played a central role in public life, and victories were celebrated with praise, public thanksgiving and permanent monuments. Wars provide one of the central themes of every history written by Romans or Greeks about Rome. On the whole, the Romans were able to persuade themselves that almost all of the wars they fought were just – near-continuous victory offered them proof of their special relationship with the gods.

This was a society comfortable with the idea of 'pacifying' peoples in distant lands and which did not accept any other state as an equal. It was important to act justly and with *fides*, because this was the correct thing to do and maintained a proper relationship with the gods, not because others had rights. The views of outsiders mattered only to the extent that they made it easier or more difficult for the Romans to achieve their objectives. This was a world without international law or any sense of an international community watching and judging. The Romans' attitude to atrocity was just as pragmatic as their attitude to the opinions of other leaders and

states. Mass enslavement, execution or mutilation – Caesar had the
hands cut off warriors who surrendered to him in 51 BC – and the
devastation of lands and settlements were acceptable if they helped
to achieve victory. Mercy and generosity to those who submitted
were equally appropriate if they achieved the same end. Brutal force
and willingness to negotiate went hand in hand in every war against
a foreign enemy – 'spare the conquered and overcome the proud in
war'. What mattered was winning.[1]

The Romans were very good at winning wars, and whatever else
we say about them we cannot doubt this basic truth. Their empire
was created and then maintained by the frequent use and ever-
present threat of military force. The circumstances in which each
community became part of the empire varied, and these helped to
determine the details of their relationship with Rome, but all were
expected to give something to the Romans, whether they had been
beaten into submission by the legions or had submitted to Roman
power without fighting. Just as they admitted their willingness to
wage war and 'overcome the proud', the Romans were equally open
in their admission that they exploited and profited from their empire.
Reluctance to undertake further conquests was justified on the basis
that the costs would outbalance profits, rather than any thought that
expansion in itself might be wrong.

For all the talk of pacification, the Romans did not pretend that
they carved out their empire for any reason other than to benefit
Rome. Roman strength and dominance were good things in their
own right, which gave them greater security and made them richer.
Provinces and allies were not acquired for their own good, but for the
good of Rome. Once they were established, then it was in Rome's
interest to maintain them in order to preserve both her prestige and
her profits. This meant dealing with rebellion, curbing civil war or
other inter-communal violence within the province, and securing it
from outside attack. These requirements were in origin self-serving,
but in the longer term led to the development of the *Pax Romana*.

I hope that the preceding chapters have shown that the Roman
Peace was a reality. The Romans did not conquer their empire to

create it, nor was it instant, and instead it grew slowly. Under the Principate, and certainly by the later first century AD, the greater part of Rome's empire was very lightly garrisoned and the prospect of rebellion was remote or non-existent. Considerable resources were devoted to maintaining Roman dominance in the frontier areas, making successful attacks on the rest of the empire very rare. The *Pax Romana* was not perfect, and it took far longer for the risk of revolt to die away in some areas than in others. The risk of banditry never wholly vanished. In some parts of the provinces, usually in mountainous or other inaccessible country, it was always a problem, often necessitating a permanent military presence. Elsewhere it existed on the fringes of society and rapidly increased in scale whenever local, provincial and imperial authorities grew weak. Yet most of the time, over most of the empire, it was kept under control – a fact of life, but not a constant and serious danger to most of the population.

Qualifying the completeness of the *Pax Romana* should not make us forget just what a remarkable achievement it was. There is no doubt that the areas under Roman rule experienced considerably less war and organised violence during this period than they did in the centuries before or since. Peace was not absolute, but the era of the Principate was more peaceful, which meant that it was more stable. Prosperity was more widespread, even if it did not reach everyone, and goods, people and ideas were able to travel further and more often than ever before, which in itself is one of the greatest proofs of the success of the *Pax Romana*. This was the world created by the Roman Empire, even if its creation was a consequence rather than a cause of Roman imperialism. Just as the Romans saw it, it was the peace brought by military victory and strength, something achieved by prolonged, large-scale violence that was costly to the Romans and even more costly to the victims of Roman warfare.

The savagery inherent in Rome's rise, which was also required to maintain her dominance of the world and her prolonged exploitation of the provinces, is difficult for many to reconcile with the stable and secure *Pax Romana*. The author of one study of Roman Britain suggested that from AD 43 to AD 84, the Roman invaders killed somewhere between 100,000 to 250,000 people from a population of perhaps 2,000,000. Like almost all numbers for this period, these are highly conjectural and impossible to prove or disprove. One reviewer commented that, if right, this represented less than 'one-third of one per cent' per annum, and wondered 'how many Britons died annually in the intertribal warfare that preceded the Roman invasion?' apart from the ones who did fall victim to Boudicca's rebels in AD 60. In a reply written in a subsequent book, the original author criticised the reviewer for trying 'to deflect criticism of Rome by implying that things might have been just as violent or bad if the Romans had never come to Britain'.[2]

There is something to be said for both sides of the argument. While there is little point in plucking a number out of the air, it is safe to say that during the Roman conquest of Britain a considerable number of human beings on the island were killed or wounded, while others were enslaved or mistreated. The flogging of Boudicca and the rape of her daughters was surely not the only instance of such abuse, although it is also worth noting that Tacitus did not consider these acts as justified and blamed them on the misconduct of the procurator and his staff. Yet they happened, and the arrival of foreign soldiers and officials and the power they held over the tribes inevitably created opportunities for abuse and cruelty quite apart from any punishment or reprisals sanctioned by the authorities. The Roman conquest of Britain, like Rome's conquests elsewhere, involved considerable use of violence and intimidation. Some leaders and communities welcomed the invaders and suffered little or no harm, but for many the experience can only have been awful.

On the other hand it is equally clear that, in Britain as in the wider world, the period before the Romans arrived was not peaceful. Intertribal warfare was common and people were killed, enslaved, injured and mistreated in these conflicts. This does not in any way exonerate the Romans from their own acts of violence and cruelty, but it does put them into context. Rome was uniquely successful at warmaking and empire-building, but other contemporary states and peoples time and again proved themselves every bit as aggressive and savage. It is possible that the Romans' highly organised, large-scale and determined war-making inflicted significantly greater violence on its victims than past conflicts, but this is not at all certain. It is true that, in Britain and elsewhere, the consequence of Roman conquest was ultimately the eradication of inter-tribal warfare. Once again it is worth repeating that there is no evidence for any rebellion or serious disturbance in lowland Britain after Boudicca. The *Pax Romana* was established, and communities and tribes lived in peace, no longer raiding and head-hunting. While it is impossible to know what would have happened if the Romans had not invaded, nothing suggests that this peace and stability was inevitable and would have emerged anyway. The probability is that wars between the tribes would have continued.

One of the main themes of this book has been the active role played in events by the leaders of the peoples with whom the Romans came into contact. From the earliest periods, when some chose to fight against Rome there were as many who instead allied with the Romans. Sometimes this was a recognition of Rome's overwhelming might, and sometimes they hoped to exploit this strength for their own benefit. These men – and occasionally women – were every bit as capable of showing ambition, skill, ruthlessness, treachery, selfishness, greed, competitiveness, cynicism, fear and courage as the Romans. One of the greatest mistakes we can make is to assume that such leaders acted primarily because their instincts were pro- or anti-Roman. Instead the presence of Rome as more or less distant neighbour or as an occupying power was just one of the many factors determining their behaviour. Often Rome could not be ignored, but even then local rivalries were of more direct concern. Roman rule simply changed the way these contests were conducted.

The *Pax Romana* came after conquest and was imposed whether or not the populations of the provinces wanted it. In the longer run, rebellions against Roman rule ceased. Fear of the terrible reprisals inflicted on rebels was one reason for this, but the absence of native revolts during the civil wars and chaos of the third century AD suggests that it eventually ceased to be the main factor. For most provincials, and especially the local aristocracies, the loss of independence and exploitation by the imperial authorities were tolerable. Over time Roman rule became normal, and any alternative either unrealistic or unappealing. This does not mean that some people did not suffer great hardships under Roman rule, but no doubt some also lived lives of miserable hardship before the Romans arrived, which again does not excuse the Romans. Yet we should not assume that being exploited by foreigners was automatically worse than being exploited by a local elite.

There is a risk, when we look back on the Roman Empire and stress the primitiveness of this society and economy in comparison with our own day and age and the harshness of life in this era, that we forget to adopt a similar approach when considering the other peoples and cultures of the ancient world. Even more importantly, we must never forget that the experience of the Western world in the post-war era is untypical in almost every way of wider human history. It should not surprise us that the Romans differed in many ways from us. Many things we take for granted are actually fairly recent innovations – from permanent diplomatic contacts between states, to detailed maps, newspapers and the media or ideas of international law, which remains very difficult to enforce.

At the start I wrote that I did not intend this book to give lessons for the modern world based on the Roman experience, and my view has not changed. It would be foolish to advise policy-makers to do things in a certain way because the Romans found that it worked. The combination of military and civil power in the person of a Roman provincial governor offered a clarity of purpose and implementation in marked contrast to the confused and conflicting command structures seen recently in Afghanistan and Iraq, where the armed forces and numerous civilian agencies worked in parallel, all in direct, real-time communication with their governments. Yet it is impossible to imagine any modern democracy entrusting so much authority to one person, let alone to a military commander. More obviously, Roman pragmatism about the use of atrocity to achieve an end could not – and obviously should not – be contemplated.

It should have been obvious from the start that the vast majority of people and leaders in these and other countries were not fundamentally pro- or anti-Western or American, but far more caught up with local politics, friendships and rivalries. There again, the Romans never attempted to invade a country with the intention of establishing a functioning democracy and then withdrawing. The Romans tended to stay, which in the end meant that most of the population had to make an accommodation with them.

The Romans were very successful at winning wars and absorbing others to create their large and long-lived empire. Yet a closer look at the processes involved shows that all of this took a long time. Along the way the Romans suffered defeats, lost interest in some regions for a while, were inconsistent in their treatment of allies and enemies alike, and made plenty of mistakes. All this occurred when the agents of the Republic and Principate behaved in the way they were supposed to, even before we allow for the incompetence, cruelty and greed of some of the men on the spot. Foreign interventions then as now were often messy and confused. It was rare for Roman conquest to take less than a generation, and quite often several passed before an area was secure.

Our world is very different from the Roman era, for which we should be grateful. In the ancient world warfare was frequent and it took the domination of an empire like Rome to establish peace over such a wide area. Whatever we think of empires in general and the Romans in particular, this was a remarkable achievement and one deserving admiration, whether or not it balances distaste for the savagery of Roman conquest. In the ancient world peace and stability were not the natural and inevitable condition of states left to their own devices. If the situation in the twenty-first century has improved, peace remains elusive over much of the globe, and is not something that simply happens on its own. This is most certainly not a call for a new Roman Empire, and is instead a reminder that so precious a thing as peace must be worked for.

CHRONOLOGY

753 BC Traditional date for foundation of Rome by Romulus.

509 Traditional date for expulsion of Rome's last king and creation of Republic. First treaty with Carthage.

496 The Romans defeat the Latin League at the Battle of Lake Regillus.

396 Capture of Veii; the Romans introduce pay for their army.

390 Rome sacked by Gauls.

340–338 League of Latin cities rebels against Rome and is defeated.

296 Romans defeat alliance of Samnites, Etruscans and Gauls at Sentinum.

280–275 War against King Pyrrhus of Epirus.

264–241 First Punic War.

225 Invading Gallic army defeated at Telamon.

218–201 Second Punic War.

214–205 First Macedonian War.

200–196 Second Macedonian War.

192–189 The Syrian War against the Seleucid King Antiochus III.

189 Manlius Vulso attacks the Galatians.

172–167 Third Macedonian War.

151–150 Sulpicius Galba governs Further Spain and massacres Lusitanians.

149–146 Third Punic War.

149–147 Fourth Macedonian War.

147–139 Career of Viriathus.

146 Destruction of Carthage and sack of Corinth.

135–132 Major slave rebellion in Sicily.

133 Fall of Numantia in Spain.

118 Colony founded at Narbo in Transalpine Gaul.

113 Romans come to assistance of king of Noricum and are defeated by Cimbri and Teutones.

112–106 War against King Jugurtha of Numidia.

105 Cimbri and Teutones destroy a large Roman army at Arausio.

102–101 Marius defeats Cimbri and Teutones.

91–88 The **Social War**, the last great rebellion by Rome's Italian allies.

88 Sulla marches his legions on Rome. Mithridates orders massacre of Romans in Asia.

88–85 First Mithridatic War.

83–82 Civil War won by Sulla.

83–82 Second Mithridatic War.

74–66 Third Mithridatic War.

74 Cicero quaestor in Sicily.

73–71 Verres governs Sicily.

73–70 Spartacus' rebellion.

67 Pompey given extraordinary command against the pirates.

66–63 Pompey defeats Mithridates, who commits suicide.

c.61 Ariovistus and the Sequani defeat the Aedui.

59 Ariovistus recognised as king and friend of the Roman people.

58–50 Caesar's Gallic campaigns.

58 Caesar defeats the Helvetii, and confronts and defeats Ariovistus.

53 Crassus defeated and killed by Parthians under Surenas at Carrhae.

52 Major Gallic rebellion led by Vercingetorix.

51–50 Cicero governs Cilicia as proconsul.

49–45 **Civil War** between Caesar and Pompey.

44 Caesar assassinated by conspiracy led by Brutus and Cassius.

44–31 Repeated Civil Wars, first between Caesar's supporters and the conspirators, and then between Antony and Octavian.

41–40 Parthians invade Syria and overrun neighbouring provinces.

38 Parthians expelled from Roman provinces.

36 Mark Antony invades Armenia and is forced into a very costly retreat by the Parthians.

31 Antony defeated by Octavian in naval battle at Actium. Octavian (soon to be given the name Augustus) becomes effectively the sole ruler of the Roman Empire.

27–AD 14 Principate of Augustus.

16–15 Conquest of the Alpine tribes.

12–7 Conquest of Pannonia and Germany.

4 Death of Herod the Great. Varus leads army into Judaea to deal with disturbances.

AD 6 Romans attack Maroboduus, but withdraw when news arrives of trouble in the Balkans.

6–9 Major revolt in Pannonia.

9 Major revolt in Germany. Varus and *Legiones XVII, XVIII* and *XIX* ambushed and massacred in the Teutoberg Wald.

14–37 Principate of Tiberius.

14–16 War against Arminius continues until halted by Tiberius.

17–24 Rebellion of Tacfarinas.

19 Death of Germanicus. Trial of Calpurnius Piso.

***c.*19** Arminius murdered by own chieftains.

21 Revolt of Florus and Sacrovir. Rebellion of some Thracian tribes.

26–36 Pontius Pilate governs Judaea as prefect.

28 Revolt of the Frisii.

37–41 Principate of Gaius (Caligula).

40–44 Mauretania rebels and is fully conquered by Suetonius Paulinus and later Hosidius Geta.

41–54 Principate of Claudius.

43 Invasion of Britain.

47 Rebellion by a group of Iceni put down by Ostorius Scapula. Corbulo campaigns east of the Rhine, but is recalled by Claudius.

54–68 Principate of Nero.

55–64 War with Parthia over control of Armenia.

59 Violent confrontation between rival crowds from Pompeii and Nuceria.

60–61 Rebellion of Boudicca in Britain.

66–74 The Jewish Rebellion.

68–69 Civil War – 'The Year of Four Emperors'. Galba, Otho and

Vitellius seize the throne in rapid succession, but war eventually won by Vespasian.

70–79 Principate of Vespasian.

70 Jerusalem captured after a long siege. Batavian Revolt.

73–74 Masada besieged and taken.

78–84 Agricola governs Britain and campaigns in the north.

79–81 Principate of Titus.

81–96 Principate of Domitian.

85–89 War with King Decebalus of Dacia.

96–98 Principate of Nerva.

98–117 Principate of Trajan.

101–102 Trajan's First Dacian War.

105–106 Trajan's Second Dacian War.

c.109–111 Pliny sent as legate to govern Bithynia and Pontus.

113–117 Trajan's Parthian War.

115–117 Rebellion by Jewish population of Egypt, Cyrenaica and Cyprus.

117–138 Principate of Hadrian.

122 Construction of Hadrian's Wall begun.

131–135 Bar Kochba Revolt in Judaea.

138–161 Principate of Antoninus Pius.

140–143 Construction of Antonine Wall begun.

161–180 Principate of Marcus Aurelius.

162–166 War with Parthia conducted and won by Marcus' co-ruler, Lucius Verus.

167–180 Warfare against German tribes on the Danube.

171/2 Revolt of the Boukoloi.

180–192 Principate of Commodus.

193–197 Civil War, eventually won by Severus.

197–211 Principate of Septimius Severus.

211–217 Caracalla's reign ends with his murder. This is followed by another period of civil war.

222–235 Principate of Severus Alexander.

476 Romulus Augustus, the last emperor in the West, is deposed.

GLOSSARY

Accensus: The senior clerk/secretary in charge of a proconsul's or propraetor's administrative staff. Such men were often well educated and trusted slaves or freedmen.

Aedile: The aediles were magistrates responsible for aspects of the day-to-day life of the City of Rome, including the staging of a number of annual festivals. Usually held between the quaestorship and the praetorship, there were fewer aediles than praetors and the post was not a compulsory part of the *cursus honorum*.

Aerarium militare: The Military Treasury or *aerarium militare* was established by Augustus in AD 6 to fund the army and in particular arrange for the pay and discharge bonuses of soldiers. Although he provided the bulk of the initial money from his own fortune, an unpopular inheritance tax was set up to support it in the future.

Aquilifer: The standard bearer who carried the legion's standard (*aquila*), a silver or gilded statuette of an eagle mounted on a staff.

Ala: (i) Republic: an *ala* was a legion-sized formation composed of Latin or other Italian soldiers. One *ala* usually accompanied each legion in the field.

(ii) Principate: an *ala* was a unit of auxiliary cavalry roughly equivalent in size to an infantry cohort.

Auctoritas: The prestige and influence of a Roman senator. *Auctoritas* was greatly boosted by military achievements.

Auxilia (**auxiliaries**): The non-citizen soldiers recruited into the army during the Late Republic and Principate were known generally as auxiliaries or supporting troops.

Ballista: A two-armed torsion catapult capable of firing bolts or stones with considerable accuracy. These were built in various sizes and most often used in sieges.

Beneficiarius: Experienced soldier attached to the staff of a provincial governor. They often performed policing functions and were detached as individuals or small groups.

Cataphract: Heavily armoured cavalryman often riding an armoured horse. These formed an important component of the Parthian army.

Centurion: Important grade of officers in the Roman army for most of its history; centurions originally commanded a century of eighty men. The most senior centurion of a legion was the *primus pilus*, a post of enormous status held only for a single year.

Century (*centuria*): The basic sub-unit of the Roman army, the century was commanded by a centurion and usually consisted of eighty men.

Cohort (*cohors*): The basic tactical unit of the legion, consisting of six centuries of eighty soldiers with a total strength of 480.

Consul: The year's two consuls were the senior elected magistrates of the Roman Republic, and held command in important campaigns. Sometimes the Senate extended their power after their year of office, in which case they were known as **proconsuls**.

Cornicularius: Clerk on the staff of a unit officer or provincial governor.

Cursus honorum: The term given to the career pattern regulating public life. Existing legislation dealing with age and other qualifications for elected magistracies was restated and reinforced by Sulla during his dictatorship, and subsequently modified by Augustus.

Decurio (**decurion**): Cavalry officer originally in command of a group of ten men. By the Principate a decurion commanded a *turma*, or about thirty men.

Dekanos: Civilian official in Egypt.

Denarius: The basic silver coin under the Principate. It was the 'penny' of the Authorised Bible, hence the pre-decimalisation abbreviation of *d* for pence.

Dictator: In times of extreme crisis a dictator was appointed for a six-month period during which he exercised supreme civil and military power. Later victors in civil wars, such as Sulla and Julius Caesar, used the title as a basis for more permanent power.

Diôgmitai: Police constables in many Hellenic cities. The name literally means 'chasers'.

Duplicarius: Soldier receiving double pay and probably acting as a junior officer.

Eirênarchai: Elected magistrates in many Hellenic cities whose duties included policing its territory.

Ephebe: Adolescent males in Greek cities underwent a process of state-supervised training at the gymnasium. This was mainly concerned with physical fitness, but often included elements of more specifically military training.

Equites (sing. *eques*): The equestrians or 'knights' were the group with the highest property qualification registered by the census. From the time of the Gracchi they were given a more formal public role as jurors in the courts, an issue that became extremely contentious. Only under Augustus was a separate senatorial order created as a distinct class.

Fasces (sing. *fascis*): An ornamental bundle of rods some 5 feet long in the middle of which was an axe. They were carried by **lictors** and were the most visible symbols of a magistrate's power and status.

Forum Augustum: The Forum constructed by Augustus with the Temple of Mars Ultor in its centre.

Forum Romanum: The political and economic heart of the City of Rome which lay between the Capitoline, Palatine, Quirinal and Velian hills. Public meetings were often held either around the **Rostra**, or at the eastern end of the Forum. The *Concilium plebis* and *Comitia tributa* also usually met in the Forum to legislate.

Frumentarii: Soldiers on detached service to supervise the military grain supply. Their duties involved regular travel to and from Rome and the provinces and over time they took on the role of an internal intelligence service.

Gladius: A Latin word meaning sword, *gladius* is conventionally used to describe the *gladius hispaniensis*, the Spanish sword which was the standard Roman sidearm until well into the third century AD. Made from high-quality steel, this weapon could be used for cutting, but was primarily intended for thrusting.

Hasmonean: In the second century BC, Judaea successfully rebelled against the Seleucids. An independent kingdom was created, ruled by the Hasmonean dynasty. Antony and Octavian eventually installed Herod the Great in place of the old royal family.

Imagines: Military standards bearing the image of the *princeps* or his family.

Immunis: Soldier exempt from fatigues, often because he possessed a specialist skill or trade.

Imperium: The power of military command held by magistrates and pro-magistrates during their term of office. Augustus and his successors were granted *maius imperium proconsulare* – i.e. proconsul power that was superior to that of all other proconsuls.

Legatus (pl. *legati*): A subordinate officer who held delegated *imperium* rather than exercising power in his own right and acted as the deputy of a governor. Under the Republic *legati* were chosen by a magistrate rather than elected. Under the Principate some were appointed by the *princeps*. Legates were also divided into two main grades, known as the *legatus legionis* who commanded a legion, and the *legatus Augusti* who commanded a province.

Legion (*legio*): Originally a term meaning levy, the legions became the main unit of the Roman army for much of its history. Under the Principate the theoretical strength of a legion was around 4,800–5,000 men in ten cohorts each of 480 men, although sometimes the first cohort was enlarged to 800 men. There was also a contingent of 120 horsemen and each legion was equipped with artillery and included many specialists in its ranks. The effective strength of a legion on campaign was often much lower than its theoretical strength.

***Librarius*:** Junior clerk in the headquarters of a unit.

Lictor: The official attendants of a magistrate who carried the *fasces* which symbolised his right to dispense justice and inflict capital and corporal punishment. Twelve lictors attended a consul, while a dictator was normally given twenty-four.

***Optio*:** A centurion's deputy and second-in-command of a century.

***Ornamenta triumphalia*:** Augustus introduced the 'ornaments' of a triumph, given as a reward in place of a triumph itself. After 19 BC, no one outside his extended family was granted a full triumph, but provincial governors who had won a victory were awarded this distinction instead.

Ovatio (**ovation**): A lesser form of the triumph, in an ovation the general rode through the City on horseback rather than in a chariot.

***Paraphylakes*:** Professional police commanders in some Hellenic cities.

Pilum (pl. *pila*): The heavy javelin which was the standard equipment of the Roman legionary for much of Rome's history. Its narrow head was designed to punch through an enemy's shield, the long, thin shank then giving it the reach to hit the man behind it.

Praesidium: A military garrison, ranging in size from small outposts to thousands of men.

Praetorian guard: Augustus established nine permanent praetorian cohorts to form his guard. At this stage they had no permanent barracks in Rome and only three cohorts were ever present in the City at one time. This changed under Tiberius, when all nine cohorts were concentrated in a fort in Rome. In most cases the praetorians only went on campaign if the emperor or a member of the imperial family led the army.

Praetor: Praetors were annually elected magistrates who under the Republic governed the less important provinces and fought Rome's smaller wars. When serving as governors their command might be extended, in which case they were given the title of propraetor.

Prefect (*praefectus*): (i) One of three senior officers leading a Republican allied *ala* and effectively equivalent to a tribune in a legion.

(ii) Governor of an equestrian province, e.g. Judaea till AD 66 and Egypt.

(iii) Commander of an auxiliary *ala* or cohort under the Principate.

Primi ordines: The centurions of the first cohort of a legion. These men were the most senior in the centurionate, and enjoyed considerable status.

Primus pilus: The commander of the first century of the first cohort and the senior centurion of the legion.

Principate: Modern term for the regime created by Augustus, meaning the rule of a *princeps*, sometimes less accurately referred to as an emperor.

Princeps: First citizen, and leader of the Senate, People and State, *princeps* was the term Augustus preferred for his own status. In the past the senatorial roll was headed by a *princeps senatus*, chosen by the censors supposedly as the council's most prestigious and respected member. In all usages, the term had no particular powers, but was a mark of esteem and respect.

Procurator: (i) Title for governor of equestrian provinces from *c.*40, replacing the earlier title of prefect.

(ii) Financial administrator similar to a quaestor, but serving in imperial provinces.

Quaestor: Magistrates whose duties were primarily financial, quaestors acted as deputies to consular governors and often held subordinate military commands.

Regionarius (fully *centurio regionarius*): A centurion placed in charge of a region or district.

Scorpion: The light bolt-shooting ballista employed by the Roman army both in the field and in sieges. They possessed a long range, as well as great accuracy and the ability to penetrate any form of armour.

Sesquiplicarius: Soldier receiving one and half times normal pay, and probably holding a specialist post or acting as a junior officer.

Signifer: The junior officer who carried the *signum* standard of a century. In the imperial army he was also responsible for a range of administrative roles within the unit, most notably supervising the soldiers' pay and savings.

Singulares: The elite bodyguards of a senior Roman officer under the Principate, such as a legionary or provincial legate. These men were normally auxiliaries seconded from their units. The *singulares Augusti* were an elite cavalry unit drawn from the entire empire and attached to the praetorian guard.

Stationarii: Soldiers detached from their unit to serve in a garrison.

Talent: The actual size of this Greek measurement of weight – and by extension money – varied considerably, from about 57 to 83 pounds. It is rarely clear from sources who employ the term which standard was in use.

Tesserarius: One of the junior officers within a century, the name was derived from the *tessera* tablet on which was written the watch-word for the day.

Tribuni aerarii: The group registered below the equestrian order in the census. Relatively little is known about them.

Tribunus militum (**military tribune**): Six military tribunes were elected or appointed to each Republican legion, one pair holding command at any one time. Under Augustus the number remained at six, but of these one was pursuing a senatorial career and was senior. This man, the *tribunus laticlavius* from the broad stripe worn around his cuirass, was second-in-command to the legionary legate. The other five tribunes, the *tribuni angusticlavii* who wore a narrow stripe, were equestrians and had usually already served in command of an auxiliary cohort.

Triumph: The great celebration granted by the Senate to a success-ful general took the form of a procession along the Sacra Via, the ceremonial main road of Rome, displaying the spoils and captives of his victory, and culminated in the ritual execution of the captured enemy leader. The commander rode in a chariot, dressed like the statues of Jupiter, a slave holding a laurel wreath of Victory over his head. The slave was supposed to whisper to the general, reminding him that he was mortal.

Triumvir: In 43 BC Antony, Lepidus and Octavian were named as *triumviri rei publicae constituendae* (board of three to reconstitute the state) by the *lex Titia* proposed by a tribune and passed by the *Concilium plebis*. The triumvirate was granted dictatorial powers, initially for five years.

Urban cohorts: Three urban cohorts were raised by Augustus as a paramilitary police force for Rome itself. They were commanded by the urban prefect. It is possible that a fourth cohort was raised under Augustus to guard the imperial mint at Lugdunum in Gaul, since the unit was certainly there under Tiberius.

Vergobret: Elected senior magistrate in many Gallic tribes such as the Aedui.

Vexillation (*vexillatio*): (i) A detachment of troops operating away from their parent unit or units.

   (ii) Name given to some cavalry units in the late Roman army.

Vexillum: A square flag mounted crosswise on a pole, the *vexillum* was used to mark a general's position and was also the standard carried by a detachment of troops. A general's *vexillum* seems usually to have been red.

Vigiles: Formed by Augustus in AD 6, the seven cohorts of *vigiles* acted as a fire brigade and night police for the City of Rome. Each cohort was placed in control of two of the fourteen regions formed at the same time.

ABBREVIATIONS

AE = *L'Année Épigraphique*

ANRW = *Aufstieg und Niedergang der römischen Welt*

Appian, *BC* = Appian, *Civil Wars*

Appian, *Bell. Hisp.* = Appian, *Spanish Wars*

Appian, *Mith.* = Appian, *The Mithridatic Wars*

Broughton, *MRR* 2 = T. Broughton & M. Patterson (1951), *The Magistrates of the Roman Republic* Vol. 2

Caesar, *BC* = Caesar, *The Civil Wars*

Caesar, *BG* = Caesar, *The Gallic Wars*

CAH² IX = J. Crook, A. Lintott & E. Rawson (eds), *The Cambridge Ancient History* 2nd edn Vol. IX: *The Last Age of the Roman Republic, 146–43 BC*

CAH² X = A. Bowman, E. Champlin & A. Lintott (eds), *The Cambridge Ancient History* 2nd edn Vol. X: *The Augustan Empire, 43 BC–AD 69*

Cicero, *ad Att.* = Cicero, *Letters to Atticus*

Cicero, *ad Fam.* = Cicero, *Letters to his friends*

Cicero, *ad Quintum Fratrem* = Cicero, *Letters to his Brother Quintus*

Cicero, *Verrines* = Cicero, *Verrine Orations*

CIG = *Corpus Inscriptionum Graecarum*

CIL = *Corpus Inscriptionum Latinarum*

Dio = Cassius Dio, *Roman History*

Galen, *Comm. In Hipp. Epid., CMG* = C. Kühn, *Galenus Medicus* (1821–33), supplemented by H. Diels *et alii* (1918–)

Hist. = *Histories*

ILLRP = A. Degrassi (ed.) (1963–5), *Inscriptiones Latinae Liberae Rei Republicae*

ILS = H. Dessau (1892–1916), *Incriptiones Latinae Selectae*

JARCE = *Journal of the American Research Center in Egypt*

Josephus, *Ant.* = Josephus, *Jewish Antiquities*

Josephus, *BJ* = Josephus, *The Jewish War*

JRA = *Journal of Roman Archaeology*

JRS = *Journal of Roman Studies*

Livy, *Pers.* = Livy, *Roman History. Periochae.*

OGIS = W. Dittenberger, *Orientis Graeci Inscriptiones Selectae* (1903–5)

PCPS = *Proceedings of the Cambridge Philological Society*

Pliny the Elder, *NH* = Pliny the Elder, *Natural History*

Pliny the Younger, *Ep.* = Pliny the Younger, *Letters*

Sallust, *Bell. Cat.* = Sallust, *The Catilinarian War*

Sallust, *Bell. Jug.* = Sallust, *The Jugurthine War*

SEG = P. Roussel, M. Tod, E. Ziebarth & J. Hondius (eds),
  Supplementum Epigraphicum Graecum (1923–)

Strabo, *Geog.* = Strabo, *Geography*

Tacitus, *Ann.* = Tacitus, *Annals*

Valerius Maximus = Valerius Maximus, *Memorable Doings and Sayings*

Velleius Paterculus = Velleius Paterculus, *Roman History*

ZPE = *Zeitschrift für Papyrologie und Epigraphik*

BIBLIOGRAPHY

G. Alföldy (trans. A. Birley), *Noricum* (1974)

R. Alston, *Soldier and Society in Roman Egypt. A Social History* (1995), pp. 20–38

R. Alston, 'The ties that bind: soldiers and societies', in A. Goldsworthy & I. Haynes (eds), *The Roman Army as a Community. JRA Supplementary Series* 34 (1999), pp. 175–95

N. Austin & B. Rankov, *Exploratio. Military and Political Intelligence in the Roman World from the Second Punic War to the Battle of Adrianople* (1995)

E. Badian, *Roman Imperialism in the Late Republic* (1968)

E. Badian, *Publicans and Sinners* (1972)

R. Bagnall, 'Army and police in upper Egypt', *JARCE* 14 (1976), pp. 67–88

R. Bagnall & B. Frier, *The Demography of Roman Egypt* (1994)

J. Barlow, 'Noble Gauls and their other', in K. Welch & A. Powell (eds), *Julius Caesar as Artful Reporter: The War Commentaries as Political Instruments* (1998), pp. 139–70

T. Barnes, 'The Victories of Augustus', *JRS* 64 (1974), pp. 21–6

D. Baronowski, 'Roman military forces in 225 BC (Polybius 2. 23–4)', *Historia* 42 (1993), pp. 181–202

A. Barrett, *Livia. First Lady of Imperial Rome* (2002)

A. Barrett, 'Aulus Caecina Severus and the Military Woman', *Historia* 54 (2005), pp. 301–14

M. Beard, *The Roman Triumph* (2007)

G. de la Bédoyère review of D. Mattingly, *An Imperial Possession. Britain in the Roman Empire 54 BC–AD 409* (2006), in *History Today* (August 2006), p. 62

K. Beloch, *Die Bevölkerung der griechisch-römischen Welt* (1886)

L. Beness & T. Hillard, '*Rei Militaris Virtus . . . Orbem Terrarum Parere*

Huic Imperio Coegit: The transformation of Roman *Imperium*', in D. Hoyos, *A Companion to Roman Imperialism* (2013), pp. 141–53

P. Bidwell, *Roman Forts in Britain* (2007)

P. Bidwell, 'Systems of obstacles on Hadrian's wall and their relationship to the turrets', in A. Moirillo, N. Hanel & E. Martín, *Limes XX: Estudios sobre la frontera romana. Roman Frontier Studies. Anejos de Gladius* 13, Vol. 3 (2009), pp. 1119–24

R. Billows, 'The religious procession of the Ara Pacis Augustae: Augustus' *supplicatio* in 13 BC', *JRA* 6 (1993), pp. 80–92

E. Birley, 'Marcus Cocceius Firmus: an epigraphic study', in E. Birley (ed.), *Roman Britain and the Roman Army. Collected papers* (1953), pp. 87–103

E. Birley, 'The origins of legionary centurions', & 'Promotion and transfer in the Roman army II: the centurionate', in E. Birley, *The Roman Army. Papers 1929–1986* (1988), pp. 189–220

E. Birley, 'Senators in the emperor's service' and 'Promotion and transfers in the Roman army: senatorial and equestrian officers', in E. Birley, *The Roman Army. Papers 1929–1986* (1988), pp. 75–114

M. Bishop, '*Praesidium*: social, military, and logistical aspects of the Roman army's provincial distribution during the early Principate', in A. Goldsworthy & I. Haynes (eds), *The Roman Army as a Community in Peace and War. JRA Supplementary Series* 34 (1999), pp. 111–18

M. Bishop & B. Coulston, *Roman Military Equipment. From the Punic Wars to the Fall of Rome* (2nd edn, 2006)

M. Bishop, *Handbook to Roman Legionary Fortresses* (2012)

J. Boardman, *The Greeks Overseas: Their Early Colonies and Trade* (4th edn, 1999)

Y. Le Bohec, *The Imperial Roman Army* (1994)

H. Bond, *Pontius Pilate in History and Interpretation. Society for New Testament Studies Monograph Series* 100 (1998), pp. 94–207

G. Bowersock, 'The mechanics of subversion in the Roman Provinces', in *Opposition et résistance à l'empire d'Auguste à Trajan*, Entretiens sur L'antiquité classique (1987), pp. 291–317

G. Bowersock, *Augustus and the Greek World* (1965)

A. Bowman, 'A letter of Avidius Cassius?', *JRS* 60 (1970), pp. 20–26

K. Bradley, 'Slavery in the Roman Republic', in K. Bradley & P. Cartledge (eds), *The Cambridge World History of Slavery* Vol. 1: *The Ancient Mediterranean* (2011), pp. 241–64

D. Braund, 'The Aedui, Troy, and the Apocolocyntosis', *Classical Quarterly* 30 (1980), pp. 420–25

D. Breeze & B. Dobson, *Hadrian's Wall* (4th edn, 2000)

D. Breeze, *Handbook to the Roman Wall* (14th edn, 2006)

D. Breeze, *The Frontiers of Imperial Rome* (2011)

T. Broughton, *The Magistrates of the Roman Republic* Vol. 3 (1986)

P. Brunt, 'Charges of provincial maladministration under the early principate' *Historia* 10 (1961), pp. 189–227

P. Brunt, *Italian Manpower 225 BC–AD 14* (1971)

P. Brunt, 'Did Imperial Rome disarm her subjects?', *Phoenix* 29 (1975), pp. 260–70

P. Brunt, *The Fall of the Roman Republic and Related Essays* (1988)

T. Burns, *Rome and the Barbarians, 100 BC–AD 200* (2003)

G. Burton, 'Proconsuls, assizes, and the administration of justice under the empire', *JRS* 65 (1975), pp. 92–106

G. Burton, 'The issuing of mandata to proconsuls and a new inscription from Cos', *ZPE* 21 (1976), pp. 63–8

C. Callwell, *Small Wars. A Tactical Textbook for Imperial Soldiers* (rev. edn, 1990)

J. Camp, *The Archaeology of Athens* (2001)

J. Campbell, 'Who were the *viri militares*?' *JRS* 65 (1975), pp. 11–31

J. Campbell, *The Emperor and the Roman Army 31 BC–AD 235* (1984)

J. Campbell, 'War and diplomacy: Rome and Parthia, 31 BC–AD 235', in J. Rich & G. Shipley (eds), *War and Society in the Roman World* (1993), pp. 213–240

A. Carandini (trans. S. Sartarelli), *Rome. Day One* (2011)

L. Casson (ed.), *The Periplus Maris Erythraei: Text with Introduction, Translation and Commentary* (1999)

D. Cherry, *Frontier and Society in Roman North Africa* (1998)

D. Conlin, *The Artists of the Ara Pacis. Studies in the History of Greece and Rome* (1997)

P. Conole & R. Milns, 'Neronian frontier policy in the Balkans: the career of Ti. Plautius Silvanus', *Historia* 32 (1983), pp. 183–200

T. Cornell, 'The end of Roman imperial expansion', in J. Rich & G. Shipley (eds), *War and Society in the Roman World* (1993), pp. 139–70

T. Cornell, *The Beginnings of Rome. Italy and Rome from the Bronze Age to the Punic Wars (c.1000–264 BC)* (1995)

T. Corsten, 'Estates in Roman Asia Minor: the case of Kibyratis', in S. Mitchell & C. Katsari (eds), *Patterns in the Economy of Roman Asia Minor* (2005), pp. 1–51

R. Cowan, *Roman Conquests – Italy* (2009)

M. Crawford, *Roman Republican Coinage* (1974)

M. Crawford, *The Roman Republic* (1978)

B. Cunliffe, *Hengistbury Head* Vol. 1 (1987)

B. Cunliffe, *Greeks, Romans and Barbarians: Spheres of Interaction* (1988)

B. Cunliffe, *Facing the Ocean: The Atlantic and its Peoples 800 BC–AD 1500* (2001)

H. Cuvigny, *Ostraca de Krokodilô. La correspondence militaire et sa circulation (O. Krok. 1–151). Praesidia du désert de Bérénice II. Fouilles de l'IFAO* 51 (2005)

R. Davies, 'The investigation of some crimes in Roman Egypt', in R. Davies (with D. Breeze and V. Maxfield, eds), *Service in the Roman Army* (1989), pp. 175–85

D. Dawson, *The Origins of Western Warfare. Militarism and Morality in the Ancient World* (1996)

B. Decharneux, 'The Carabas affair (in Flacc 36–39): An incident emblematic of Philo's political philosophy', in P. Tomson & J. Schwartz (eds), *Jews and Christians in the First and Second Centuries: How to Write their History* (2014), pp. 70–79

H. Delbrück (trans. J. Renfroe), *History of the Art of War* Vol. 1: *Warfare in Antiquity* (1975)

T. Derks, *Gods, Temples and Ritual Practices: The Transformation of Religious Ideas and Values in Roman Gaul* (1998)

P. Derow, 'Polybius, Rome and the east', *JRS* 69 (1979), pp. 1–5

S. Dmitriev, *City Government in Hellenistic and Roman Asia Minor* (2005)

B. Dobson, 'Legionary centurion or equestrian officer? A comparison of pay and prospects', *Ancient Society* 3 (1972), pp. 193–207

B. Dobson, 'The significance of the centurion and *primipilaris* in the Roman army and administration', *ANRW* 2. 1 (1974), pp. 392–434

B. Dobson, 'The rôle of the fort', in W. Hanson (ed.), *The Army and the Frontiers. JRA Supplementary Series* 74 (2009), pp. 25–32

J. Drinkwater, *The Alamanni and Rome 213–496 (Caracalla to Clovis)* (2007)

S. Dyson, 'Native Revolts in the Roman Empire', *Historia* 20 (1971), pp. 239–74

S. Dyson, 'Native Revolt Patterns in the Roman Empire', *ANRW* 2. 3 (1975), pp. 138–75

S. Dyson, *The Creation of the Roman Frontier* (1985)

S. Dyson, *Rome. A Living Portrait of an Ancient City* (2010)

W. Eck, *The Age of Augustus* (2003)

A. Eckstein, *Mediterranean Anarchy, Interstate War, and the Rise of Rome* (2006)

A. Eckstein. 'Hegemony and annexation beyond the Adriatic 230–146 BC', in D. Hoyos (ed.), *A Companion to Roman Imperialism* (2013), pp. 79–97

C. Edwards & G . Woolf (eds), *Rome the Cosmopolis* (2003)

R. Errington, *The Dawn of Empire: Rome's Rise to World Power* (1971)

C. Esdaile, *Outpost of Empire. The Napoleonic Occupation of Andalucia, 1810–1812* (2012)

N. Faulkner, *Apocalypse. The Great Jewish Revolt against Rome* AD 66–73 (2002)

E. Fentress, *Numidia and the Roman Army. BAR International Series* 53 (1979)

J. Ferrary, 'The powers of Augustus', in J. Edmondson (ed.), *Augustus* (2009), pp. 90–136

T. Frank (ed.), *An Economic Survey of Ancient Rome* Vol. 1 (1933)

T. Frazel, 'The composition and circulation of Cicero's "In Verrem"', *The Classical Quarterly* 54. 1 (2004), pp. 128–42

S. Freyne, 'The Revolt from a regional perspective', in A. Berlin & J. Overman (eds), *The First Jewish Revolt. Archaeology, History, and Ideology* (2002), pp. 43–56

B. Frier, 'Roman Demography', in D. Potter & D. Mattingly (eds),

Life, Death and Entertainment in the Roman Empire (1999), pp. 95–109

C. Fuhrmann, *Policing the Roman Empire. Soldiers, Administration and Public Order* (2012)

K. Galinsky, *Augustus. Introduction to the Life of an Emperor* (2012)

J. Gardner, 'The "Gallic menace" in Caesar's Propaganda', *Greece and Rome* 30 (1983), pp. 181–9

R. Garland, *The Wandering Greeks: The Ancient Greek Diaspora from the Age of Homer to the Death of Alexander* (2014)

P. Garnsey, *Famine and Food Supply in the Graeco-Roman World* (1988)

M. Gelzer (trans. P. Needham), *Caesar. Politician and Statesman* (1968)

R. Gibson, 'On the nature of ancient letter collections', *JRS* 102 (2012), pp. 56–78

M. Gichon, 'Life on the borders reflected in rabbinical sources', in A. Morillo, N. Hanl & E. Martín (eds), *Limes XX. Estudios Sobre La Frontera Romana Roman Frontier Studies* Vol. 1 (2009), pp. 113–18

A. Goldsworthy, *The Roman Army at War 100 BC–AD 200* (1996)

A. Goldsworthy, *The Punic Wars* (2000) (= *The Fall of Carthage*, 2003)

A. Goldsworthy, *The Complete Roman Army* (2003)

A. Goldsworthy, *In the Name of Rome* (2003)

A. Goldsworthy, *Caesar: The Life of a Colossus* (2006)

A. Goldsworthy, 'War', in P. Sabin, H. van Wees & M. Whitby (eds), *The Cambridge History of Greek and Roman Warfare* Vol. 2: *Rome from the Late Republic to the Late Empire* (2007), pp. 76–121

A. Goldsworthy, *The Fall of the West. The Death of the Roman Superpower* (= *How Rome Fell*) (2009)

A. Goldsworthy, *Antony and Cleopatra* (2010)

A. Goldsworthy, *Augustus. From Revolutionary to Emperor* (= *Augustus. The First Emperor*) (2014)

A. Goldsworthy, '"Men casually armed against fully equipped regulars": The Roman military response to Jewish insurgence 63 BCE–135 CE', in P. Tomson & J. Schwartz (eds), *Jews and Christians in the First and Second Centuries: How to Write their History* (2014), pp. 207–37

M. Goodman, *The Ruling Class of Judaea. The Origins of the Jewish Revolt against Rome AD 66–70* (1987)

C. Goudineau, *César et la Gaule* (1995)

P. Green, *Alexander to Actium* (1990)

B. Grenfell, A. Hunt, H. Bell *et alii* (eds), *The Oxyrhynchus Papyri* (1898–)

M. Griffin, 'The Senate's story. Review of Das Senatus Consultum de Cn. Pisone Patre by Werner Eck; Antonio Caballos; Fernando Fernández', *JRS* 87 (1997), pp. 249–63

E. Gruen, *The Hellenistic World and the Coming of Rome* (1984)

E. Gruen, 'Material rewards and the drive for empire', in W. Harris (ed.), *The Imperialism of Mid-Republican Rome* (1984), pp. 59–82

E. Gruen, 'Roman perspectives on the Jews in the age of the Great Revolt', in A. Berlin & J. Overman (eds), *The First Jewish Revolt. Archaeology, History, and Ideology* (2002), pp. 27–42

T. Grünewald (trans. J. Drinkwater), *Bandits in the Roman Empire. Myth and Reality* (2004)

N. Hammond, 'The western part of the via Egnatia', *JRS* 64 (1974), pp. 185–94

D. Harding, *The Iron Age in Northern Britain. Celts, Romans, Natives and Invaders* (2004)

W. Harris, *War and Imperialism in Republican Rome 327–70 BC* (1979)

W. Harris, 'Demography, Geography, and the supply of slaves', *JRS* 89 (1999), pp. 62–75

M. Hassall, M. Crawford & J. Reynolds, 'Rome and the Eastern Provinces at the end of the Second Century BC', *JRS* 64 (1974), pp. 195–220

J. Hatzfield, 'Les Italiens résidant à Délos', *Bulletin de Correspondance Hellénique* 36 (1912), 143

I. Haynes, *Blood of the Provinces. The Roman Auxilia and the Making of Provincial Society from Augustus to Severus* (2013)

J. Hind, 'A. Plautius' campaign in Britain: an alternative reading of the narrative in Cassius Dio (60. 19. 5–21. 2)', *Britannia* 38 (2007), pp. 93–106

E. Hobsbawm, *Bandits* (1969)

N. Hodgson, 'Gates and passages across the frontiers: the use of openings through the barriers of Britain, Germany and Raetia', in

Z. Visy, *Limes XIX. Proceedings of the XIXth International Congress of Roman Frontier Studies held in Pécs, Hungary, September 2003* (2005), pp. 183–7

G. Hölbl (trans. T. Saavedra), *A History of the Ptolemaic Empire* (2001)

K. Hopkins, *Conquerors and Slaves* (1978)

K. Hopkins, 'Rome, taxes, rent and trade', in W. Scheidel & S. von Reden (eds), *The Ancient Economy* (2002), pp. 190–230

R. Horsley, 'Power vacuum and power struggle 66–7 CE', in A. Berlin & J. Overman (eds), *The First Jewish Revolt. Archaeology, History, and Ideology* (2002), pp. 87–109

F. Hunter, 'Iron age hoarding in Scotland and northern Britain', in A. Gwilt & C. Haselgrove (eds), *Reconstructing Iron Age Societies* (1997), pp. 108–33

F. Hunter, 'Roman and native in Scotland: new approaches', *JRA* 14 (2001), pp. 289–309

F. Hunter, 'The lives of Roman objects beyond the frontier', in P. Wells (ed.), *Rome Beyond its Frontiers; Imports, Attitudes and Practices*, *JRA Supplementary Series* 95 (2013), pp. 15–28

J. Ilkjaer, 'Danish war booty sacrifices', in B. Stoorgard & L. Thomsen (eds), *The Spoils of Victory. The North in the Shadow of the Roman Empire* (2003), pp. 44–65

B. Isaac, *The Limits of Empire. The Roman Army in the East* (rev. edn, 1992)

S. James, *Rome and the Sword. How Warriors and Weapons Shaped Roman History* (2011)

X. Jensen, L. Jørgensen & U. Hansen, 'The Germanic army: warriors, soldiers and officers', in B. Stoorgard & L. Thomsen (eds), *The Spoils of Victory. The North in the Shadow of the Roman Empire* (2003), pp. 310–28

A. Johnson, *Roman Forts* (1983)

M. Johnson, *Boudicca* (2012)

A. Jørgensen, 'Fortifications and the control of land and sea traffic in the Pre-Roman and Roman Iron Age', in B. Stoorgard & L. Thomsen (eds), *The Spoils of Victory. The North in the Shadow of the Roman Empire* (2003), pp. 194–209

R. Kallet-Marx, *Hegemony to Empire. The Development of the Roman Imperium in the East from 148 to 62 BC* (1995)

D. Kennedy, 'Parthia and Rome: Eastern Perspectives', in D. Kennedy (ed.), *The Roman Army in the East. JRA Supplement* 18 (1996), pp. 67–90

T. Kinsella, *The Táin. From the Irish Epic Táin Bó Cuailnge* (1969)

C. Kokkinia, 'Ruling, inducing, arguing: how to govern (and survive) a Greek province', in L. de Light, E. Hemelrijk & H. Singor (eds), *Roman Rule and Civic Life: Local and Regional Perspectives. Impact of Empire* Vol. 4 (2004), pp. 39–58

W. Lacey, *Augustus and the Principate. The Evolution of a System* (1996)

S. Lancel, *Carthage* (Oxford, 1995)

J. Lazenby, *The First Punic War* (1996)

J. Lazenby, *Hannibal's War. A Military History of the Second Punic War* (1998)

J. Lendon, *Empire of Honour. The Art of Government in the Roman World* (1997)

J. Lendon, *Song of Wrath. The Peloponnesian War Begins* (2010)

F. Lepper & S. Frere, *Trajan's Column* (1988)

B. Levick, 'The Veneti Revisited: C. E. Stevens and the tradition of Caesar the propagandist', in K. Welch & A. Powell (eds), *Julius Caesar as Artful Reporter: The War Commentaries as Political Instruments* (1998), pp. 61–83

B. Levick, *The Government of the Roman Empire. A Sourcebook* (2nd edn, 2000)

J. Liebeschuetz, 'The settlement of 27 BC', in C. Deroux, *Studies in Latin Literature and Roman History* (2008), pp. 346–53

A. Lintott, '*Leges Repetundae* and associate measures under the Republic', *Zeitschrift der Savigny-Stiftung für Rechtsgeschichte: Romanistische Abteilung* 98 (1981) pp. 194–5

A. Lintott, *Imperium Romanum. Politics and Administration* (1993)

A. Lintott, *The Constitution of the Roman Republic* (1999)

E. Luttwak, *The Grand Strategy of the Roman Empire: From the First Century ad to the Third* (1976)

L. Keppie, *The Making of the Roman Army* (1984)

C. Kraus, 'Bellum Gallicum', in M. Griffin (ed.), *A Companion to Julius Caesar* (2009), pp. 159–74

J. Ma, 'Peer Polity Interaction in the Hellenistic Age', *Past & Present* 180 (2003), pp. 9–39

R. MacMullen, *Enemies of the Roman Order* (1966)

R. MacMullen, *Roman Government's Response to Crisis AD 235–337* (1976)

J. Madsen, *Eager to be Roman. Greek Response to Roman Rule in Pontus and Bithynia* (2009)

J. Manley, *AD 43. The Roman Invasion of Britain – A Reassessment* (2002)

A. Marshall, 'The Structure of Cicero's Edict', *The American Journal of Philology* 85 (1964), pp. 185–91

A. Marshall, 'Governors on the Move', *Phoenix* 20 (1966), pp. 231–46

A. Marshall, 'The *Lex Pompeia de provinciis* (52 BC) and Cicero's *Imperium* in 51–50 BC: Constitutional aspects', *ANRW* I. 1 (1972), pp. 887–921

A. Marshall, 'Tacitus and the governor's lady: a note on Annals iii. 31–4', *Greece and Rome* 22 (1975), pp. 11–18

R. Marichal, *Les Ostraca du Bu Njem* (1979), pp. 436–52

S. Mason, 'Why did Judaeans go to war with Rome in 66–67 CE? Realist-Regional perspectives', in P. Tomson & J. Schwartz (eds), *Jews and Christians in the First and Second Centuries: How to Write their History* (2014), pp. 126–206

S. Mattern, *Rome and the Enemy. Imperial Strategy in the Principate* (1999)

D. Mattingly (ed.), *The Archaeology of the Fazzān* Vol. 1: *Synthesis* (2003)

D. Mattingly, *An Imperial Possession. Britain in the Roman Empire* (2006)

D. Mattingly, *Imperialism, Power, and Identity. Experiencing the Roman Empire 54 BC–AD 409* (2011)

P. Matyszak, *Mithridates the Great. Rome's Indomitable Enemy* (2008)

V. Maxfield, *The Military Decorations of the Roman Army* (1981)

V. Maxfield, 'Ostraca and the Roman army in the eastern desert', in J. Wilkes (ed.), *Documenting the Roman Army. Essays in Honour of Margaret Roxan* (2003), pp. 153–73

A. Mayor, *The Poison King. The Life and Legend of Mithridates, Rome's Deadliest Enemy* (2010)

P. McKechnie, 'Judaean embassies and cases before Roman Emperors, AD 44–66', *Journal of Theological Studies* 56 (2005), pp. 339–61

C. Meier (trans. D. McLintock), *Caesar* (1996)

E. Meyers, 'Roman Sepphoris in the light of new archaeological evidence and recent research', in L. Levine (ed.), *The Galilee in Late Antiquity* (1992), pp. 321–28

R. Miles, *Carthage Must Be Destroyed. The Rise and Fall of an Ancient Civilization* (2010)

F. Millar, *The Emperor in the Roman World (31 BC–AD 337)* (1977)

F. Millar, 'The world of the Golden Ass', *JRS* 71 (1981), pp. 63–75

F. Millar, 'Emperors, frontiers and foreign relations, 31 BC to AD 378', *Britannia* 13 (1982), pp. 1–23

F. Millar, 'The Mediterranean and the Roman Revolution: Politics, war and the economy', *Past & Present* 102 (1984), pp. 3–24

F. Millar, 'State and Subject: the impact of monarchy', in F. Millar & E. Segal (eds), *Caesar Augustus. Seven Aspects* (corrected paperback edn, 1990), pp. 37–60

F. Millar, *The Roman Near East 31 BC–AD 337* (1993)

S. Mitchell, 'Requisitioned transport in the Roman empire: a new inscription from Pisidia', *JRS* 66 (1976), pp. 106–31

S. Mitchell, *Anatolia. Land, Men, and Gods in Asia Minor* Vol. 1: *The Celts in Anatolia and the Impact of Roman Rule* (1993)

S. Mitchell, 'Olive oil cultivation in the economy of Roman Asia Minor', in S. Mitchell & C. Katsari (eds), *Patterns in the Economy of Roman Asia Minor* (2005), pp. 83–113

A. Morillo Cerdán, 'The Augustean Spanish Experience: The origin of the *limes* system?', in A. Moirillo, N. Hanel & E. Martín, *Limes XX: Estudios sobre la frontera romana. Roman Frontier Studies. Anejos de Gladius* 13, Vol. 1 (2009), pp. 239–51

N. Morley, *The Roman Empire. Roots of Imperialism* (2010)

A. Murdoch, *Rome's Greatest Defeat. Massacre in the Teutoburg Forest* (2006)

H. Musurillo, *The Acts of the Pagan Martyrs, Acta Alexandrinorum* (1954)

D. Nappo & A. Zerbini, 'Trade and taxation in the Egyptian desert', in O. Hekster & T. Kaizer (eds), *Frontiers in the Roman World. Proceedings of the Ninth Workshop of the International Network Impact of Empire (Durham, 16–19 April 2009)* (2011), pp. 61–77

O. van Nijf, 'Local heroes: athletics, festivals and elite self-fashioning in the Roman East', in S. Goldhill (ed.), *Being Greek under Rome. Cultural Identity, the Second Sophistic and the Development of Empire* (2001), pp. 306–34

J. North, 'The development of Roman imperialism', *JRS* 71 (1981), pp. 1–9

S. Oakley, 'The Roman conquest of Italy', in J. Rich & G. Shipley (eds), *War and Society in the Roman World* (1993), pp. 9–37

J. Oliver, 'A Roman governor visits Samothrace', *American Journal of Philology* 87 (1966), pp. 75–80

J. Osgood, *Caesar's Legacy: Civil War and the Emergence of the Roman Empire* (2006)

J. Osgood, 'The Pen and the Sword: Writing and Conquest in Caesar's Gaul', *Classical Antiquity* 28 (2009), pp. 328–58

F. Queseda Sanz, *Arma de la Antigua Iberia de Tatessos a Numancia* (2010)

E. Palmer, *Carthage and Rome at Peace* (1997)

T. Parkin, *Demography and Roman Society* (1992)

T. Pekàry, 'Seditio: Unruhen und Revolten im römischen Reich von Augustus bis Commodus', *Ancient Society* 18 (1987), pp. 133–150

G. Picard & C. Picard, *Carthage* (rev. edn, 1987)

L. Pitts, 'Relations between Rome and the German "kings" on the Middle Danube in the first to fourth centuries AD', *JRS* 79 (1989), pp. 45–58

S. Pomeroy, 'Coprynyms and the exposure of infants in Egypt', in A. Cameron & A. Kuhrt (eds), *Images of Women in Antiquity* (1983), pp. 207–22

D. Potter, 'Empty areas and Roman frontier policy', *American Journal of Philology* 113 (1992), pp. 269–74

D. Potter, 'Emperors, their borders and their neighbours: the scope of imperial *mandata*', in D. Kennedy (ed.), *The Roman Army in the East. JRA Supplementary Series* 18 (1996), pp. 49–66

J. Prag, '*Auxilia* and *gymnasia*: A Sicilian model of Roman Imperialism', *JRS* 97 (2007), pp. 68–100

J. Prag, *Sicilia Nutrix Plebis Romanae. Rhetoric, Law, and Taxation in Cicero's Verrines* (2007)

R. Preston, 'Roman questions, Greek answers: Plutarch and the construction of identity', in S. Goldhill (ed.), *Being Greek under Rome. Cultural Identity, the Second Sophistic and the Development of Empire* (2001), pp. 86–119

N. Purcell, 'The creation of provincial landscape: the Roman imprint on Cisalpine Gaul', in T. Blagg & M. Millet (eds), *The Early Roman Empire in the West* (1990), pp. 7–29

B. Rankov, 'The governor's men: the *officium consularis*', in A. Goldsworthy & I. Haynes (eds), *The Roman Army as a Community in Peace and War. JRA Supplementary Series* 34 (1999), pp. 15–34

B. Rankov, 'Do rivers make good frontiers?', in Z. Visy, *Limes XIX. Proceedings of the XIXth International Congress of Roman Frontier Studies held in Pécs, Hungary, September 2003* (2005), pp. 175–81

B. Rankov, 'A "secret of empire" (*imperii arcanum*): an unacknowledged factor in Roman imperial expansion', in W. Hanson (ed.), *The army and the frontiers of Rome: papers offered to David Breeze on the occasion of his sixty-fifth birthday and his retirement from historic Scotland. JRA Supplementary Series* 74 (2009), pp. 163–72

D. Rathbone, 'Villages, land and population in Graeco-Roman Egypt', *PCPS* 36 (1990), pp. 103–42

L. Rawlings, 'Caesar's portrayal of the Gauls as warriors', in K. Welch & A. Powell (eds), *Julius Caesar as Artful Reporter: The War Commentaries as Political Instruments* (1998), pp. 171–92

E. Rawson, 'Caesar's Heritage. Hellenistic kings and their Roman equals', *JRS* 65 (1975), pp. 148–59

J. Rea, 'Lease of a Red Cow called Thayris', *The Journal of Egyptian Archaeology* 68 (1982), pp. 277–82

T. Rice Holmes, *Caesar's Conquest of Gaul* (1911)

J. Rich, 'Fear, greed and glory: the causes of Roman war-making in the middle Republic', in J. Rich & G. Shipley (eds), *War and Society in the Roman World* (1993), pp. 38–68

J. Rich, 'Augustus, War and Peace', in J. Edmondson (ed.), *Augustus* (2009), pp. 137–64 = L. de Blois, P. Erdkamp, G. de Kleijn & S. Mols (eds), *The Representation and Perception of Roman Imperial Power: Proceedings of the Third Workshop of the International Network, Impact of Empire (Roman Empire 200 BC to AD 476). Netherlands Institute in Rome, March 20–23, 2002* (2003), pp. 329–57

J. Richardson, 'The Tabula Contrebiensis: Roman law in Spain in the early first century BC', *JRS* 73 (1983), pp. 33–41

J. Richardson, *Hispaniae. Spain and the Development of Roman Imperialism, 218–82 BC* (1986)

J. Richardson, 'The purpose of the Lex Calpurnia de Repedundis', *JRS* 77 (1987), pp. 1–12

J. Richardson, *Augustan Rome 44 BC to AD 14. The Restoration of the Republic and the Establishment of the Empire* (2012)

J. Ritterling, 'Military forces in senatorial provinces', *JRS* 17 (1927), pp. 28–32

L. Robert & J. Robert, *Claros* Vol. 1: Décrets hellénistiques (1989)

N. Rosenstein, 'Marriage and Manpower in the Hannibalic War: *Assidui, Proletarii* and Livy 24. 18. 7–8.', *Historia* 51 (2002), pp. 163–91

N. Rosenstein, *Rome at War: Farms, Families, and Death in the Middle Republic* (2004)

N. Rosenstein, 'General and imperialist', in M. Griffin (ed.), *A Companion to Julius Caesar* (2009), pp. 85–99

N. Rosenstein, *Rome and the Mediterranean 290 to 146 BC. The Imperial Republic* (2012)

A. Rost, 'The Battle between Romans and Germans in Kalriese: Interpreting the Archaeological Remains from an ancient battlefield', in A. Moirillo, N. Hanel & E. Martín, *Limes XX: Estudios sobre la frontera romana. Roman Frontier Studies. Anejos de Gladius* 13 Vol. 3 (2009), pp. 1339–45

N. Roymans, *Tribal Societies in Northern Gaul: An Anthropological Perspective. Cingula* 12 (1990)

S. Rutledge, 'The Roman destruction of sacred sites', *Historia* 56 (2007), pp. 179–95

Z. Safrai, 'Socio-economic and cultural developments in the Galilee from the late first to early third century CE', in P. Tomson & J. Schwartz (eds), *Jews and Christians in the First and Second Centuries: How to Write their History* (2014), pp. 278–310

W. Scheidel, *Measuring Sex, Age, and Death in the Roman Empire. Explorations in Ancient Demography. JRA Supplementary Series* 21 (1996)

W. Scheidel, 'Germs for Rome', in C. Edwards & G. Woolf (eds), *Rome the Cosmopolis* (2003), pp. 158–76

W. Scheidel, 'The Roman slave supply', in K. Bradley & P. Cartledge (eds), *The Cambridge World History of Slavery* Vol. 1: *The Ancient Mediterranean* (2011), pp. 287–310

C. Schmidt, 'Just recycled? New light on the Roman imports at the "central farmstead" of Friensted (central Germany)', in P. Wells (ed.), *Rome Beyond its Frontiers: Imports, Attitudes and Practices. JRA Supplementary Series* 95 (2013), pp. 57–70

E. Schürer, G. Vermes & F. Millar, *The History of the Jewish People in the Age of Jesus Christ* Vol. 1 (1973)

D. Schwartz, *Studies in the Jewish Background of Christianity* (1992)

S. Schwartz, 'The Rabbi in Aphrodite's bath: Palestinian society and Jewish identity in the High Roman Empire', in S. Goldhill (ed.), *Being Greek under Rome. Cultural Identity, the Second Sophistic and the Development of Empire* (2001), pp. 335–61

K. Scott, 'The Political Propaganda of 44–30 BC', *Memoirs of the American Academy in Rome* 11 (1933), pp. 7–49

C. Sebastian Sommer, 'The Roman army in SW Germany as an instrument of colonisation: the relationship of forts to military and civilian *vici*', in A. Goldsworthy & I. Haynes (eds), *The Roman Army as a Community. JRA Supplementary Series* 34 (1999), pp. 81–93

C. Serafina, 'A Roman engineer's tales', *JRS* 101 (2011), pp. 143–65

Y. Sharar, 'The underground hideouts in Galilee and their historical meaning', in P. Schäfer (ed.), *The Bar Kokhba War Reconsidered: New Perspectives on the Second Jewish Revolt against Rome* (2003), pp. 217–40

B. Shaw, 'Bandits in the Roman Empire', *Past & Present* 105 (1984), pp. 3–52

B. Shaw, 'The bandit', in A. Giardina (ed.), *The Romans* (1993), pp. 3–52

B. Shaw, 'Tyrants, bandits and kings: personal power in Josephus', *Journal of Jewish Studies* 44 (1993), pp. 176–204

B. Shaw, 'Fear and Loathing: the nomad menace and Roman Africa', in B. Shaw, *Rulers, Nomads, and Christians in Roman North Africa* (1995), VII, pp. 25–46

B. Shaw (ed.), *Spartacus and the Slave Wars. A Brief History with Documents* (2001)

R. Sheldon, *Rome's Wars in Parthia: Blood in the Sand* (2010)

A. Sherwin-White, *The Letters of Pliny. A Historical and Social Commentary* (1966)

A. Sherwin-White, 'The date of the Lex Repetundarum and its consequences', *JRS* 62 (1972), pp. 83–99

A. Sherwin-White, 'Rome the aggressor?', *JRS* 70 (1979), pp. 177–81

A. Sherwin-White, *The Roman Citizenship* (2nd edn, 1996)

D. Shotter, *Caesar Augustus* (2nd edn, 1991)

M. Siani-Davies, 'Ptolemy XII Auletes and the Romans', *Historia* 46 (1997), pp. 306–40

H. Sidebotham, 'International Relations', in P. Sabin, H. van Wees & M. Whitby (eds), *The Cambridge History of Greek and Roman Warfare* Vol. 2: *Rome from the Late Republic to the Late Empire* (2007), pp. 3–29

R. Smith, *Service in the Post-Marian Roman Army* (1958)

P. de Souza, *Piracy in the Graeco-Roman World* (1999)

P. de Souza, 'Pirates and politics in the Roman world', in V. Grieb & S. Todt (eds), *Piraterie von de Antike bis zur Gegenwart* (2012), pp. 47–73

J. Spaul, *Ala²* (1994)

A. Spawforth, *Greece and the Augustan Cultural Revolution. Greek Culture in the Roman World* (2012)

M. Speidel, 'The Roman army in Judaea under the Procurators', in M. Speidel, *Roman Army Studies* Vol. 2: *Mavors* (1992), pp. 224–32

M. Speidel, *Emperor Hadrian's Speeches to the African Army – A New Text* (2006)

M. Speidel, 'The missing weapons at Carlisle', *Britannia* 38 (2007), pp. 237–39

D. Stockton, *Cicero: A Political Biography* (1971)

T. Strickland, 'What kind of community existed at Chester during the hiatus of the 2nd c.?', in A. Goldsworthy & I. Haynes (eds), *The Roman Army as a Community. JRA Supplementary Series* 34 (1999), pp. 105–9

R. Syme, *The Roman Revolution* (1960)

R. Syme, 'Who was Vedius Pollio?', *JRS* 51 (1961), pp. 23–30

R. Syme, 'Military Geography at Rome', *Classical Antiquity* 7 (1988), pp. 227–51

A. Tchernia, 'Italian wine in Gaul at the end of the Republic', in P. Garnsey, K. Hopkins & C. Whittaker (eds), *Trade in the Ancient Economy* (1983), pp. 87–104

P. Temin, *The Roman Market Economy* (2013)

J. Thomas & R. Davies, 'A new military strength report on papyrus', *JRS* 67 (1977), pp. 50–61

J. Thorne, 'The Chronology of the Campaign against the Helvetii: A Clue to Caesar's Intentions?', *Historia* 56 (2007), pp. 27–36

M. Todd, *The Northern Barbarians* (1987)

M. Todd, *Roman Britain* (3rd edn, 1999)

M. Todd, *The Early Germans* (2nd edn, 2004)

R. Tomber, 'Pots, coins and trinkets in Rome's trade with the East', in P. Wells (ed.), *Rome Beyond its Frontiers: Imports, Attitudes and Practices. JRA Supplementary Series* 95 (2013), pp. 87–104

R. Tomlin, 'Making the machine work', in A. Goldsworthy & I. Haynes (eds), *The Roman Army as a Community. JRA Supplementary Series* 34 (1999), pp. 127–38

M. Torelli, *Typology and Structure of Roman Historical Reliefs* (1982)

M. Trümper, *Greaco-Roman Slave Markets. Fact or Fiction?* (2009)

R. Utley, *The Last Days of the Sioux Nation* (2nd edn, 2004)

A. Vasaly, 'Cicero, domestic politics and the first action of the Verrines', *Classical Antiquity* 28. 1 (2009), pp. 101–37

F. Walbank, 'Polybius and Rome's eastern policy', *JRS* 53 (1963), pp. 1–13

F. Walbank, *A Historical Commentary on Polybius* Vol. 1 (1970)

G. Watson, *The Roman Soldier* (1969)

G. Webster, *The Roman Invasion of Britain* (rev. edn, 1993)

G. Webster, *Rome against Caratacus* (rev. edn, 1993)

G. Webster, *The Roman Imperial Army of the First and Second Centuries AD* (3rd edn, 1998)

J. Webster, 'At the end of the world: Druidic and other revitalization movements in post-conquest Gaul and Britain', *Britannia* 30 (1999), pp. 1–20

H. Van Wees, *Greek Warfare – Myths and Realities* (2004)

K. Wellesley, *The Year of Four Emperors* (3rd edn, 2000)

C. Wells, *The German Policy of Augustus* (1972)

P. Wells, *The Barbarians Speak. How the Conquered Peoples Shaped Roman Europe* (1999)

P. Wells, *The Battle that Stopped Rome* (2003)

E. Wheeler, 'Methodological limits and the mirage of Roman Strategy. Parts 1 & 2', *The Journal of Military History* 57 (1993), pp. 7–41 & 215–40

C. Whittaker, *Frontiers of the Roman Empire. A Social and Economic Study* (1994)

C. Whittaker, *Rome and its Frontiers. The Dynamics of Empire* (2004)

S. Wilbers-Rost, 'The site of the Varus Battle at Kalkriese. Recent Results from Archaeological Research', in A. Moirillo, N. Hanel & E. Martín, *Limes XX: Estudios sobre la frontera romana. Roman Frontier Studies. Anejos de Gladius* 13, Vol. 3 (2009), pp. 1347–52

A. Wilson, *Emigration from Italy in the Republican Age of Expansion* (1966)

A. Wilson, 'Machines, power and the Ancient Economy', *JRS* 92 (2002), pp. 1–32

J. Winkler, 'Lollianos and the desperadoes', *Journal of Hellenic Studies* 100 (1980), pp. 155–81

P. Wiseman, 'The publication of the *De Bello Gallico*', in K. Welch & A. Powell (eds), *Julius Caesar as Artful Reporter: The War Commentaries as Political Instruments* (1998), pp. 1–9

R. Wolters, *Die Schlacht im Teutoburger Wald* (2008)

G. Woolf, 'Roman Peace', in J. Rich & G. Shipley, *War and Society in the Roman World* (1993), pp. 171–94

G. Woolf, *Becoming Roman. The Origins of Provincial Civilization in Gaul* (1998)

G. Woolf, 'Pliny's province', in T. Bekker-Nielsen (ed.), *Rome and the Black Sea Region: Domination, Romanization, Resistance* (2006), pp. 93–108

D. Wooliscroft, *Roman Military Signalling* (2001)

D. Wooliscroft & B. Hoffman, *Rome's First Frontier. The Flavian Occupation of Northern Scotland* (2006)

P. Zanker (trans. A. Shapiro), *The Power of Images in the Age of Augustus* (1988)

A. Ziolkowski, '*Urbs direpta*, or how the Romans sacked cities', in J. Rich & G. Shipley (eds), *War and Society in the Roman World* (1993), pp. 69–91

NOTES

PREFACE

1 Tacitus, *Agricola* 30. 5.

INTRODUCTION – A GLORY GREATER THAN WAR

1 Virgil, *Aeneid* 1. 278–9 (Loeb translation).
2 E. Gibbon, *The Decline and Fall of the Roman Empire* Vol. 1 (1776; Penguin Classics edn, 1995), p. 103; this passage seems to have been inspired by very similar comments made by William Robertson some years before, see R. Porter, *Gibbon* (1988), pp. 135–6.
3 In the UK, very large protests were staged against the Iraq War, without in any way preventing most of the people involved for voting for the same government at the next election. Earlier this year there was a general election. The violence in Ukraine, Iraq and Syria and so many other places was barely mentioned by any of the parties, whose focus was almost entirely domestic. Clearly the opinion polls guiding the parties did not suggest that voters cared about such things. However, given that the opinion polls were proved dramatically wrong in their prediction of the outcome, this may be just another reminder of their many flaws.
4 Ovid, *Fasti* 1. 709–18 (Loeb translation).
5 Virgil, *Aeneid* 6. 851–3 – *tu regere imperio populos, Romane, memento*
(Hae tibi erunt artes) pacisque imponere morem,
parcere subiectis et debellare superbos.
6 G. Woolf, 'Roman Peace', in J. Rich & G. Shipley, *War and Society in the Roman World* (1993), pp. 171–94, 189; 'robbery with violence', see N. Faulkner, *The Decline and Fall of Roman Britain* (2nd edn, 2004), p. 12.
7 N. Morley, *The Roman Empire. Roots of Imperialism* (2010), p. 69.

CHAPTER I – THE RISE OF ROME

1　Polybius 1. 2. 7, 3. 6 (Loeb translation).

2　For Rome's early history, T. Cornell, *The Beginnings of Rome. Italy and Rome from the Bronze Age to the Punic Wars (c.1000–264 BC)* (1995) is an excellent introduction, see esp. pp. 1–30 on sources, and pp. 48–80 on Rome's origins. A lively and challenging look at similar questions is A. Carandini (trans. S. Sartarelli), *Rome. Day One* (2011). Nearly every aspect of this period and the evidence for it continues to be fiercely debated by scholars.

3　On early warfare, see S. Oakley, 'The Roman conquest of Italy', in J. Rich & G. Shipley (eds), *War and Society in the Roman World* (1993), pp. 9–37, esp. pp. 12–14; on the treaty with Carthage, Polybius 3. 22. 1–23.6, 26. 1–2 with comments in F. Walbank, *A Historical Commentary on Polybius* Vol. 1 (1970), pp. 337–55 for detailed discussion.

4　Livy 1. 6, 9–10, 2. 16, 4. 4.

5　Cornell (1995), pp. 304–9; Herodotus 7. 170 for the quote.

6　Cornell (1995), pp. 309–13; pay, see Diodorus Siculus 14. 16. 5, Livy 4. 59. 11.

7　Cornell (1995), pp. 313–22.

8　For a good recent narrative of the Roman conquest of Italy see R. Cowan, *Roman Conquests – Italy* (2009), with Cornell (1995), pp. 322–6, 345–68 and Oakley (1993), pp. 14–33.

9　Refusal of Latin communities to accept Roman citizenship, see Livy 23. 20. 2–3; for a rare example of enfranchisement by Athens of surviving Plataeans, see J. Lendon, *Song of Wrath. The Peloponnesian War Begins* (2010), pp. 202–3, p. 472 n. 3; on Athenian manpower see H. Van Wees, *Greek Warfare – Myths and Realities* (2004), pp. 241–3.

10　Pliny the Elder, *NH* 33. 16 with comments in Cornell (1995), p. 208; Polybius 2. 24. 1–15, with Walbank (1970), pp. 196–203, and more recently D. Baronowski, 'Roman military forces in 225 BC (Polybius 2. 23–4)', *Historia* 42 (1993), pp. 181–202.

11　On the Roman army see L. Keppie, *The Making of the Roman Army* (1984), pp. 14–56.

12　On politics see the useful survey in M. Crawford, *The Roman Republic* (1978), pp. 30–37, 74–83, Cornell (1995), pp. 242–71, 327–44; for more detailed discussion of the magistrates see A. Lintott, *The Constitution of the Roman Republic* (1999), esp. pp. 94–120.

13 On the triumph see in general M. Beard, *The Roman Triumph* (2007); for aristocratic self-advertisement see in particular Polybius 6. 53. 1–54. 5.

14 On the military obligations of citizens and their impact on society see N. Rosenstein, *Rome at War: Farms, Families, and Death in the Middle Republic* (2004).

15 Cowan (2009), pp. 103–47, Cornell (1995), pp. 363–8.

16 On the Punic Wars in general see J. Lazenby, *The First Punic War* (1996), *Hannibal's War. A Military History of the Second Punic War* (1998) and A. Goldsworthy, *The Punic Wars* (2000) (= *The Fall of Carthage*, 2003) as surveys and introductions to the vast literature on the subject.

17 See S. Dyson, *The Creation of the Roman Frontier* (1985), esp. pp. 7–125 for northern Italy and pp. 174–98 for Spain; on the wars against the Hellenistic world see E. Gruen, *The Hellenistic World and the Coming of Rome* (1984), F. Walbank, 'Polybius and Rome's eastern policy', *JRS* 53 (1963), pp. 1–13 and P. Derow, 'Polybius, Rome and the east', *JRS* 69 (1979), pp. 1–15 for a glimpse of the extensive literature on the subject.

18 N. Purcell, 'The creation of provincial landscape: the Roman imprint on Cisalpine Gaul', in T. Blagg & M. Millet (eds), *The Early Roman Empire in the West* (1990), pp. 7–29.

CHAPTER II – WAR

1 Sallust, *Bell. Cat.* 7. 3–6 (Loeb translation).

2 For age of service, see the plausible suggestions in N. Rosenstein, *Rome and the Mediterranean 290 to 146 BC. The Imperial Republic* (2012), pp. 94–6, 112–16 and 'Marriage and Manpower in the Hannibalic War: *Assidui*, *Proletarii* and Livy 24. 18. 7–8', *Historia* 51 (2002), pp. 163–91; on military decorations see Polybius 6. 39. 1–11, with in general V. Maxfield, *The Military Decorations of the Roman Army* (1981).

3 For centurions, see the case of Spurius Ligustinus in Livy 42. 34. 1–35. 1 and discussion in R. Smith, *Service in the Post-Marian Roman Army* (1958), pp. 4–6; on governors see A. Lintott, *Imperium Romanum. Politics and Administration* (1993), pp. 43–69.

4 For Galba and his campaign, the fullest account is in Appian, *Bell. Hisp.* 55–60, with comments in S. Dyson, *The Creation of the Roman Frontier* (1985), pp. 203–9, J. Richardson, *Hispaniae. Spain and the Development of Roman Imperialism, 218–82 BC* (1986), pp. 126–7, 136–7; for the Lusitanians, see Strabo, *Geog.* 3. 3. 3–8, with 3. 3. 7 on wearing their hair long.

5 On fear of Carthage in 149 BC see J. Rich, 'Fear, greed and glory: the causes of Roman war-making in the middle Republic', in J. Rich & G. Shipley (eds), *War and Society in the Roman World* (1993), pp. 38–68, esp. 63–64, and for the course of the war see A. Goldsworthy, *The Punic Wars* (2000) (= *The Fall of Carthage*, 2003), pp. 331–56; Polybius 35. 1 for the 'fiery war' and 4. 3–14 on the problems of recruiting and the role of Scipio Aemilianus, the popular young nobleman.

6 Appian, *Bell. Hisp.* 56–57 on the captured Roman standards and crossing to Africa.

7 For the quote see Appian, *Bell. Hisp.* 59 (Loeb translation); Galba had served in the Third Macedonian War, see Livy 45. 35. 8–39. 20, but nothing else is known of any other time with the army; on the use of resettlement, see Dyson (1985), pp. 54–5, 100–01, 104–5, 213–14, 226.

8 Suetonius, *Galba* 3. 2 for the total of 30,000 Lusitanians, and note that later Appian, *Bell. Hisp.* 61 claims that 10,000 survivors gathered by 148 BC; women's costume, Strabo, *Geog.* 3. 3. 7.

9 For Wounded Knee, see the thorough reconstruction in R. Utley, *The Last Days of the Sioux Nation* (2nd edn, 2004), pp. 200–30.

10 Frontinus, *Stratagems* 1. 12. 4 for blood on shields and chests of horses; Livy 31. 34. 4–5 (Loeb translation) for Livy's description of wounds inflicted by the Spanish sword in a skirmish during the Second Macedonian War.

11 Livy, *Pers.* 49, Strabo, *Geog.* 3. 3. 6–7 on human sacrifice and comments in Dyson (1985), pp. 204–6.

12 There is a convenient list of temples and other monuments vowed and constructed by victorious commanders in the list of building work at Rome in the early centuries in S. Oakley, 'The Roman conquest of Italy', in Rich & Shipley (1993), pp. 9–37, 33–5.

13 Polybius 1. 1. 5 (Loeb translation).

14 On Polybius see F. Walbank, *A Historical Commentary on Polybius* Vol. 1 (1970), pp.1–6.

15 For the traditional view see E. Badian, *Roman Imperialism in the Late Republic* (1968), R. Errington, *The Dawn of Empire: Rome's Rise to World Power* (1971); the most powerful criticism of this came with the hugely influential W. Harris, *War and Imperialism in Republican Rome 327–70 BC* (1979), but important contributions include K. Hopkins, *Conquerors and Slaves* (1978) and Richardson (1986) which looks at the Spanish

experience emphasising the aggression and opportunism of provincial governors eager for plunder and glory.

16 See Harris (1979), pp. 9–53 on attitudes to warfare; Richardson (1986), pp. 128–37 on the shifting pattern or sending consular or praetorian governors to the Spanish provinces.

17 On the change to the start of the consular year, see Richardson (1986), pp. 12–129.

18 First Punic War, see Polybius 1. 11. 1–3; Second Macedonian War, Polybius 18. 1. 1–12. 5, Livy 32. 32. 1–37. 6; Third Macedonian War, Livy 43. 1. 4–12.

19 Appian, *Bell. Hisp.* 50–55, with Dyson (1985), pp. 202–3, Richardson (1986), pp. 136–7 for contrasting assessments.

20 Livy 38. 44–50.

21 E.g. Livy 39. 6, 45. 40, Plutarch, *Aemilius Paulus* 34.

22 On triumphs see Rich (1993), pp. 4–53; for 1,192,000 deaths in Caesar's campaigns see Pliny the Elder, *NH* 7. 92, although Velleius Paterculus 2. 47. 1 gives a figure of 400,000; on the Roman sword see the provocative study by S. James, *Rome and the Sword. How Warriors and Weapons Shaped Roman History* (2011), *passim*.

23 Polybius 10. 15. 4–5 (Loeb translation).

24 For emphasis on Roman ferocity, citing this passage, see Harris (1979), pp. 50–53.

25 On Roman looting see A. Ziolkowski, '*Urbs direpta*, or how the Romans sacked cities', in Rich & Shipley (1993), pp. 69–91.

26 P. Brunt, *Italian Manpower 225 BC–AD 14* (1971), pp. 391–472 , Harris (1979), pp. 44–6.

27 Polybius 31. 13. 7 (Loeb translation) for the quote; more generally on the profits of expansion see Harris (1979), pp. 54–104, Hopkins (1978), pp. 1–98 and E. Gruen, 'Material rewards and the drive for empire', in W. Harris (ed.), *The Imperialism of Mid-Republican Rome* (1984), pp. 59–82.

28 'massive violence' see Harris (1979), p. 53; for a good survey of problems with Harris' thesis see Rich (1993).

29 Rich (1993), pp. 47–55 on triumphs; Harris (1979), pp. 189–90 on alliances pretext for war and 201–05 with Richardson (1986), pp. 20–30 on Saguntum and the start of the Second Punic War.

30 By far the most important recent contribution to the debate on Roman imperialism is A. Eckstein, *Mediterranean Anarchy, Interstate War, and the*

Rise of Rome (2006), which thoroughly demolishes the idea of Rome as uniquely aggressive.

31 On Greek warfare in general see H. Van Wees, *Greek Warfare – Myths and Realities* (2004), esp. pp. 77–85, 115–50, D. Dawson, *The Origins of Western Warfare. Militarism and Morality in the Ancient World* (1996), pp. 47–107, and Eckstein (2006), pp. 37–180; piracy and trade at Athens, see van Wees (2004), pp. 202–3; none of this is to claim that Greek states were in permanent conflict. Peaceful co-operation did occur, see for instance J. Ma, 'Peer Polity Interaction in the Hellenistic Age', *Past & Present* 180 (2003), pp. 9–39.

32 Eckstein (2006), pp. 200–04 comparing Roman ferocity with that of others, and noting that Polybius believed the Macedonians and not the Romans to be the most naturally fierce and effective soldiers.

33 Caesar, *BG*. 6. 15, 23, cf. 1. 2.

34 See for instance the evidence for significant fighting at the very large and organised Iron Age *oppidum* or town at Manching in P. Wells, *The Barbarians Speak. How the Conquered Peoples Shaped Roman Europe* (1999), pp. 28–31, 77–79; on head-hunting see Poseidonius quoted in Strabo, *Geog*. 4. 4. 5, and Diodorus Siculus 5. 29. 2–5; on the use of heads and other body parts in ritual, one example is Ribemont-sur-Ancre, for which see T. Derks, *Gods, Temples and Ritual Practices: The Transformation of Religious Ideas and Values in Roman Gaul* (1998), pp. 48, 234–5.

35 Eckstein (2006), pp. 244–316.

36 Harris (1979), pp. 175–254 attempted a survey of Rome's wars in the period he covered presenting almost all as caused by Roman aggression. This has generally been seen as the weakest section of his book by critics and supporters alike, e.g. A. Sherwin-White, 'Rome the aggressor?', *JRS* 70 (1979), pp. 177–181 and J. North, 'The development of Roman imperialism', *JRS* 71 (1981), pp. 1–9.

37 Diodorus Siculus 5. 34. 6–7.

38 Strabo, *Geog*. 3. 3. 5.

39 On weaponry see F. Queseda Sanz, *Arma de la Antigua Iberia de Tatessos a Numancia* (2010), with pp. 171–80 on mercenary service.

40 Attempt to permit owners to reclaim recaptured booty in 193 BC, see Livy 35. 1.

41 Livy, *Pers*. 49.

42 Cato quoted in Cicero, *de Oratore* 1. 228 (Loeb translation), see also

Cicero, *Brutus* 89, Livy, *Pers.* 49, Appian, *Bell. Hisp.* 60, with comments and further references in Dyson (1985), pp. 205–6.

43 Valerius Maximus 6. 4. 2.

44 On Viriathus see Appian, *Bell. Hisp.* 61–75, with Dyson (1985), pp. 206–13; for locals rather than Romans as the chief focus of his attacks, note that the stratagems attributed to him, Frontinus, *Stratagems* 2. 5. 7, 13. 4 describe tactics used against the Romans, but 3. 10. 6, 11. 4, 4. 5. 22 all deal with fighting the Segobrigenses.

45 Dyson (1985), pp. 220–24 on lessening of warfare first in Nearer Spain and then in Further Spain, while noting repeated talk of banditry, e.g. Diodorus Siculus 3. 54. 7, Plutarch, *Marius* 6.

CHAPTER III – FRIENDS AND RIVALS

1 Cicero, *ad Att.* 1. 19.

2 Caesar, *BG* 1. 44 (Loeb translation).

3 In general see Caesar, *BG* 1. 31–43, 6. 12.

4 Caesar, *BG* 1. 42, and for the nickname *equestris* see L. Keppie, *The Making of the Roman Army* (1984), pp. 84, 204.

5 For the dating of the *Commentaries* see M. Gelzer, *Caesar* (1968), pp. 170–72, C. Meier, *Caesar* (1996), pp. 254–64. For the arguments in favour of annual publication see K. Welch & A. Powell (eds), *Julius Caesar As Artful Reporter* (1998), and especially the article by P. Wiseman, 'The publication of the *De Bello Gallico*', pp. 1–9, and also T. Rice Holmes, *Caesar's Conquest of Gaul* (1911), pp. 202–9. See also Caesar, *BG* 8 preface and Suetonius, *Caesar* 56. 3–4. In general also C. Kraus, '*Bellum Gallicum*', in M. Griffin (ed.), *A Companion to Julius Caesar* (2009), pp. 159–74, and J. Osgood, 'The Pen and the Sword: Writing and Conquest in Caesar's Gaul', *Classical Antiquity* 28 (2009), pp. 328–58.

6 On the archaeological evidence see S. Dyson, *The Creation of the Roman Frontier* (1985), pp. 126–73, B. Cunliffe, *Greeks, Romans and Barbarians: Spheres of Interaction* (1988), esp. pp. 38–58 and 80–105, N. Roymans, *Tribal Societies in Northern Gaul: An Anthropological Perspective. Cingula* 12 (1990), esp. pp. 17–47, P. Wells, *The Barbarians Speak* (1999), pp. 48–85 and T. Burns, *Rome and the Barbarians, 100 BC–AD 200* (2003), pp. 88–139.

7 On the power of noblemen expressed by the number of retainers see Caesar, *BG* 6. 15; on the wine trade see Cunliffe (1988), pp. 59–105, esp. 74, and Roymans (1990), pp. 147–67 and A. Tchernia, 'Italian wine in

Gaul at the end of the Republic', in P. Garnsey, K. Hopkins & C. Whittaker (eds), *Trade in the Ancient Economy* (1983), pp. 87–104.

8 Strabo, *Geog.* 4. 3. 2 on conflict to control the Saône and its trade route. More generally see Dyson (1985), pp. 141–3, 172.

9 See discussion in Wells (1999), pp. 44–7, 75–85, Burns (2003), pp. 76–87.

10 Caesar, *BG* 1. 3, 4–5, 31, 6. 12, Cicero, *ad Att.* 1. 19. 2.

11 On *amicitia* in general see P. Brunt, *The Fall of the Roman Republic and Related Essays* (1988), pp. 351–81, C. Steel, 'Friends, associates, wives', in Griffin (2009), pp. 112–25, esp. 112–14; on the Aedui see D. Braund, 'The Aedui, Troy, and the Apocolocyntosis', *Classical Quarterly* 30 (1980), pp. 420–25.

12 Diviciacus in Rome, see Cicero, *de Divinatione* 1. 41. 90, cf. *ad Att.* 1. 19. 2–3, and Caesar, *BG* 1. 31, 35, 43 and 6. 13–14 on druids and druidic training ; Pliny the Elder, *NH* 2. 67 describes an encounter between a Metellus as proconsul with a king of the Suebi. The purpose of the anecdote is the unlikely claim that the German leader handed over sailors who had come from India and been washed ashore in his territory.

13 See Dyson (1985), pp. 169–71.

14 Caesar, *BG* 1. 3–4, 18; for differing views on what the Helvetii and their leaders planned see T. Rice Holmes, *Caesar's Conquest of Gaul* (1911), pp. 218–24, and H. Delbrück (trans. J. Renfroe), *History of the Art of War* Vol. 1: *Warfare in Antiquity* (1975), pp. 459–78, and A. Goldsworthy, *Caesar: The Life of a Colossus* (2006), pp. 205–11.

15 Desire to be first, Plutarch, *Caesar* 11; the focus on the Balkans, see C. Goudineau, *César et la Gaule* (1995), pp. 130–48.

16 Caesar, *BG* 1. 9; in general see the useful discussion in J. Thorne, 'The Chronology of the Campaign against the Helvetii: A Clue to Caesar's Intentions?', *Historia* 56 (2007), pp. 27–36.

17 Caesar, *BG* 1. 11 for raiding; for the narrative of the campaign see Goldsworthy (2006), pp. 212–23.

18 Caesar, *BG* 1. 17–20.

19 Caesar, *BG* 1. 30–33.

20 Caesar, *BG* 1. 34–6, with quote from 1. 34.

21 See N. Rosenstein, 'General and imperialist', in Griffin (2009), pp. 85–99, esp. 88–91; on depiction of the Germans see J. Gardner, 'The "Gallic menace" in Caesar's Propaganda', *Greece and Rome* 30 (1983), pp. 181–9; see M. Todd, *The Northern Barbarians* (1987), pp. 11–13, *The Early Germans* (1992), pp. 8–13, C. Wells, *The German Policy of Augustus* (1972),

pp. 14–31 and Wells (1999), pp. 42–7, 99–121, and Burns (2003), pp. 111–18.

22 Caesar, *BG* 1. 39–41; Dio 38. 35. 2 claims that some felt Caesar was exceeding his remit as governor by leading his army so far from his province.

23 Caesar, *BG* 1. 47.

24 Caesar, *BG* 1. 43–47.

25 Caesar, *BG* 1. 47–54; women 1. 51, cf. Tacitus, *Germania* 7–8, with the unnecessarily sceptical comments in Burns (2003), p. 120–22; subsequent death of Ariovistus, Caesar, *BG* 5. 29.

26 Caesar, *BG* 1. 54; on displays of submission see H. Sidebotham, 'International Relations', in P. Sabin, H. van Wees & M. Whitby (eds), *The Cambridge History of Greek and Roman Warfare* Vol. 2: *Rome from the Late Republic to the Late Empire* (2007), pp. 3–29, esp. 16–22; Caesar's inexperience in 58 BC see Goldsworthy (2006), pp. 184–5, Rosenstein (2009), pp. 86–8.

27 Caesar, *BG* 2. 1, 3–5.

28 Caesar, *BG* 2. 6–7, 12–15.

29 E.g. Caesar, *BG* 4. 21 and 7. 76 on favours to Commius of the Atrebates, and other cases in 5. 25, 27.

30 Caesar, *BG* 5. 6–7.

31 Caesar, *BG* 5. 2–4.

32 Caesar, *BG* 5. 24–25, 26–27, 54, 55–58; for the narratives of the campaigns see Goldsworthy (2006), pp. 297–312 or M. Sage, *Roman Conquests: Gaul* (2011), pp. 84–95.

33 Caesar, *BG* 5. 54, 6. 2, 4, 9.

34 Caesar, *BG* 7. 1–2; on Caesar's attitude to the Gauls see J. Barlow, 'Noble Gauls and their other in Caesar's propaganda' and L. Rawlings, 'Caesar's portrayal of the Gauls as warriors', both in in K. Welch & A. Powell (eds), *Julius Caesar as Artful Reporter: the War Commentaries as Political Instruments* (1998), pp. 139–170, and 171–192 respectively.

35 Caesar, *BG* 7. 4, 6. 6, 7. 76; friendly relations between Vercingetorix and Caesar, see Dio 40. 41. 1, 3.

36 Caesar, *BG* 7. 32–3, 37–43, 54–5, 59.

37 Caesar, *BG* 7. 63 on Aedui seeking to lead rebellion; for the campaign overall see Goldsworthy (2006), pp. 315–342, Sage (2011), pp. 105–40.

38 Caesar, *BG* 8. 49.

39 For Commius see Caesar, *BG* 8. 6, 7, 22–23, 47–48, and Frontinus, *Stratagems* 2. 13. 11; for quote 8. 48.

40 On 'pacifying' see for instance Caesar, *BG* 3. 7, 20.

CHAPTER IV – TRADERS AND SETTLERS

1 Cicero, *Verrines* 2. 5. 167–8 (Loeb translation).

2 He was awarded twenty days of public thanksgiving, see Caesar, *BG* 4. 38; for excitement see Cicero, *ad Att.* 4. 17, *ad Quintum Fratrem* 2. 16. 4.

3 Marcus Mettius, Caesar, *BG* 1. 47, 53.

4 Caesar, *BG* 1. 1 for Belgians rarely visited by traders, 2. 15 for the refusal of the Nervii to admit any traders and 4. 2 for the Germans, with comments in J. Barlow, 'Noble Gauls and their other in Caesar's propaganda', in K. Welch & A. Powell (eds), *Julius Caesar as Artful Reporter: The War Commentaries as Political Instruments* (1998), pp. 139–70; the use of the alleged morality of the simple Germanic peoples in contrast to the decadence of 'sophisticated' society in Rome is especially pronounced in Tacitus, *Germania*.

5 Caesar, *BG* 4. 20–21; see in general M. Todd, *Roman Britain* (3rd edn, 1999), pp. 1–3, B. Cunliffe, *Hengistbury Head* Vol. 1 (1987) and *Facing the Ocean: The Atlantic and its peoples 800 BC–AD 1500* (2001) pp. 261–310, on Caesar and the Veneti see B. Levick, 'The Veneti Revisted: C. E. Stevens and the tradition on Caesar the propagandist', in Welch & Powell (1998), pp. 61–83.

6 For very different attempts to understand events in Britain after 54 BC see G. Webster, *The Roman Invasion of Britain* (rev. edn, 1993), pp. 41–74, J. Manley, *AD 43. The Roman Invasion of Britain – A Reassessment* (2002), pp. 37–50.

7 Cicero, *ad Att.* 4. 17; Caesar and pearls, see Suetonius, *Caesar* 47; Strabo, *Geog.* 4. 6. 12 on Scipio Aemilianus; on the absence of commercial motives in Roman decision-making see W. Harris, *War and Imperialism in Republican Rome 327–70 BC* (1979), pp. 54–104.

8 Polybius 34. 10. 10, with Strabo, *Geog.* 4. 6. 12.

9 See Appian, *Celtica* 13, with S. Dyson, *The Creation of the Roman Frontier* (1985), pp. 75–6; see G. Alföldy (trans. A. Birley), *Noricum* (1974), pp. 44 for Pompaius Senator, 44–47 on the Magdalensberg settlement.

10 On Romans abroad see A. Wilson, *Emigration from Italy in the Republican Age of Expansion* (1966); for Greek colonisation see in general R. Garland, *The Wandering Greeks: The Ancient Greek Diaspora from the Age of Homer to the Death of Alexander* (2014), J. Boardman, *The Greeks Overseas: Their Early Colonies and Trade* (4th edn, 1999).

11 Polybius 3. 22. 1–23. 6; on the treaties with Carthage. F. Walbank, *A Historical Commentary on Polybius* Vol. 1 (1970), pp. 337–56; on Carthage in general see G. Picard & C. Picard, *Carthage* (rev. edn, 1987), S. Lancel, *Carthage* (Oxford, 1995) and R. Miles, *Carthage Must be Destroyed. The Rise and Fall of an Ancient Civilization* (2010), pp. 1–176.

12 Strabo, *Geog.* 3. 5. 11.

13 For Romans in Carthage see Appian, *Punic Wars* 92; E. Palmer, *Carthage and Rome at Peace* (1997), pp. 32–62.

14 Exchanging a slave for an amphora see Diodorus Siculus 5. 26. 3–4; on coinage see C. Howgego, 'The Monetization of Temperate Europe', *JRS* 103 (2013), pp. 16–45, esp. 26–31, 35–7.

15 Livy 44. 13. 1; Cunliffe (2001), pp. 311–64.

16 Polybius 2. 8. 1–4, with T. Frank (ed.), *An Economic Survey of Ancient Rome* Vol. 1 (1933), pp. 102–3 and Harris (1979) pp. 195–7 noting that the Romans appear to have let this piracy continue for some time before taking action; Cicero, *Verrines* 2. 5. 149–50, 167–8

17 Colonisation see Wilson (1966), pp. 44–5, 64–5; inscription from Sicily, *ILS* 1. 864 = *CIL* 1². 612; Cossutius see *Inscriptiones Graecae* 3. (1) 561 and Vitruvius, *De architectura* 8. 160, with Wilson (1966), pp. 96–7.

18 Strabo, *Geog.* 14. 2. 5; on Delos in general see Wilson (1966), pp. 99–121, with J. Hatzfeld, 'Les Italiens résidant à Délos', *Bulletin de Correspondance Hellénique* 36 (1912), 143¹ for dealers in oil; on the Agora of the Italians see M. Trümper, *Greaco-Roman Slave Markets. Fact or Fiction?* (2009), pp. 34–49 who is sceptical, but presents a good bibliography of the debate over this site.

19 A. Sherwin-White, *The Roman Citizenship* (2nd edn, 1996), pp. 399–402.

20 Caesar, *BG.* 6. 37 for traders caught outside the camp; *BG* 7. 3, 38, 42, 55 for massacres of Romans in 53–52 BC.

21 Appian, *Iberica* 38. 115, with J. Richardson, *Hispaniae. Spain and the Development of Roman Imperialism, 218–82 BC* (1986), pp. 53, 57; Carteia, see Livy 43. 3. 1–4, with Richardson (1986), pp. 118–19.

22 Strabo, *Geog.* 4. 1. 5, with Wilson (1966), pp. 64–7.

23 Cicero, *pro Fronteio* 11–12, cf. *pro Quinctio* 11 describing Romans buying cattle from the province, and *in Catilinam* 2. 14 and Sallust, *Bell. Cat.* 34. 2 on a merchant who had done business with the Allobroges tribe.

24 Caesar, *BG* 7. 3, 38, 42, 55; Cicero, *pro Fronteio* 46; raising forces from Roman citizens in the provinces, see Josephus, *Jewish Antiquities* 14. 84

for armed civilians in Judaea, and Cicero, *ad Fam.* 15. 4 for re-enlisting demobilised soldiers in Cilicia.

25 Sallust, *Bell. Jug.* 21, 23–7, 47, 67.

26 Appian, *Mith.* 22 (Loeb translation).

27 Appian, *Mith.* 22, Athanaeus *frag.* 5. 213, Tacitus, *Ann.* 4. 14; Valerius Maximus 9. 2. 3 gives a death toll of 80,000, although Plutarch, *Sulla* 24 claims the total was 150,000; for handy introductions to the background see P. Matyszak, *Mithridates the Great. Rome's Indomitable Enemy* (2008), pp. 43–7, A. Mayor, *The Poison King. The Life and Legend of Mithridates, Rome's Deadliest Enemy* (2010), pp. 170–75.

28 Cicero, *de imperio Cn. Pompeio* 11; 20,000 massacred on Delos and else-where, see Appian, *Mith.* 28; on the general hatred of Romans see Sherwin-White (1996), pp. 399–402, referring to the Sibylline Oracles circulating in the eastern Mediterranean. However, it should be noted that similar prophecies in the past had foretold the humbling of other nations, notably the Macedonians.

29 Cicero, *Verrines* 2. 1. 63–76.

30 Romans in provinces seen as greedy, see Cicero, *ad Quintum Fratrem* 1. 1. 16.

31 Humiliation and execution of Q. Oppius by Mithridates, see Appian, *Mith.* 20–21; see Matyszak (2008), pp. 43–8 for a good analysis of Mithridates' motives.

32 However, anger at such an outrage might make Roman legionaries fight with more than usual fury, e.g. at Avaricum in 52 BC, Caesar, *BG* 7. 17, 29.

CHAPTER V – 'HOW MUCH DID YOU MAKE?' – GOVERNMENT

1 Cicero, *ad Fam.* 15. 5 (Loeb translation).

2 Cicero, *ad Att.* 5. 1–15 for letters written on the journey and describing his itinerary. The month of July was not yet named after Julius Caesar and was still called Quinctilis, but I have used the later term to avoid confusion.

3 In general see A. Lintott, *Imperium Romanum. Politics and Administration* (1993), pp. 22–7, 46–8.

4 On Cicero's career in general and his appointment to Cilicia see D. Stockton, *Cicero: A Political Biography* (1971), esp. pp. 225–6; for a detailed

discussion of his appointment see A. Marshall, 'The *Lex Pompeia de provinciis* (52 BC) and Cicero's *Imperium* in 51–50 BC: Constitutional aspects', *ANRW* I. I (1972), pp. 887–921.

5   Cicero, *ad Att.* 5. 15 for the quote; for pleas to prevent any extension of his command e.g. Cicero. *ad Att.* 5. 14, 15, 18, 20, 21, 6. 1, 3, with letters to incoming magistrates *ad Fam.* 15. 7, 8, 9, 12.

6   Cicero, *ad Fam.* 2. 12.

7   On Petreius see Sallust, *Bell. Cat.* 59. 6 describing him in 62 BC, but probably referring to his entire career; for Caesar see A. Goldsworthy, *Caesar. The Life of a Colossus* (2006), pp. 184–5; Catullus 10. 8.

8   Cicero, *pro Cn. Plancio* 64–6.

9   Cicero, *ad Att.* 6. I. 15, Valerius Maximus 8. 15. 6; on edicts see Lintott (1993), pp. 60–62, A. Marshall, 'The Structure of Cicero's Edict', *The American Journal of Philology* 85 (1964), pp. 185–91.

10 For a survey of the province and Cicero's governorship see Stockton (1971), pp. 227–53; on relations with the Parthians see D. Kennedy, 'Parthia and Rome: Eastern Perspectives', in D. Kennedy (ed.), *The Roman Army in the East. JRA Supplementary Series* 18 (1996), pp. 67–90.

11 For subordinates and staff see Lintott (1993), pp. 50–52, and on quaestors see A. Lintott, *The Constitution of the Roman Republic* (1999), pp. 133–7; on the *accensus*, Cicero, *ad Quintum Fratrem* I. I. 13.

12 Lintott (1993), pp. 53–4; Cicero, *Verrines* 2. 5. 29, 39–42.

13 A. Marshall, 'Governors on the Move', *Phoenix* 20 (1966), pp. 231–46, Lintott (1993), pp. 54–65; captured praetor killed because he was old and fat, Appian, *Bell. Hisp.* 63.

14 Marshall (1966), p. 246; for Caesar see Suetonius, *Julius Caesar* 56–7.

15 Cicero, *ad Att.* 5. 14, 15, 16, 17, *ad Fam.* 3. 6, 15. 4.

16 assizes as he travelled along the road, Cicero, *ad Att.* 5. 20.

17 For the quote, Cicero, *ad Att.* 5. 20, and the campaign in general see also *ad Fam.* 2. 7, 10, 15. 1, 2, 4, with discussion in A. Goldsworthy, *The Roman Army at War* 100 BC–AD 200 (1996), pp. 95–7, 99–100.

18 'perpetual enemies', Cicero, *ad Fam.* 2. 10, Bibulus' defeat, *ad Att.* 5. 20; tribes in the Alps, Caesar, *BG.* 3. 1.

19 E.g. Lintott (1993), pp. 53–4, Marshall (1966), pp. 239–40.

20 Cicero, *ad Att.* 5. 21.

21 Cicero, *Verrines* 2. 4 *passim* on Verres' alleged thefts or compulsory purchases of artworks.

22 Cicero, *ad Att.* 5. 21.

23 Quotes from Cicero, *ad Att.* 5. 15; efforts to keep tight control over expenses, e.g. *ad Att.* 5. 15, 16, 17, 21 (for a blemish on the record), 6. 2, 3.

24 Cicero, *ad Att.* 6. 1, with R. Syme, 'Who was Vedius Pollio?', *JRS* 51 (1961), pp. 23–30.

25 Polybius 6. 17. 1–9, and in general see E. Badian, *Publicans and Sinners* (1972).

26 Second Punic War, Livy 23. 48. 4–49. 4, 25. 3. 9–5. 1, with Badian (1972), pp. 17–20; Strabo, *Geog* 3. 2. 10 on mining, quoting a lost passage from Polybius, with Badian (1972), pp. 31–6; the latter's visit to the area, Polybius 3. 59. 7; mines in Macedonia, Livy 45. 18. 3–5, with Badian (1972), pp. 40–41, 127–8 ns. 40–41.

27 Cicero, *ad Att.* 1. 17. 9, 18. 3, 2. 1. 8, with Badian (1972), pp. 101–04.

28 On size of contracts see Badian (1972), pp. 67–70; quote from Cicero, *ad Quintum Fratrem* 1. 1. 32–5, cf. *ad Att.* 6. 1 for his own relations with the *publicani* in Cilicia.

29 Cicero, *Verrines* 2. 3 which deals at length with abuse of the grain tithe; 2. 182, 3. 167, 182 for companies keeping records. This oration was never delivered in court because Verres had already gone into exile. For recent discussion see the collection of papers in J. Prag, *Sicilia Nutrix Plebis Romanae. Rhetoric, Law, and Taxation in Cicero's Verrines* (2007); quote from Livy 45. 18. 4; on Rutilius Rufus see Badian (1972), pp. 90–92, and for suggestion of guilt A. Lintott, '*Leges Repetundae* and associate measures under the Republic', *ZSS* 98 (1981) pp. 194–5.

30 Badian (1972), pp. 102–5.

31 Cicero, *Verrines* 2. 5. 158–73.

32 Cicero, *ad Fam.* 13. 55, 53, and 56 respectively (Loeb translation).

33 Cicero, *ad Fam.* 8. 9, 2. 11, *ad Fam.* 5. 21.

34 Cicero, *ad Att.* 5. 21, 6. 1, 2, 3.

35 Quote from Plutarch, *Brutus* 6.

36 For Ariobarzanes see Cicero, *ad Fam.* 15. 2, *ad Att.* 5. 20, 6. 1.

37 Cicero, *ad Fam.* 3. 1, 2, 3, 4, 5, 6, 7, 8, 9, 10, 11, 12, 13 for letters to Appius, *ad Att.* 5. 15, 16, 6. 1, 2, with 6. 1 for the joke about a doctor resenting someone else curing his patient.

38 Cicero, *ad Att.* 6. 2 on corruption among local magistrates.

39 Cicero, *ad Fam.* 15. 4, 5, 6 for exchange of letters with Cato.

40 In 44 BC Decimus Brutus Albinus, one of Caesar's assassins and by this time governor of Cisalpine Gaul, sent a punitive expedition into the Alps 'not so much in quest of the title *imperator* as desiring to satisfy my

men and make them firm for the defence of our concerns', see Cicero, *ad Fam.* 11. 4 (Loeb translation).

41 Risk of famine, Cicero, *ad Att.* 5. 21.

42 On putting his quaestor in charge see Marshall (1972), pp. 899–921.

CHAPTER VI – PROVINCIALS AND KINGS

1 Polybius 31. 20 (Loeb translation).

2 On the establishment of a permanent presence in Macedonia see discussion in R. Kallet-Marx, *Hegemony to Empire. The Development of the Roman* Imperium *in the East from 148 to 62 BC* (1995), pp. 11–41, and for Asia, pp. 97–122.

3 Kallet-Marx (1995), pp. 30–40, E. Gruen, *The Hellenistic World and the Coming of Rome* (1984), pp. 429–36, and A. Eckstein, 'Hegemony and annexation beyond the Adriatic 230–146 BC', in D. Hoyos (ed.), *A Companion to Roman Imperialism* (2013), pp. 79–97; on the course of the Via Egnatia see Kallet-Marx (1995), pp. 347–9 and N. Hammond, 'The western part of the via Egnatia', *JRS* 64 (1974), pp. 185–94.

4 M. Hassall, M. Crawford & J. Reynolds, 'Rome and the Eastern Provinces at the end of the Second Century BC', *JRS* 64 (1974), pp. 195–220, esp. pp. 201–7 for text and 207–29 for translation of the law.

5 Plutarch, *Cimon* 1. 2–2. 1 tells the story but is unclear about the date of the incident. For this see Kallet-Marx (1995), pp. 280–81, and esp. p. 280 n. 77.

6 On homosexuality in the army see Polybius 6. 37 and the incident in Plutarch *Marius* 13–14 where a soldier received the highest award for valour, the *corona civica*, when he killed his commander after the latter had abused his authority in an effort to seduce the man.

7 In general see Gruen (1984), pp. 523–8 on Greece, pp. 529–610 on Asia, Kallet-Marx (1995), pp. 223–334.

8 Polybius 31. 2. 1–6, Appian, *Syrian Wars* 45–46, with Gruen (1984), p. 664 esp. fn. 244 with fuller references, pp. 714–15 for another tour by a delegation led by a distinguished senator, in this case Scipio Aeminilianus.

9 For a good survey see Kallet-Marx (1995), pp. 161–83, and for the background see J. Ma, 'Peer Polity Interaction in the Hellenistic Age', *Past & Present* 180 (2003), pp. 9–39.

10 For the declaration of the Second Macedonian War see Livy 31. 5. 1–8. 4; and comments and doubts over the true motive in W. Harris, *War and*

Imperialism in Republican Rome 327–70 BC (1979), pp. 212–18, F. Walbank, 'Polybius and Rome's eastern policy', *JRS* 53 (1963), pp. 1–13, P. Derow, 'Polybius, Rome and the east', *JRS* 69 (1979), pp. 1–15, and in general J. Rich, *Declaring War in the Roman Republic in the Period of Transmarine Expansion. Collection Latomus 149* (1976); On Popillius Laenas see Livy 44. 20. 1, 29. 1–5, 10. 45. 2–15, 12. 1–3, with Gruen (1984), pp. 656–60.

11 On declining offers of aid see the case of the Ptolemies in Gruen (1984), pp. 672–85; on Roman decisions to act and priorities see T. Hillard & L. Beness, 'Choosing friends, foes and fiefdoms in the second century BC', in Hoyos (2013), pp. 127–40.

12 In general see Kallet-Marx (1995), pp. 162–77; on receiving embassies in February see T. Broughton, *The Magistrates of the Roman Republic* Vol. 3 (1986), pp. 97–8.

13 Caesar and Cicero as students, see Cicero, *Brutus* 316, Suetonius, *Caesar* 4; Horace, *Epistles* 2. 1. 156–7 for quote.

14 On Athens see Kallet-Marx (1995), pp. 203–5, with Cicero, *de Oratore* 3. 75 for Crassus; on Ptolemies and the cat incident see Diodorus Siculus 1. 83. 1–9, 1. 44. 1; in general see M. Siani-Davies, 'Ptolemy XII Auletes and the Romans', *Historia* 46 (1997), pp. 306–40, esp. 317–22, and G. Hölbl (trans. T. Saavedra), *A History of the Ptolemaic Empire* (2001), pp. 225–7.

15 Delegation led by philosophers, see Pausanius 7. 11. 4–8, Polybius 33. 2, Plutarch, *Cato the Elder* 22; on Menippus see L. Robert & J. Robert, *Claros* Vol. 1: Décrets hellénistiques (1989), Menippus 23–44 with Kallet-Marx (1995), p. 128.

16 Cicero, *ad Att.* 15. 15; Sallust, *Bell. Jug.* 35. 10; ban on delegation borrowing money, see Diodorus Siculus 40. 1. 1.

17 Sallust, *Bell. Jug.* 33. 1; Polybius 30. 18. 1–19. 17, cf. Gruen (1984), p. 574; on Roman attitudes towards monarchs see E. Rawson, 'Caesar's Heritage. Hellenistic kings and their Roman equals', *JRS* 65 (1975), pp. 148–59.

18 Valerius Maximus 5. 1f, Diodorus Siculus 31. 18. 1–2, with comments in Gruen (1984), pp. 694–6.

19 In general see J. Prag, '*Auxilia* and *gymnasia*: A Sicilian model of Roman Imperialism', *JRS* 97 (2007), pp. 68–100; on Caesar and the pirates and Mithridates see Suetonius, *Caesar* 4. 2, 74, Plutarch *Caesar* 2.

20 Slave rebellions in Sicily, see the useful collection of sources in B. Shaw (ed.), *Spartacus and the Slave Wars. A Brief History with Documents* (2001), pp. 79–129; one or two slave revolts against Athens, see Orosius 5. 9.

5, Athaneus 6. 272e; house at Segesta, see Prag (2007), pp. 98–9 with references.

21 Cicero, *Verrines* 2. 2. 95–100, cf. 2. 4. 41; Silanus, see Valerius Maximus 5. 8. 3, Cicero, *de finibus* 1. 7. 24, Livy, *Pers.* 54.

22 Ref. Popillius Laenas from Lintott in 173 attacking the Ligurians; Livy 43. 2–3 (Loeb translation for quote).

23 On the *repetundae* court see A. Lintott, '*Leges Repetundae* and associate measures under the Republic', *ZSS* 98 (1981), pp. 162–212 and *Imperium Romanum. Politics and Administration* (1993), pp. 97–107, J. Richardson, 'The purpose of the Lex Calpurnia de Repedundis', *JRS* 77 (1987), pp. 1–12, A. Sherwin-White, 'The date of the Lex Repetundarum and its consequences', *JRS* 62 (1972), pp. 83–99; Lintott (1981), pp. 209–12 for results of trials between 149–50 BC.

24 Verres' comment from Cicero, *Verrines* 1. 14; in general see T. Frazel, 'The composition and circulation of Cicero's "In Verrem"', *The Classical Quarterly* 54. 1 (2004), pp. 128–42, A. Vasaly, 'Cicero, domestic politics and the first action of the Verrines', *Classical Antiquity* 28. 1 (2009), pp. 101–37 and the papers in J. Prag, *Sicilia Nutrix Plebis Romanae. Rhetoric, Law, and Taxation in Cicero's Verrines* (2007).

25 For the sums of money involved in Verres' trial see Lintott (1993), pp. 106–7, quoting Cicero, *Verrines* 1. 56 for forty million and Plutarch, *Cicero* 8 for three million.

26 Cicero, *de Officiis* 2. 26–7 (Loeb translation, slightly modified).

27 On Caesar see A. Goldsworthy, *Caesar. The Life of a Colossus* (2006), pp. 70–74; for the theme of changing attitudes to the empire see L. Beness & T. Hillard, '*Rei Militaris Virtus . . . Orbem Terrarum Parere Huic Imperio Coegit:* The transformation of Roman *Imperium*', in Hoyos (2013), pp. 141–53.

28 Cicero, *de imperio Cn. Pompei* 2. 6 (Loeb translation).

29 Power over the globe, e.g. Cicero, *de Republica* 3. 35, with Beness & Hillard (2013), pp. 142–3, cf. the theme of Pompey's triumph in 61 BC see Pliny, *NH* 7. 97, Plutarch, *Pompey* 45, Dio 37. 21. 1–4, Appian, *Mith.* 116–17; Sicily see Cicero, *Verrines* 2. 2, 3. 12; Cicero, *de prov. consularibus* 31 (Loeb translation).

30 Cicero, *de prov. consularibus* 4 (Loeb translation, slightly modified).

31 Cicero, *de prov. consularibus* 31 (Loeb translation).

32 Cicero, *de imperio Cn. Pompei* 55 (Loeb translation).

33 On the pirate problem see Appian, *Mith.* 91–3, Plutarch, *Pompey* 24–5,

and for Pompey's campaign see Appian, *Mith.* 94–6, Plutarch, *Pompey* 26–8.

34 Epirus, see Polybius 30. 15, Livy 45. 34. 1–6, Plutarch, *Aemilius Paullus* 29. 1–3; Caesar in Gaul, see Plutarch, *Caesar* 15, Pliny, *NH* 7. 92, Velleius Paterculus 2. 47. 1, with comments in C. Goudineau, *César et la Gaule* (1995), pp. 308–11; *publicani* enslaving debtors see Diodorus Siculus 36. 3. 1–2.

35 On supply of slaves, see W. Harris, 'Demography, Geography, and the supply of slaves', *JRS* 89 (1999), pp. 62–75; Spartacus, see Appian, *BC* 1. 118.

36 On slavery in general see K. Bradley, 'Slavery in the Roman Republic', in K. Bradley & P. Cartledge (eds), *The Cambridge World History of Slavery* Vol. 1: *The Ancient Mediterranean* (2011), pp. 241–64 and W. Scheidel, 'The Roman slave supply', in Bradley & Cartledge (2011), pp. 287–310.

37 For Flamininus see Polybius 18. 46. 1–15, with Gruen (1984), pp. 133–47, 448–9; on free and other cities see Lintott (1993), pp. 36–41.

38 For the framing of legal questions in the Roman style, see the law discussed in J. Richardson, 'The Tabula Contrebiensis: Roman law in Spain in the early first century BC', *JRS* 73 (1983), pp. 33–41; Cicero, *ad Att.* 6. 1 for quote, with Kallet-Marx (1995), pp. 130–35.

39 See Hillard & Beness (2013), pp. 138–40, Beness & Hillard (2013), pp. 141–53.

40 F. Millar, 'The Mediterranean and the Roman Revolution: Politics, war and the economy', *Past & Present* 102 (1984), pp. 3–24.

41 For Cleopatra's career see A. Goldsworthy, *Antony and Cleopatra* (2010), *passim*.

42 For an introduction to the depiction of Cleopatra see A. Goldsworthy, *Augustus. From Revolutionary to Emperor* (2014), pp. 180–85, with more detail in K. Scott, 'The Political Propaganda of 44–30 BC', *Memoirs of the American Academy in Rome* 11 (1933), pp. 7–49, esp. 33–49, J. Osgood, *Caesar's Legacy: Civil War and the Emergence of the Roman Empire* (2006), pp. 335–49, Pelling in *CAH²* X, pp. 40–48, and R. Syme, *The Roman Revolution* (1960), pp. 276–8.

CHAPTER VII – EMPERORS

1 Virgil, *Aeneid* 6. 851–3 (Loeb translation, slightly modified).

2 Dio 47. 25. 3, and Appian, *BC* 4. 100–01; for examples of Brutus' coinage

see M. Crawford, *Roman Republican Coinage* (1974), pp. 498–508.

3 Josephus, *Jewish Antiquities* 14. 314–16, and 14. 301–12 (quotes from Loeb translation); see also in general J. Osgood, *Caesar's Legacy: Civil War and the Emergence of the Roman Empire* (2006), pp. 105–6.

4 On the Parthian invasion see D. Kennedy, 'Parthia and Rome: eastern perspectives', in D. Kennedy (ed.), *The Roman Army in the East. JRA Supplementary Series* 18 (1996), pp. 67–90, esp. 77–81, Osgood (2006), pp. 185, 225–8, G. Bowersock, 'The mechanics of subversion in the Roman Provinces', in *Opposition et résistance à l'empire d'Auguste à Trajan*, Entretiens sur L'antiquité classique (1987), pp. 291–317, esp. 295–6.

5 *Historia Augusta, Hadrian* 15. 13; on the emperor and the army in general see J. Campbell, *The Emperor and the Roman Army 31 BC–AD 235* (1984), *passim*; on Augustus and the army see A. Goldsworthy, *Augustus. From Revolutionary to Emperor* (2014), pp. 245–53, 436–7.

6 For concise introductions to the career of Augustus and the system he created see D. Shotter, *Caesar Augustus* (2nd edn, 1991), W. Eck, *The Age of Augustus* (2003), K. Galinsky, *Augustus. Introduction to the Life of an Emperor* (2012), J. Richardson, *Augustan Rome 44 BC to AD 14. The Restoration of the Republic and the Establishment of the Empire* (2012), and for more detail see Goldsworthy (2014).

7 The fullest discussion of the imagery of the Augustan regime is P. Zanker (trans. A. Shapiro), *The Power of Images in the Age of Augustus* (1988).

8 Dio 53. 12. 2–16. 3, with W. Lacey, *Augustus and the Principate. The Evolution of a System* (1996), pp. 89–95, J. Liebeschuetz, 'The settlement of 27 BC', in C. Deroux, *Studies in Latin Literature and Roman History* (2008), pp. 346–53, J. Ferrary, 'The powers of Augustus', in J. Edmondson (ed.), *Augustus* (2009), pp. 90–136, esp. 90–99; on the role of provinces and warfare in general for Caesar's justification of his position see J. Rich, 'Augustus, War and Peace', in Edmondson (2009), pp. 137–64, esp. 153–7.

9 Dio 53. 13. 1.

10 For quote see *Res Gestae* 34 (Loeb translation, slightly modified), on the *ara pacis Augusti* see D. Conlin, *The Artists of the Ara Pacis. Studies in the History of Greece and Rome* (1997), M. Torelli, *Typology and Structure of Roman Historical Reliefs* (1982), pp. 27–61, Zanker (1990), esp. pp. 158–60, 179–83, 203–4, K. Galinsky, *Augustan Culture* (1996), pp. 141–55, and R. Billows, 'The religious procession of the Ara Pacis Augustae: Augustus' *supplicatio* in 13 BC', *JRA* 6 (1993), pp. 80–92.

11 Horace, *Epodes* 7. 1–10 (Loeb translation); on the popular desire for a victory over the Parthians and conquests in Britain see Rich (2009), pp. 137–64, esp. 143–6, = L. de Blois, P. Erdkamp, G. de Kleijn & S. Mols (eds), *The Representation and Perception of Roman Imperial Power: Proceedings of the Third Workshop of the International Network, Impact of Empire (Roman Empire 200 BC to AD 476). Netherlands Institute in Rome, March 20–23, 2002* (2003), pp. 329–57.

12 Ovid, *Fasti* 1. 709–18 (Loeb translation) for the *ara pacis*.

13 Dio 51. 20. 4–5, 53. 26. 1–5, 27. 1–2 and 54. 36. 2 (where a third opening was ordered, but then countermanded because a fresh war broke out), Suetonius, *Augustus* 22, *Res Gestae* 13, with comments in T. Barnes, 'The Victories of Augustus', *JRS* 64 (1974), pp. 21–6.

14 Rich (2009), pp. 137–64, and E. Gruen, 'The expansion of the Empire under Augustus', in *CAH²* X, pp. 147–97.

15 Virgil, *Aeneid* 6. 853, Horace, *Odes* 3. 5. 2–4 (Loeb translation, slightly modified).

16 On the Temple of Mars Ultor and the Forum of Augustus see Zanker (1990), pp. 81–2, 113–14, 193–215, S. Dyson, *Rome. A Living Portrait of an Ancient City* (2010), pp. 128–31, and Lacey (1996), pp. 193, 197–202; embassies from India and Britain, *Res Gestae* 31–2.

17 R. Syme, 'Military Geography at Rome', *Classical Antiquity* 7 (1988), pp. 227–51.

18 For accounts of the campaigns see Goldsworthy (2014), pp. 433–9, 446–55; ten legions concentrated, see Velleius Paterculus 2. 113. 1.

19 Suetonius, *Augustus* 23. 2 for the quote about Varus; Tacitus, *Ann.* 1. 11 for Augustus' advice.

20 There is an especially useful discussion of this question in T. Cornell, 'The end of Roman imperial expansion', in J. Rich & G. Shipley (eds), *War and Society in the Roman World* (1993), pp. 139–70.

21 See Suetonius, *Augustus* 25. 2, Velleius Paterculus 2. 110. 6–111. 2, with L. Keppie, *The Making of the Roman Army* (1984), pp. 168–9; Tacitus, *Ann.* 2. 5 on Gaul and other provinces.

22 Cornell (1993), pp. 145–9 provides a good survey with references of the debate over these questions, and B. Rankov, 'A "secret of empire" (*imperii arcanum*): an unacknowledged factor in Roman imperial expansion', in W. Hanson (ed.), *The army and the frontiers of Rome: papers offered to David Breeze on the occasion of his sixty-fifth birthday and his retirement from historic Scotland. JRA Supplementary Series* 74 (2009), pp. 163–72.

23 Strabo, *Geog.* 17. 3. 24, and 2. 5. 8.

24 Appian, *praef* 7.

25 Suetonius, *Nero* 18 for the claim that he considered abandoning Britain, with the scepticism of M. Todd, *Roman Britain* (3rd edn, 1999), pp. 67–8.

26 B. Levick, *Claudius* (1990), pp. 29–39 for discussion of the circumstances of his accession.

27 Campbell (1984), pp. 59–69, 417–27.

28 Tacitus, *Ann.* 11. 20; for a range of views on the invasion of Britain see Todd (1999), pp. 45–6, G. Webster, *The Roman Invasion of Britain* (rev. edn, 1993), pp. 84–5, and Levick (1990), pp. 137–44.

29 'Shameful peace', Tacitus, *Ann.* 15. 25; suicide of Corbulo, note the interesting comments in Bowersock (1987), pp. 316–17.

30 Comparisons with Alexander, Dio 68. 29. 1–4.

31 Dio 69. 1. 1 denied Hadrian's adoption.

32 Hadrian's prediction of his own death, *Historia Augusta, Hadrian* 16. 7; Marcus Aurelius' campaigns, see A. Birley, *Marcus Aurelius* (rev. edn, 1987), pp. 159–79, 206–10.

33 Dio 75. 3. 2–3

34 Contrast Dio 68. 6. 1–2, with 68. 17. 1.

35 Strabo, *Geog.* 6. 4. 2 (Loeb translation).

36 Velleius Paterculus 2. 126 .3

CHAPTER VIII – REBELLION

1 Josephus, *BJ* 2. 356 (Loeb translation).

2 For the invasion army in AD 43 see G. Webster, *The Roman Invasion of Britain* (rev. edn, 1993), pp. 85–92.

3 Dio 60. 19. 1–22. 2, Suetonius, *Vespasian* 4. 1, with discussion in Webster (1993), pp. 94–110; on the Roman army in the field and levels of fighting see A. Goldsworthy, *The Roman Army at War 100 BC–AD 200* (1996), pp. 79–105 and 'War', in P. Sabin, H. van Wees & M. Whitby (eds), *The Cambridge History of Greek and Roman Warfare* Vol. 2: *Rome from the Late Republic to the Late Empire* (2007), pp. 76–121, esp. 85–9.

4 Tacitus, *Ann.* 12. 34–37, with quote from 12. 37.

5 Togidubnus, see *Roman Inscriptions in Britain* 91, Tacitus, *Agricola* 14, with G. Webster, *Rome against Caratacus* (rev. edn, 1993), pp. 24–7, 124–30, J. Manley, *AD 43. The Roman Invasion of Britain – A Reassessment* (2002), pp. 64–5, 114–15, 120–21; J. Hind, 'A. Plautius' campaign in Britain: an

alternative reading of the narrative in Cassius Dio (60. 19. 5–21. 2)', *Britannia* 38 (2007), pp. 93–106, esp. 96–100, argues that Togidubnus was the Togodumnus, son of Cunobelinus who fought the Romans in AD 43, but then made peace and became a client king. While possible, the evidence is inadequate to prove the case one way or the other.

6 Tacitus, *Ann.* 12. 31–2 for the rebellion; in general see P. Brunt, 'Did Imperial Rome disarm her subjects?', *Phoenix* 29 (1975), pp. 260–70.

7 Tacitus, *Ann.* 14. 31.

8 The main narratives of the rebellion are Tacitus, *Ann.* 14. 29–39 and *Agricola* 5, 14–16, Dio 62. 1. 1–12. 6; a concise and critical survey of the evidence is provided by M. Johnson, *Boudicca* (2012).

9 Tacitus, *Ann.* 12. 32, 14. 31–2.

10 Caesar, *BG* 6. 13–14, 16–18; for an insightful assessment of the changing role of druids before and after conquest by Rome see J. Webster, 'At the end of the world: Druidic and other revitalization movements in post-conquest Gaul and Britain', *Britannia* 30 (1999), pp. 1–20; on Roman attitudes to the cult see also M. Goodman, *The Ruling Class of Judaea. The Origins of the Jewish Revolt against Rome AD 66–70* (1987), pp. 240–48.

11 Roman hostility to human sacrifice, see Pliny, *NH* 30. 13, with comments and further references in Webster (1999), p. 13; on the destruction of the groves on Mona see S. Rutledge, 'The Roman destruction of sacred sites', *Historia* 56 (2007), pp. 179–95, esp. 191–2; for the tendency for rebellion to catch the Romans by surprise see S. Dyson, 'Native Revolts in the Roman Empire', *Historia* 20 (1971), pp. 239–74, esp. 250, 252–4, 263–4.

12 For these towns and the rebellion in general see J. Wacher in *CAH²* X, pp. 508–9, 511–13.

13 Dio 52. 7. 2 (Loeb translation). It should be noted that this lurid passage comes from a later epitome of Dio's longer history. The author of this summarised version was inclined to include the most dramatic passages and make them more prominent than in the original version, but it is unlikely that he invented them; Tacitus, *Ann.* 14. 33 for casualties and the rebels' unwillingness to take prisoners.

14 *RIB* 12.

15 M. Todd, *Roman Britain* (3rd edn, 1999), pp. 71–3.

16 On rebellions in general see S. Dyson, 'Native Revolts in the Roman Empire', *Historia* 20 (1971), pp. 239–74 and 'Native Revolt Patterns in the Roman Empire', *ANRW* 2. 3 (1975), pp. 138–75.

17 For an overview of AD 9 see A. Goldsworthy, *Augustus. From Revolutionary to Emperor* (2014), pp. 446–53, and for more detail see P. Wells, *The Battle that Stopped Rome* (2003) and A. Murdoch, *Rome's Greatest Defeat. Massacre in the Teutoburg Forest* (2006).

18 On Lanhau-Waldgirmes see R. Wolters, *Die Schlacht im Teutoburger Wald* (2008), pp. 65–9.

19 Dio 54. 21. 1–8.

20 For Varus see Velleius Paterculus 2. 117. 2–4 including the quotes, Dio 56.l 18. 1–5; for Pannonia see Dio 56. 16. 3 (Loeb translation).

21 Tacitus, *Ann.* 4. 72–4; for the size of cattle and livestock see M. Todd, *The Early Germans* (2nd edn, 2004), pp. 76–8.

22 Tacitus, *Ann.* 4. 46–51; for the quote see Tacitus, *Hist.* 4. 14; on the origins of the Batavian rebellion see Dyson (1971), pp. 264–7 and K. Wellesley, *The Year of Four Emperors* (3rd edn, 2000), pp. 168–83.

23 For Arminius and his early life see esp. Velleius Paterculus 2. 118. 1–3, Tacitus, *Ann.* 2. 9–10, 88.

24 For attempts to interpret the remarkable archaeology of part of this battle, see A. Rost, 'The Battle between Romans and Germans in Kalriese: Interpreting the Archaeological Remains from an ancient battlefield' and S. Wilbers-Rost, 'The site of the Varus Battle at Kalkriese. Recent Results from Archaeological Research', both in A. Moirillo, N. Hanel & E. Martín, *Limes XX: Estudios sobre la frontera romana. Roman Frontier Studies. Anejos de Gladius* 13 Vol. 3 (2009), pp. 1339–45, 1347–52; the main ancient sources are Dio 56. 19. 1–22. 2, Velleius Paterculus 2. 119. 1–5, Tacitus, *Ann.* 1. 61–2.

25 Tacitus, *Germania* 37.

26 Josephus, *BJ* 2. 39–79 for Varus in 4 BC; there is much of relevance to the way rebellions develop in the early twentieth-century military manual, C. Callwell, *Small Wars. A Tactical Textbook for Imperial Soldiers* (rev. edn, 1990), pp. 26, and esp. 71–84.

27 Tacitus, *Ann.* 12. 31.

28 Tacitus, *Ann.* 14. 37, Dio 62. 8. 1.

29 Tacitus, *Ann.* 2. 88.

30 Tacitus, *Ann.* 1. 57–9, Velleius Paterculus 2. 118. 4.

31 E.g. Dio 54. 20. 4–6, Suetonius, *Augustus* 23. 1, with Dyson (1975), pp. 154–6.

32 Dyson (1975), pp. 156–8.

33 See J. Spaul, *Ala²* (1994), pp. 52–3.

34 Caesar, *BG* 6. 15 for aristocrats basing their power on the number of warriors in their household.

35 For the full narrative see Tacitus, *Ann.* 3. 41–7.

36 Tacitus, *Hist.* 4. 54 for druidic prophecies and 2. 61 for Mariccus.

37 For instance, G. Woolf, 'Roman Peace', in J. Rich & G. Shipley, *War and Society in the Roman World* (1993), pp. 171–94, esp. 186–8, and S. Mattern, *Rome and the Enemy. Imperial Strategy in the Principate* (1999), pp. 100–03, esp. 101 fn. 95, citing T. Pekàry, 'Seditio: Unruhen und Revolten im römischen Reich von Augustus bis Commodus', *Ancient Society* 18 (1987), pp. 133–50, but of his list, pp. 136–45, only a handful of incidents could be described as revolts against Roman rule.

38 Herod Agrippa II's speech, Josephus, *BJ* 3. 348–404, with quote from 3. 352; Petilius Cerealis in Tacitus, *Hist.* 4. 43–4.

39 The literature on this subject is vast and there are a range of opinions about almost every detail. For the Roman military viewpoint see A. Goldsworthy, '"Men casually armed against fully equipped regulars": The Roman military response to Jewish insurgence 63 BCE–135 CE', in P. Tomson & J. Schwartz (eds), *Jews and Christians in the First and Second Centuries: How to Write their History* (2014), pp. 207–37; for the narrative of rebellion from AD 66–73, a lively and provocative account is N. Faulkner, *Apocalypse. The Great Jewish Revolt against Rome AD 66–73* (2002).

40 Dio 69. 14. 1; on Galilee see S. Freyne, 'The Revolt from a regional perspective', in A. Berlin & J. Overman (eds), *The First Jewish Revolt. Archaeology, History, and Ideology* (2002), pp. 43–56, and R. Horsley, 'Power vacuum and power struggle 66–7 CE', in Berlin & Overman (2002), pp. 87–109 and other papers in the same volume, Z. Safrai, 'Socio-economic and cultural developments in the Galilee from the late first to early third century CE', in Tomson and Schwartz (2014), pp. 278–310, E. Meyers, 'Roman Sepphoris in the light of new archaeological evidence and recent research', in L. Levine (ed.), *The Galilee in Late Antiquity* (1992), pp. 321–8.

41 F. Millar, *The Roman Near East 31 BC–AD 337* (1993), pp. 337–74.

42 For some notable discussions of the causes of the revolt see Goodman (1987) and S. Mason, 'Why did Judaeans go to war with Rome in 66–67 CE? Realist-Regional perspectives', in Tomson & Schwartz (2014), pp. 126–206; for Roman attitudes see E. Gruen, 'Roman perspectives on the Jews in the age of the Great Revolt', in Berlin & Overman (2002), pp. 27–42.

CHAPTER IX – RESISTANCE, RIOTING AND ROBBERY

1 Dio 72. 4. 1 (Loeb translation).

2 For the garrison of Egypt see R. Alston, *Soldier and Society in Roman Egypt. A Social History* (1995), pp. 20–38.

3 For the rebellion see Dio 72. 24, with Alston (1995), pp. 77–8; for a document possibly demonstrating Avidius Cassius' connection with Egypt see A. Bowman, 'A letter of Avidius Cassius?', *JRS* 60 (1970), pp. 20–26.

4 For discussion see J. Winkler, 'Lollianos and the desperadoes', *Journal of Hellenic Studies* 100 (1980), pp. 155–81, esp. 180–81.

5 Diodorus Siculus 20. 100. 3–4, and P. Green, *Alexander to Actium* (1990), pp. 80–91 for a good survey of Alexandria's origins and culture.

6 Tacitus, *Hist.* 1. 65–6 for Gaul, 4. 50 for Africa.

7 Tacitus, *Hist.* 2. 21 for Placentia; Tacitus, *Ann.* 14. 17 for Pompeii and Nuceria, with R. MacMullen, *Enemies of the Roman Order* (1966), pp. 169–70.

8 *ILS* 5947 = *CIL* 10. 7852, with B. Shaw, 'Bandits in the Roman Empire', *Past & Present* 105 (1984), pp. 3–52, 7 fn. 12.

9 S. Mason, 'Why did Judaeans go to war with Rome in 66–67 CE? Realist-Regional perspectives', in P. Tomson & J. Schwartz (eds), *Jews and Christians in the First and Second Centuries: How to Write their History* (2014), pp. 126–206, esp. 170–74, and for the history in general E. Schürer, G. Vermes & F. Millar, *The History of the Jewish People in the Age of Jesus Christ* Vol. 1 (1973), pp. 125–232; Good Samaritan, Luke 10. 30–35, cf. John 4. 4–30 for the Samaritan woman at the well.

10 For Cleopatra see Plutarch, *Antony* 36, Dio 49. 32. 5, Strabo, *Geog.* 14. 669, 671, with M. Grant, *Cleopatra* (1971), pp. 135–41, G. Hölbl (trans. T. Saavedra), *A History of the Ptolemaic Empire* (2001), p. 242; for Herod see Schürer, Vermes & Millar (1973), pp. 287–329.

11 On the Olympic Games see Josephus, *Jewish Antiquities* 16. 149, *Jewish War* 1. 427, and his own Hellenic-style festival 15. 268–71; on Herod's gifts to Greek communities see G. Bowersock, *Augustus and the Greek World* (1965), pp. 54–6, and A. Spawforth, *Greece and the Augustan Cultural Revolution. Greek Culture in the Roman World* (2012), pp. 84–6; on Herod's troops see M. Speidel, 'The Roman army in Judaea under the Procurators', in M. Speidel, *Roman Army Studies* Vol. 2: *Mavors* (1992), pp. 224–32.

12 Josephus, *Ant.* 19. 356–9 for joy at Herod Agrippa I's death; for the region

in general see F. Millar, *The Roman Near East 31 BC–AD 337* (1993), pp. 43–69, 337–66.

13 For Augustus' joke see Macrobius, *Saturnalia* 2. 4. 11; for a public act of opposition to Herod and the subsequent executions see Josephus, *BJ* 1. 648–53.

14 Herod's war, see Josephus, *Ant.* 16. 271–99; Herod Antipas' campaign against the Nabataeans, see *Ant.* 18. 109–15, 120–25.

15 D. Schwartz, *Studies in the Jewish Background of Christianity* (1992), pp. 182–217 has suggested that Pontius Pilate held office for even longer, from AD 18 to 36/37; for the standards see Josephus, *BJ* 2. 169–74, *Ant.* 18. 55–9.

16 Josephus, *BJ* 2. 184–7, 192–203, *Ant.* 18. 257–309, Philo, *Legatio* 199–205; for discussion see Mason (2014), p. 178.

17 Josephus, *BJ* 175–7, *Ant.* 60–62.

18 Josephus, *Ant.* 18. 85–9.

19 Josephus, *Ant.* 20. 97–9 (quote from Loeb translation), Acts 5. 36.

20 Josephus, *BJ* 2. 261–3, *Ant.* 20. 97–8 and Acts 21. 38.

21 Josephus, *Ant.* 20. 106–12, *BJ* 2. 224–7

22 Josephus, *Ant.* 20. 113–17, *BJ* 2. 228–31, and in general Mason (2014), pp. 180–82.

23 Josephus, *BJ* 2. 232–46, *Ant.* 20. 118–36; Claudius considers posting the garrison to Pontus, *Ant.* 19. 365–6, with Mason (2014), p. 180.

24 For embassies and decisions in favour of the Jewish leaders see P. McKechnie, 'Judaean embassies and cases before Roman Emperors, AD 44–66', *Journal of Theological Studies* 56 (2005), pp. 339–61; agitators, see Philo, *in Flaccum* 20; on the incident at Alexandria see Philo, *in Flaccum* 18–114, with B. Decharneux, 'The Carabas affair (in Flacc 36–39): An incident emblematic of Philo's political philosophy', in Tomson & Schwartz (2014), pp. 70–79.

25 Josephus, *BJ* 2. 1. 408–16, 266–70, *Ant.* 20. 173–8, 182–4, with McKechnie (2005), pp. 353–6.

26 Josephus, *BJ* 2. 289–90 (Loeb translation).

27 Josephus *BJ* 2. 285–92, with Mason (2014), pp. 184–7; cohort massacred in Jerusalem, but commander spared, see *BJ* 2. 450–554.

28 Josephus, *BJ* 2. 460–62 (Loeb translation).

29 Josephus, *BJ* 2. 461–80.

30 Josephus, *Ant.* 20. 121, *BJ*. 2. 235 also mentions an 'Alexander' as one of the leaders of these raids; bandits hired as mercenaries in Galilee,

Josephus, *BJ* 3. 581–3; *sicarii*, see *BJ* 2. 254–7, 425, *Ant.* 20. 162–6, 186, 204.

31 Digest 49. 15. 24

32 On bandits and pirates in general see R. MacMullen, *Enemies of the Roman Order* (1966), pp. 192–212, 255–68, B. Shaw, 'Bandits in the Roman Empire', *Past & Present* 105 (1984), pp. 3–52, 'The bandit', in A. Giardina (ed.), *The Romans* (1993), pp. 3–52, T. Grünewald (trans. J. Drinkwater), *Bandits in the Roman Empire. Myth and Reality* (2004), P. de Souza, *Piracy in the Graeco-Roman world* (1999), and C. Fuhrmann, *Policing the Roman Empire. Soldiers, Administration and Public Order* (2012).

33 See Grünewald (2004), pp. 72–90, P. de Souza, 'Pirates and politics in the Roman world', in V. Grieb & S. Todt (eds), *Piraterie von de Antike bis zur Gegenwart* (2012), pp. 47–73, esp. 61–73.

34 Strabo, *Geog.* 3. 3. 8, and A. Morillo Cerdán, 'The Augustean Spanish Experience: The origin of the *limes* system?', in A. Moirillo, N. Hanel & E. Martín, *Limes XX: Estudios sobre la frontera romana. Roman Frontier Studies. Anejos de Gladius* 13 Vol. 1 (2009), pp. 239–51, esp. 244–7.

35 Grünewald (2004), pp. 91–109, B. Shaw, 'Tyrants, bandits and kings: personal power in Josephus', *Journal of Jewish Studies* 44 (1993), pp. 176–204; Matthew 22. 17, 'sons of thunder', Mark 3. 17, and for Barabbas Luke 23. 19.

36 For discussion of the social and economic problems see M. Goodman, *The Ruling Class of Judaea. The Origins of the Jewish Revolt against Rome AD 66–70* (1987), pp. 51–75.

37 Velleius Paterculus 2. 126. 3.

38 See B. Isaac, *The Limits of Empire. The Roman Army in the East* (rev. edn, 1992), pp. 68–100.

39 Sifre Deuteronomy, 318 (ed. Finkelstein) quoted in Isaac (1992), p. 115.

40 Examples taken from Isaac (1992), pp. 83–4, 85–8, 117–18.

41 Dio 69. 12. 3 (Loeb translation); Y. Sharar, 'The underground hideouts in Galilee and their historical meaning', in P. Schäfer (ed.), *The Bar Kokhba War Reconsidered: New Perspectives on the Second Jewish Revolt against Rome* (2003), pp. 217–40.

42 Isaac (1992), pp. 85–9 suggests some ambiguity in rabbinic attitudes to bandits, but no active or enthusiastic support for them; Marcus Aurelius' comment mentioned because it was misquoted by the Emperor Julian in the fourth century AD, Ammianus Marcellinus 22. 5. 5.

43 Isaac (1992), pp. 116–17.

44 MacMullen (1966), pp. 84–90, and for the texts see H. Musurillo, *The Acts of the Pagan Martyrs, Acta Alexandrinorum* (1954).

45 Millar (1993), pp. 337–66, 408–14.

CHAPTER X – IMPERIAL GOVERNORS

1 Suetonius, *Domitian* 8. 2 (Loeb translation).

2 Pliny the Younger, *Ep.* 10. 15–18. Pliny's letters are not dated and there is a question over whether his provincial command began in AD 109, 110 or 111, but there is no means to resolve this debate and it does not matter for our purpose. On his appointment and for background to the province and the letters, see A. Sherwin-White, *The Letters of Pliny. A Historical and Social Commentary* (1966), pp. 526–55.

3 Sherwin-White (1966), pp. 1–84; see also R. Gibson, 'On the nature of ancient letter collections', *JRS* 102 (2012), pp. 56–78, esp. 67–9.

4 For *mandata* see G. Burton, 'The issuing of *mandata* to proconsuls and a new inscription from Cos', *ZPE* 21 (1976), pp. 63–8, and D. Potter, 'Emperors, their borders and their neighbours: the scope of imperial *mandata*', in D. Kennedy (ed.), *The Roman Army in the East. JRA Supplementary Series* 18 (1996), pp. 49–66.

5 Pliny the Younger, *Ep.* 10. 106–7, mentioning a centurion from a *cohors VI equitata*, and in general see J. Ritterling, 'Military forces in senatorial provinces', *JRS* 17 (1927), pp. 28–32, esp. 28.

6 e.g. Pliny the Younger, *Ep.* 4. 9, 5. 20, 6. 5, 13, 7. 6, 10, with P. Brunt, 'Charges of provincial maladministration under the early principate', *Historia* 10 (1961), pp. 189–227, esp. 213–14, 227.

7 For an early-third-century AD summary of the two types of governors see Dio 3. 13. 2–14. 4; on senatorial careers see E. Birley, 'Senators in the emperor's service' and 'Promotion and transfers in the Roman army: senatorial and equestrian officers', in E. Birley, *The Roman Army. Papers 1929–1986* (1988), pp. 75–114, with J. Campbell, 'Who were the *viri militares?*' *JRS* 65 (1975), pp. 11–31.

8 Note the scepticism of this raised in G. Woolf, 'Pliny's province', in T. Bekker-Nielsen (ed.), *Rome and the Black Sea Region: Domination, Romanization, Resistance* (2006), pp. 93–108.

9 Suetonius, *Augustus* 53. 1.

10 For the province see J. Madsen, *Eager to be Roman. Greek Response to Roman Rule in Pontus and Bithynia* (2009), esp. pp. 11–57.

11 Pliny the Younger, *Ep.* 10. 21–2.

12 Pliny the Younger, *Ep.* 10. 25, cf. Sherwin-White (1966) pp. 394–5 on legates; Fronto, *Correspondence with Antoninus Pius* 8. 1 with translation and comments in B. Levick, *The Government of the Roman Empire. A Sourcebook* (2nd edn, 2000), p. 14.

13 J. Oliver, 'A Roman governor visits Samothrace', *American Journal of Philology* 87 (1966), pp. 75–80; prefect of Pontic Shore, Pliny the Younger, *Ep.* 10. 21–2; Maximus, Pliny the Younger, *Ep.* 27–8.

14 Pliny the Younger, *Ep.* 19–20, 77–8.

15 See B. Rankov, 'The governor's men: the *officium consularis*', in A. Goldsworthy & I. Haynes (eds), *The Roman Army as a Community in Peace and War. JRA Supplementary Series* 34 (1999), pp. 15–34, esp. 23–5 on numbers, A. Goldsworthy, *The Roman Army at War 100 BC–AD 200* (1996), pp. 22–5 on men on detached service; for *Legio III Augusta* see M. Speidel, *Emperor Hadrian's Speeches to the African Army – A New Text* (2006), p. 8, field 2, lines 3–4 of the inscription; for a discussion of literacy and the importance of the written word for auxiliaries see I. Haynes, *The Blood of the Provinces. The Roman Auxilia and the Making of Provincial Society from Augustus to Severus* (2013), pp. 313–36.

16 Matthew 27. 19, 24.

17 Tacitus, *Ann.* 3. 33–4, with A. Marshall, 'Tacitus and the governor's lady: a note on Annals iii. 31–4', *Greece and Rome* 22 (1975), pp. 11–18 and A. Barrett, 'Aulus Caecina Severus and the Military woman', *Historia* 54 (2005), pp. 301–14.

18 Pliny the Younger, *Ep.* 10. 120–21 for use of the imperial post by Pliny's wife; see also S. Mitchell, 'Requisitioned transport in the Roman empire: a new inscription from Pisidia', *JRS* 66 (1976), pp. 106–31.

19 G. Burton, 'Proconsuls, assizes, and the administration of justice under the empire', *JRS* 65 (1975), pp. 92–106, A. Lintott, *Imperium Romanum. Politics and Administration* (1993), pp. 148–60.

20 Pliny the Younger, *Ep.* 10. 81–2.

21 Pliny the Younger, *Ep.* 10. 47–8.

22 Pliny the Younger, *Ep.* 10. 58–9, 79–80, 112–15.

23 Lintott (1993), pp. 122–3, and E. Badian, *Publicans and Sinners* (1972) for an overview of organisation of the *publicani*.

24 Pliny the Younger, *Ep.* 10. 96–7 (quotes from Loeb), with Sherwin-White (1966), pp. 691–712.

25 Pliny the Younger, *Ep.* 10. 19–20, 32–3 (quote from Loeb).

26 Pliny the Younger, *Ep.* 10. 37–41 for these projects.

27 Pliny the Younger, *Ep.* 10. 22–3.

28 Pliny the Younger, *Ep.* 10. 41–2, 60–61, 90–91, 98–9.

29 *AE* 1954, 137, and see C. Serafina, 'A Roman engineer's tales', *JRS* 101 (2011), pp. 143–65 for discussion.

30 Pliny the Younger, *Ep.* 10. 34–5 (quote from Loeb)

31 Pliny the Younger, *Ep.* 10. 34–5 (quote from Loeb), with Sherwin-White (1966), pp. 606–10; 10. 65–6 on foundlings.

32 Dio Chrysostom, *Discourse* 46. esp. 8, 11–14; on Dio see Madsen (2006), pp. 107–19.

33 Suetonius, *Vespasian* 4. 3.

34 Digest 1. 18. 13

35 For banditry see especially R. MacMullen, *Enemies of the Roman Order* (1966), pp. 192–241, 255–68, and B. Shaw, 'Bandits in the Roman empire', *Past & Present* 105 (1984), pp. 3–52 and 'The Bandit', in A. Giardina (ed.), *The Romans* (1993), pp. 300–41.

36 Pliny the Younger, *Ep.* 6. 25 (Loeb translation).

37 *CIL* 3. 8242, and for other tombstones see Shaw (1984), pp. 10–12, fn. 25; 2 Corinthians 11. 26; Epictetus, *Diss.* 4. 1. 91, praise of governor, see Apuleius, *Florida* 9. 36 and discussion in C. Fuhrmann, *Policing the Roman Empire* (2012), pp. 182–4.

38 On soldiers see Fuhrmann (2012), pp. 186–94, 201–38, R. Davies, 'The investigation of some crimes in Roman Egypt', in R. Davies, D. Breeze & V. Maxfield (eds), *Service in the Roman Army* (1989), pp. 175–85; Apuleius, *Metamorphoses* 2. 18 (Loeb translation).

39 Apuleius, *Metamorphoses* 7. 7–8 (Loeb translation).

40 *AE* 1956, 124 and F. Millar, 'The world of the Golden Ass', *JRS* 71 (1981), pp. 63–75, 66–7.

41 Apuleius, *Metamorphoses* 8. 16–17 (Loeb translation); Aelius Aristides, see Fuhrmann (2012), pp. 67–8, fn. 76, citing *Orations* 50. 63–94.

42 Shaw (1984), pp. 14–18, Fuhrmann (2012), pp. 66–87.

43 Florida Ostraka 2, cf. O. Mons Claudianus 175 requesting that a man be sent to serve in a watch-tower as a *skopelarios*.

44 Quote from Mons Claudianus Ostraka 48; in general see R. Bagnall, 'Army and police in upper Egypt', *JARCE* 14 (1976), pp. 67–88, V. Maxfield, 'Ostraca and the Roman army in the eastern desert', in J. Wilkes (ed.), *Documenting the Roman Army. Essays in Honour of Margaret Roxan* (2003), pp. 153–73.

45 M. Bishop, 'Praesidium: social, military, and logistical aspects of the Roman army's provincial distribution during the early Principate', in A. Goldsworthy & I. Haynes (eds), *The Roman Army as a Community in Peace and War. JRA Supplementary Series* 34 (1999), pp. 111–18.

46 Galen, *On anatomical procedures* 1. 2 (trans. C. Singer, 1956); for Social Bandits see E. Hobsbawm, *Bandits* (1969), with critical comments in Shaw (1984), pp. 4–5, and 'The Bandit', in A. Giardina (ed., trans. L. Cochrane), *The Romans* (1993), pp. 300–41, and Fuhrmann (2012), pp. 134–6, 156 with the fictionalised stories about Bulla Felix and Maternus; for another period, see the comments on Hobsbawm in C. Esdaile, *Outpost of Empire. The Napoleonic Occupation of Andalucía, 1810–1812* (2012), pp. 119–23, 158–9.

47 Shaw (1984), pp. 9–10.

CHAPTER XI – LIFE UNDER ROMAN RULE

1 Tacitus, *Hist.* 4. 74 (Loeb translation).

2 For the importance of courtesy in dealing with provincials especially in the eastern provinces, see C. Kokkinia, 'Ruling, inducing, arguing: how to govern (and survive) a Greek province', in L. de Light, E. Hemelrijk & H. Singor (eds), *Roman Rule and Civic Life: Local and Regional Perspectives. Impact of Empire* Vol. 4 (2004), pp. 39–58; on the importance of formality and courtesy in general see J. Lendon, *Empire of Honour. The Art of Government in the Roman World* (1997), *passim*.

3 See S. Schwartz, 'The Rabbi in Aphrodite's bath: Palestinian society and Jewish identity in the High Roman Empire', in S. Goldhill (ed.), *Being Greek under Rome. Cultural Identity, the Second Sophistic and the Development of Empire* (2001), pp. 335–61, esp. 337 emphasising how rare it is for rabbinic literature to express hostility to the pagan environment; on the Greeks see Dio Chrysostom, *Orations* 45. 6, 48. 2, Plutarch, *Praecepta gerendae reipublicae* 17, with S. Dmitriev, *City Government in Hellenistic and Roman Asia Minor* (2005), esp. pp. 289–328, R. Preston, 'Roman questions, Greek answers: Plutarch and the construction of identity', in Goldhill (2001), pp. 86–119.

4 Matthew 22. 17–22, with F. Millar, 'State and Subject: the impact of monarchy', in F. Millar & E. Segal (eds), *Caesar Augustus. Seven Aspects* (corrected paperback edn, 1990), pp. 37–60, esp. 44–5.

5 Strabo, *Geog.* 10. 5. 3 (Loeb translation), with Millar (1990), pp. 44–5 and

J. Rea, 'Lease of a Red Cow called Thayris', *The Journal of Egyptian Archaeology* 68 (1982), pp. 277–82.

6 Dio 69. 6. 3 (Loeb translation); on emperors as benefactors see F. Millar, *The Emperor in the Roman World (31 BC–AD 337)* (1977), pp. 135–9.

7 Arrian, *Periplus* 1.

8 *SEG* 28. 1462. 1–3, see O. van Nijf, 'Local heroes: athletics, festivals and elite self-fashioning in the Roman East', in Goldhill (2001), pp. 306–34, esp. 318; for the cities in Asia Minor see R. Sherk, *Roman Documents from the Greek East* (1969), no. 65.

9 On Hadrian's buildings in Athens see J. Camp, *The Archaeology of Athens* (2001), pp. 199–208.

10 See G. Woolf, *Becoming Roman. The Origins of Provincial Civilization in Gaul* (1998), pp. 48–76, 112–41.

11 D. Mattingly, *An Imperial Possession. Britain in the Roman Empire* (2006), pp. 271–2.

12 S. Mitchell, *Anatolia. Land, Men, and Gods in Asia Minor* Vol. 1: *The Celts in Anatolia and the Impact of Roman Rule* (1993), pp. 80–98, esp. 87–8 on the tribal boundaries.

13 Tacitus, *Agricola* 21 (Loeb translation).

14 Tacitus, *Agricola* 21 (Loeb translation).

15 Woolf (1998), pp. 135–68, Mattingly (2006), pp. 255–350.

16 Dio Chrysostom, *Orations* 35.15.

17 Tacitus, *Agricola* 24, Strabo, *Geog.* 17. 24, Appian, *praef.* 7.

18 For taxation and the economy in general important studies include K. Hopkins, 'Rome, taxes, rent and trade', in W. Scheidel & S. von Reden (eds), *The Ancient Economy* (2002), pp. 190–230, which restates his earlier argument that tax stimulated production, and the recent P. Temin, *The Roman Market Economy* (2013); on deforestation see Mattingly (2006), pp. 363–6.

19 Suetonius, *Tiberius* 32. 2 for quote; surprise at rarity of rebellion provoked by over-taxation see D. Mattingly, *Imperialism, Power, and Identity. Experiencing the Roman Empire* (2011), pp. 137–8.

20 For a good discussion of several estates in an eastern province see T. Corsten, 'Estates in Roman Asia Minor: the case of Kibyratis', in S. Mitchell & C. Katsari (eds), *Patterns in the Economy of Roman Asia Minor* (2005), pp. 1–51, esp. 17–27.

21 For some discussion of olive oil see S. Mitchell, 'Olive oil cultivation in the economy of Roman Asia Minor', in Mitchell & Katsari (2005), pp.

83–113; on levels of pollution see A. Wilson, 'Machines, power and the Ancient Economy', *JRS* 92 (2002), pp. 1–32, esp. 17–29.

22 On the roads in Anatolia see Mitchell (1993), pp. 124–36, 245–53.

23 Josephus, *Vitae* 16, on Livia as a patron see A. Barrett, *Livia. First Lady of Imperial Rome* (2002), pp. 195–9.

24 P. Brunt, 'Charges of provincial maladministration under the early Principate', *Historia* 10 (1961), pp. 189–227, with A. Lintott, *Imperium Romanum. Politics and Administration* (1993), pp. 120–21; Pliny the Younger, *Ep.* 3. 9. 4. 7, 9. 2–3, quote from Loeb translation.

25 Figures from Brunt (1961), pp. 224–7; Tacitus, *Agricola* 19, Licinus in Gaul from Dio 54. 21. 2–8.

26 Pliny the Younger, *Ep.* 3. 9. 13 for the quote, and the whole letter for the case.

27 On overall effectiveness see the pessimistic assessment of Brunt (1961), pp. 206–23.

28 On *frumentarii* see N. Austin & B. Rankov, *Exploratio. Military and Political Intelligence in the Roman World from the Second Punic War to the Battle of Adrianople* (1995), pp. 136–7, 150–54; on Lucullus see Suetonius, *Domitian* 10. 3; for Avidius Cassius see A. Goldsworthy, *The Fall of the West* (= *How Rome Fell*) (2009), p. 51.

29 For Piso see Tacitus, *Ann.* 2. 55, 57–8, 69–81, 3. 7–18, with M. Griffin, 'The Senate's story', *JRS* 87 (1997), pp. 249–63 for the inscription.

30 Pliny the Younger, *Ep.* 3. 4. 5–6.

31 I. Haynes, *Blood of the Provinces. The Roman Auxilia and the Making of Provincial Society from Augustus to the Severus* (2013), pp. 339–67; on veterans and villagers see R. Alston, 'The ties that bind: soldiers and societies', in A. Goldsworthy & I. Haynes (eds), *The Roman Army as a Community. JRA Supplementary Series* 34 (1999), pp. 175–95.

32 Strabo, *Geog.* 3. 5. 3; on citizenship in general see A. Sherwin-White, *The Roman Citizenship* (1973), pp. 221–87.

33 Pliny the Younger, *Ep.* 3. 9. 3; Claudius and the Gauls, see Tacitus, *Ann.* 11. 23–4, *ILS* 212, with a convenient translation in B. Levick, *The Government of the Roman Empire. A Sourcebook* (2nd edn, 2000), pp. 178–82.

34 *Scriptores Historiae Augustae*, *Pertinax* 1. 1–4. 4, 5. 7–13. 8, with Goldsworthy (2009), pp. 56–7.

35 Woolf (1998), pp. 148–60.

36 Mattingly (2006), pp. 367, 375–7, 383.

37 See P. Garnsey, *Famine and Food Supply in the Graeco-Roman World* (1988), *passim*.

38 Josephus, *Ant.* 15. 305–16.

39 Pliny the Younger, *Ep.* 10. 65–6, S. Pomeroy, 'Coprynyms and the exposure of infants in Egypt', in A. Cameron & A. Kuhrt (eds), *Images of Women in Antiquity* (1983), pp. 207–22, and also T. Parkin, *Demography and Roman Society* (1992), pp. 91–133; Varro, *de re rustica* 2. 10. 9.

40 On runaway slaves see C. Fuhrmann, *Policing the Roman Empire* (2012), pp. 21–43, on demands for services see S. Mitchell, 'Requisitioned transport in the Roman empire: a new inscription from Pisidia', *JRS* 66 (1976), pp. 106–31; on the mining in Jordan see Mattingly (2011), pp. 167–99, esp. 181–2, 197.

41 B. Frier, 'Roman Demography', in D. Potter & D. Mattingly (eds), *Life, Death and Entertainment in the Roman Empire* (1999), pp. 95–109, W. Scheidel, 'Germs for Rome', in C. Edwards & G. Woolf (eds), *Rome the Cosmopolis* (2003), pp. 158–76.

42 Apuleius, *Metamorphoses* 9. 39–10. 1; John the Baptist, see Luke 3. 14; for Simon the Cyrenian see Matthew 27. 32, Mark 15. 21, Luke 23. 26.

43 Acts 16. 16–40.

44 Acts 18. 12–17.

45 Acts 21. 35–7, 22. 24–9, 24. 22–7, 25. 1–21.

46 Acts 27. 1–28. 31; on the *cohors Augusta* see M. Speidel, 'The Roman army in Judaea under the Procurators', in M. Speidel, *Roman Army Studies* Vol. 2: *Mavors* (1992), pp. 224–32; on the executions under Nero see Eusebius, *Ecclesiastical History* 2. 25.

47 Josephus, *Vitae* 13.

48 John 18. 3; a useful historical survey of the trial of Jesus and Pontius Pilate's role in it is H. Bond, *Pontius Pilate in History and Interpretation. Society for New Testament Studies Monograph Series* 100 (1998), pp. 94–207.

49 John 19. 12 for quote; Joseph of Arimathea, Matthew 27. 57–60 (not mentioning his membership of the Sanhedrin), Mark 15. 42–6, Luke 23. 50–53, John 19. 38–40 (again not mentioning his membership of the Sanhedrin); on the Tiberieum see Bond (1999), pp. 11–12.

50 Luke 23. 16, 22; for Barabbas and the release of a prisoner, Matthew 27. 15–26, Mark 15. 6–15, Luke 23. 18–25, John 18. 40; Pilate's wife, Matthew 27. 19; placard, Matthew 27. 37, Mark 15. 26, Luke 23. 38, John 19. 19–22.

51 Bond (1998) is a good survey of all that is known about Pilate. In the fourth century AD Eusebius, *Ecclesiastical History* 2. 7 claimed that

'tradition' maintained that the former prefect later committed suicide, but there is no earlier evidence for this and it may well be an invention. The so-called *Acts of Pilate* were certainly a later invention by a pagan author hostile to Christians. We should note that such obscurity over an individual after he held office is normal for equestrians and very common even for senators.

CHAPTER XII – THE ARMY AND THE FRONTIERS

1 Josephus, *BJ* 3. 72–4 (Loeb translation).

2 For the army in general see G. Webster, *The Roman Imperial Army of the First and Second Centuries* AD (3rd edn, 1998), Y. Le Bohec, *The Imperial Roman Army* (1994), and A. Goldsworthy, *The Complete Roman Army* (2003).

3 On demography see B. Frier, 'Roman Demography', in D. Potter & D. Mattingly (eds), *Life, Death and Entertainment in the Roman Empire* (1999), pp. 95–109. Estimates based on the ability of land to support population remain heavily influences by K. Beloch, *Die Bevölkerung der griechisch-römischen Welt* (1886); for more recent studies see R. Bagnall & B. Frier, *The Demography of Roman Egypt* (1994), T. Parkin, *Demography and Roman Society* (1992), W. Scheidel, *Measuring Sex, Age, and Death in the Roman Empire. Explorations in Ancient Demography. JRA Supplementary Series* 21 (1996), and D. Rathbone, 'Villages, land and population in Graeco-Roman Egypt', *PCPS* 36 (1990), pp. 103–42, and C. Edwards & G. Woolf (eds), *Rome the Cosmopolis* (2003), esp. W. Scheidel, 'Germs for Rome', pp. 158–76 for a very bleak assessment of urban life.

4 Tacitus, *Ann.* 4. 5; M. Bishop, *Handbook to Roman Legionary Fortresses* (2012) offers an excellent survey of all known legionary fortresses and their garrisons.

5 For the movements of the legions, a useful survey is Le Bohec (1994), pp. 24–6, 165–78.

6 Aelius Aristides, *Roman Oration* 80–82 (Brill translation), Appian, *Praef.* 7 (Loeb translation), Herodian 2. 11. 5 (Loeb translation).

7 Webster (1998), pp. 167–230; see also B. Dobson, 'The rôle of the fort', in W. Hanson (ed.), *The Army and the Frontiers. JRA Supplementary Series* 74 (2009), pp. 25–32.

8 See A. Goldsworthy, *The Roman Army at War 100 BC–AD 200* (1996), pp. 13–38.

9 Quote from Tacitus, *Agricola* (Loeb translation); on the differences between legionary and auxiliary equipment see M. Bishop & B. Coulston, *Roman Military Equipment. From the Punic Wars to the Fall of Rome* (2nd edn, 2006), pp. 254–9.

10 Tacitus, *Agricola* 35; on order in the pursuit see Arrian, *Ectaxis* 27–8.

11 Josephus, *BJ* 3. 73–6 (Loeb translation).

12 R. Fink, *Roman Military Rewards on Papyrus* (1971), p. 87.

13 R. Fink, *Roman Military Rewards on Papyrus* (1971), p. 99.

14 N. Austin & B. Rankov, *Exploratio. Military and Political Intelligence in the Roman World from the Second Punic War to the Battle of Adrianople* (1995), pp. 158–9 for *thetatus*; discharge document B. Grenfell, A. Hunt, H. Bell *et alii* (eds), *The Oxyrhynchus Papyri* (1898–), p. 39 and R. Davies, *Service in the Roman Army* (1989), p. 227.

15 Arrian, *Periplus Ponti Euxini* (trans. A. Liddle, 2003), 6. 1–2, 9. 3–4, 9. 5; Latin report, 6. 2; exercises, 3. 1, 10. 3–4; pay, 6. 1, 10. 3.

16 The excellent M. Speidel, *Emperor Hadrian's Speeches to the African Army – A New Text* (2006) provides the best text and analysis of this inscription and the quotes are from his translation; to III Augusta, 2. 1–8; archers, 22. 1–11; 'nothing must ever . . .' 26. 9; legionary cavalry, 6. 5–10; *ala I Pannoniorum* 29. 5–7.

17 Speidel (2006), fields 19, 20, 30 for Hadrian's comments on mounting horses and jumping.

18 R. Tomlin, 'Making the machine work', in A. Goldsworthy & I. Haynes (eds), *The Roman Army as a Community. JRA Supplementary Series* 34 (1999), pp. 127–38, with M. Speidel, 'The missing weapons at Carlisle', *Britannia* 38 (2007), pp. 237–9, esp. 238–9 on the *subarmales*.

19 Austin & Rankov (1995), pp. 155–69.

20 On centurions see E. Birley, 'The origins of legionary centurions', and 'Promotion and transfer in the Roman army II: the centurionate', in E. Birley, *The Roman Army. Papers 1929–1986* (1988), pp. 189–220, B. Dobson, 'The significance of the centurion and *primipilaris* in the Roman army and administration', *ANRW* 2. 1 (1974), pp. 392–434, 'Legionary centurion or equestrian officer? A comparison of pay and prospects', *Ancient Society* 3 (1972), pp. 193–207; Fortunatus *ILS* 2658 = *CIL* 8. 217, Honoratus, *ILS* 2655 = *CIL* 8. 14698.

21 J. Thomas & R. Davies, 'A new military strength report on papyrus', *JRS* 67 (1977), pp. 50–61, col. 1, lines 2–7.

22 Pliny the Younger, *Ep.* 2. 13. 2 (Loeb translation); on the *ab epistulis* and

his military role and the *frumentarii* see Austin & Rankov (1995), pp. 135–41.

23 Tacitus, *Ann.* 2. 55 (Loeb translation).

24 M. Griffin, 'The Senate's story. Review of Das Senatus Consultum de Cn. Pisone Patre by Werner Eck; Antonio Caballos; Fernando Fernández', *JRS* 87 (1997), pp. 249–63, quote from p. 251.

25 Germanicus, see Tacitus, *Ann.* 1. 35.

26 Statius, *Silvae* 5. 1. 83–100 on the duties of the *ab epistulis*.

27 Suetonius, *Tiberius* 25; for the relationship with the army see B. Campbell, *The Emperor and the Roman Army 31 BC–AD 235* (1984).

28 Dio 77. 15. 2.

29 Much of the debate was sparked by E. Luttwak, *The Grand Strategy of the Roman Empire: From the First Century AD to the Third* (1976); significant contributions include F. Millar, 'Emperors, frontiers and foreign relations, 31 BC to AD 378', *Britannia* 13 (1982), pp. 1–23, B. Isaac, *The Limits of Empire. The Roman Army in the East* (rev. edn, 1992), E. Wheeler, 'Methodological limits and the mirage of Roman Strategy. Parts 1 & 2', *The Journal of Military History* 57 (1993), pp. 7–41 and 215–40, C. Whittaker, *Frontiers of the Roman Empire. A Social and Economic Study* (1994) and *Rome and its Frontiers. The Dynamics of Empire* (2004), S. Mattern, *Rome and the Enemy. Imperial Strategy in the Principate* (1999) and D. Breeze, *The Frontiers of Imperial Rome* (2011).

30 For Roman relations with Parthia see B. Campbell, 'War and diplomacy: Rome and Parthia, 31 BC–AD 235', in J. Rich & G. Shipley (eds), *War and Society in the Roman World* (1993), pp. 213–40, and D. Kennedy, 'Parthia and Rome: eastern perspectives', in D. Kennedy (ed.), *The Roman Army in the East. JRA Supplementary Series* 18 (1996), pp. 67–90.

31 Plutarch, *Crassus* 21.

32 On Parthian armies see Goldsworthy (1996), pp. 60–68, Kennedy (1996), pp. 83–4.

33 Isaac (1992), pp. 20–23.

34 Tacitus, *Ann.* 6. 35.

35 Tacitus, *Germania* 13–14, and in general Goldsworthy (1996), pp. 42–60.

36 Tacitus, *Germania* 30 (Loeb translation).

37 Caesar, *BG* 6. 23.

38 Velleius Paterculus 2. 109. 1–2, Tacitus, *Ann.* 2. 45.

39 Goldsworthy (1996), pp. 74–5.

40 See B. Rankov, 'A "secret of empire" (*imperii arcanum*): an unacknow-ledged factor in Roman imperial expansion', in Hanson (2009), pp. 163–72.

41 Strabo, *Geog.* 17. 1. 54 (Loeb translation); in general see A. Goldsworthy, 'War', in P. Sabin, H. van Wees, & M. Whitby (eds), *The Cambridge History of Greek and Roman Warfare* Vol. 2: *Rome from the Late Republic to the Late Empire* (2007), pp. 76–85, 106–20.

42 An insightful survey of Roman relations with the Parthians is found in Wheeler (1993), pp. 30–37.

43 Tacitus, *Hist.* 4. 51.

44 Tacitus, *Ann.* 12. 50; for an overview of the campaign see A. Goldsworthy, *In the Name of Rome* (2003), pp. 273–87.

45 Tacitus, *Ann.* 13. 9; for a narrative of the wars between Rome and Parthia see R. Sheldon, *Rome's Wars in Parthia: Blood in the Sand* (2010).

46 Dio 75. 3. 2.

47 *Tabulae Vindolandenses II* 164.

48 B. Campbell, 'Who were the *viri militares*?', *JRS* 65 (1975), pp. 11–31 is sceptical about clear career paths for a distinct group of military men, but this does not mean that ability was not an important factor in appointments.

49 Suetonius, *Domitian* 7. 3.

50 E.g. J. Drinkwater, *The Alamanni and Rome 213–496 (Caracalla to Clovis)* (2007), pp. 14, 49 on women.

51 *ILS* 986, see P. Conole & R. Milns, 'Neronian frontier policy in the Balkans: the career of Ti. Plautius Silvanus', *Historia* 32 (1983), pp. 183–200; translation taken from B. Levick, *The Government of the Roman Empire. A Sourcebook* (2nd edn, 2000), pp. 34–5.

CHAPTER XIII – GARRISONS AND RAIDS

1 Ammianus Marcellinus 27. 2. 11 (Loeb translation).

2 For Tacfarinas and the first campaign see Tacitus, *Ann.* 2. 52.

3 For the region under Augustus and Tacfarinas see D. Whittaker in *CAH²* X, pp. 591–6, E. Fentress, *Numidia and the Roman Army. BAR International Series* 53 (1979), pp. 66–8 and D. Cherry, *Frontier and Society in Roman North Africa* (1998), pp. 24–43.

4 Tacitus, *Ann.* 3. 21, Aulus Gellius, *Attic Nights* 5. 6. 14, *ILS* 2637; on veterans see A. Goldsworthy, *The Roman Army at War 100 BC–AD 200*

(1996), p. 16, on decimation see G. Watson, *The Roman Soldier* (1969), pp. 119–20.

5   Tacitus, *Ann.* 3. 20–21.

6   Tacitus, *Ann.* 3. 32, 73.

7   Tacitus, *Ann.* 3. 74.

8   Tacitus, *Ann.* 4. 23–6.

9   Cherry (1998), pp. 24–71, esp. 63–6 on the *fossatum*.

10 'To separate the Romans from the barbarians', *Scriptores Historiae Augustae, Vita Hadriani* 11. 2; on the sources for Hadrian's Wall see D. Breeze, *Handbook to the Roman Wall* (14th edn, 2006), pp. 25–34, and for the wall in general see this and D. Breeze & B. Dobson, *Hadrian's Wall* (4th edn, 2000); two fragments of an inscription, *RIB* 1051, have been reconstructed to state Hadrian's official intention in building the wall, but this is highly conjectural.

11 See B. Rankov, 'Do rivers make good frontiers?', in Z. Visy, *Limes XIX. Proceedings of the XIXth International Congress of Roman Frontier Studies held in Pécs, Hungary, September 2003* (2005), pp. 175–81.

12 For the frontiers in general see D. Breeze, *The Frontiers of Imperial Rome* (2011); on caution on guessing the function of a fort's garrison purely from its position see the cautionary comments in B. Isaac, *The Limits of Empire* (rev. edn, 1992), pp. 409–10.

13 For arguments that the severe limitations of Roman maps made many aspects of central strategic planning impossible see Isaac (1992), pp. 387–408, with emphasis on political geography, and C. Whittaker, 'Mental maps and frontiers: seeing like a Roman', in *Rome and its Frontiers. The Dynamics of Empire* (2004), pp. 63–87, which opens with the naive assertion that Julius Caesar getting lost on the way to the River Rubicon reflects a lack of maps. Given how easy it is to lose the way even with a map, especially in poor visibility or at night, this is strange. For sensible criticism of pushing such views to an extreme see E. Wheeler, 'Methodological limits and the mirage of Roman Strategy' Part 2, *The Journal of Military History* 57 (1993), pp. 236–9.

14 D. Wooliscroft, *Roman Military Signalling* (2001), pp. 51–78, 95–7, 109–35, 155–7.

15 Tacitus, *Agricola* 22. 1–2.

16 On forts in general see A. Johnson, *Roman Forts* (1983) and P. Bidwell, *Roman Forts in Britain* (2007); on South Shields see summary and references in Breeze (2006), pp. 115–28.

17 On Hadrian's Wall see Breeze & Dobson (2000), pp. 25–83; on the Gask ridge see D. Wooliscroft & B. Hoffman, *Rome's First Frontier. The Flavian Occupation of Northern Scotland* (2006), esp. pp. 175–88.

18 *Tabulae Vindolandenses II* 154.

19 *RMR* 100, and see discussion in F. Lepper & S. Frere, *Trajan's Column* (1988), pp. 244–59; on dispersal of units see Goldsworthy (1996), pp. 22–8.

20 On forts and their function see M. Bishop, 'Praesidium: social, military, and logistical aspects of the Roman army's provincial distribution during the early Principate', in A. Goldsworthy & I. Haynes (eds), *The Roman Army as a Community. JRA Supplementary Series* 34 (1999), pp. 111–18 and B. Dobson, 'The rôle of the fort', in W. Hanson (ed.), *The Army and the Frontiers. JRA Supplementary Series* 74 (2009), pp. 25–32; on Chester see T. Strickland, 'What kind of community existed at Chester during the hiatus of the 2nd c.?', in Goldsworthy & Haynes (1999), pp. 105–9.

21 *RMR* 10, Florida Ostraka 3, 5.

22 P. Bidwell, 'Systems of obstacles on Hadrian's wall and their relationship to the turrets', in A. Moirillo, N. Hanel & E. Martín, *Limes XX: Estudios sobre la frontera romana. Roman Frontier Studies. Anejos de Gladius* 13 Vol. 3 (2009), pp. 1119–24.

23 N. Hodgson, 'Gates and passages across the frontiers: the use of openings through the barriers of Britain, Germany and Raetia', in Visy (2005), pp. 183–7; *centurio regionarius Tab. Vind. II* 250. 8, centurions attending tribal councils, Dio 73. 2. 4.

24 *CIL* 8. 2495.

25 T. Kinsella, *The Táin. From the Irish Epic Táin Bó Cuailnge* (1969), p. 52; Homer, *Odyssey* 11. 397–403 (Loeb translation).

26 The expressions are used by E. Luttwak, *The Grand Strategy of the Roman Empire: From the First Century AD to the Third* (1976). His usage is subtle and does not imply a sharp divide between these levels of warfare, but this seems assumed by many who have used his works, including his critics; accepting raiding, but seeing this as not a threat, see J. Drinkwater, *The Alamanni and Rome 213–496* (2007), pp. 11–42, who suggests emperors invented a 'barbarian threat' to satisfy their own political needs.

27 *CIL* 3. 3385.

28 Tacitus, *Germania* 5. 1–2.

29 On *comites* see Tacitus, *Germania* 13; finds of weapons and other equipment dedicated as the spoils of victory in Scandinavian bogs can be interpreted to suggest forces of 200–300 men as the followers of a war leader, see X. Jensen, L. Jørgensen & U. Hansen, 'The Germanic army: warriors, soldiers and officers', in B. Stoorgard & L. Thomsen (eds), *The Spoils of Victory. The North in the Shadow of the Roman Empire* (2003), pp. 310–28.

30 Caesar, *BG* 6. 34–5, 41; fourth century, Ammianus Marcellinus 17. 10. 5–6, 18. 2. 2–3, 7–8; Hannibal, see Livy 22. 13. 5–9.

31 Tacitus, *Germania* 41 (Loeb translation); Dio 72. 11. 2–3.

32 Jerusalemite Talmud, *Erubin* 4, p. 21, col. 4, Babylonian Talmud, tractate Yebamoth 48 and see discussion in M. Gichon, 'Life on the borders reflected in rabbinical sources', in A. Morillo, N. Hanl & E. Martín (eds), *Limes XX. Estudios Sobre La Frontera Romana Roman Frontier Studies* Vol. 1 (2009), pp. 113–18.

33 Tacitus, *Ann.* 13. 54. 1, *Hist.* 1. 79, Ammianus Marcellinus 31. 10.

34 Caesar, *BG* 8. 3, Cicero, *Verrines* 2. 4. 95, 96, Babylonian Talmud, *Baba Qama* 83a.

35 H. Cuvigny, *Ostraca de Krokodilô* (2005), p. 87, with V. Maxfield, 'Ostraca and the Roman army in the eastern desert', in J. Wilkes (ed.), *Documenting the Roman Army. Essays in Honour of Margaret Roxan* (2003), pp. 153–73, esp. 166–7.

36 Observation of nomads and others by military outposts in North Africa, see R. Marichal, *Les Ostraca du Bu Njem* (1979), pp. 436–52; villa at Regensburg-Harting, Drinkwater (2007) pp. 78–9; Apuleius, *Metamorphoses* 8. 16–17.

37 Caesar, *BG* 6. 34 (Loeb translation).

38 Tacitus, *Ann.* 12. 27 for quote (Loeb translation), 12. 39 for the Silures, Ammianus Marcellinus 27. 1–2.

39 M. Todd in A. Bowman, P. Garnsey & A. Cameron, *The Cambridge Ancient History, Vol. 12 (Second Edition): The Crisis of Empire*, AD 193–337 (2005), p. 442; Ammianus Marcellinus 19. 6. 2.

40 Tacitus, *Ann.* 12. 27–8.

41 *RIB* 1142.

42 D. Potter, 'Empty areas and Roman frontier policy', *American Journal of Philology* 113 (1992), pp. 269–74.

43 Tacitus, *Ann.* 12. 31, *Agricola* 18.

CHAPTER XIV – BEYOND THE *PAX ROMANA*

1   Tacitus, *Agricola* 24. 1–2 (Loeb translation).

2   On maps and boundaries, note the sensible comments in E. Wheeler, 'Methodological limits and the mirage of Roman Strategy. Parts 1 & 2', *The Journal of Military History* 57 (1993), pp. 7–41 and 215–40, esp. 24–6 and 228–30.

3   Tacitus, *Hist.* 4. 64–65 (Loeb translation).

4   H. Cuvigny, *Ostraca de Krokodilô* (2005), p. 252, with translation and discussion in D. Nappo & A. Zerbini, 'Trade and taxation in the Egyptian desert', in O. Hekster & T. Kaizer (eds), *Frontiers in the Roman World. Proceedings of the Ninth Workshop of the International Network Impact of Empire (Durham, 16–19 April 2009)* (2011), pp. 61–77, esp. 72–74; see also V. Maxfield, 'Ostraca and the Roman army in the eastern desert', in J. Wilkes (ed.), *Documenting the Roman Army. Essays in Honour of Margaret Roxan* (2003), pp. 153–73, esp. 154–6, 164–7.

5   P. Wells, *The Barbarians Speak. How the Conquered People Shaped Roman Europe* (1999), pp. 122–47, D. Whittaker, *Frontiers of the Roman Empire. A Social and Economic Study* (1994), pp. 98–131.

6   In general see C. Sebastian Sommer, 'The Roman army in SW Germany as an instrument of colonisation: the relationship of forts to military and civilian *vici*', in A. Goldsworthy & I. Haynes (eds), *The Roman Army as a Community. JRA Supplementary Series* 34 (1999), pp. 81–93.

7   B. Shaw, 'Fear and Loathing: the nomad menace and Roman Africa', in B. Shaw, *Rulers, Nomads, and Christians in Roman North Africa* (1995), VII, pp. 25–46, esp. 42–5.

8   J. Drinkwater, *The Alamanni and Rome 213–496 (Caracalla to Clovis)* (2007), pp. 80–116.

9   *Periplus Maris Erythraei* 49, translation taken from L. Casson (ed.), *The Periplus Maris Erythraei: Text with Introduction, Translation and Commentary* (1999).

10 On Roman trade with India see R. Tomber, 'Pots, coins and trinkets in Rome's trade with the East', in P. Wells (ed.), *Rome Beyond its Frontiers: Imports, Attitudes and Practices. JRA Supplementary Series* 95 (2013), pp. 87–104, C. Whittaker, 'Indian trade within the Roman imperial network', in Whittaker (2004), pp. 163–80; Pliny the Elder, *NH* 12. 84.

11 Tacitus, *Ann.* 2. 62 (Loeb translation, slightly modified); Pliny the Elder,

NH 37. 45; Q. Atilius Primus, see *AE* 1978, 635; on Marcomani and Quadi see L. Pitts, 'Relations between Rome and the German "kings" on the Middle Danube in the first to fourth centuries AD', *JRS* 79 (1989), pp. 45–58, esp. 46–51.

12 In general see D. Mattingly (ed.), *The Archaeology of the Fazzān* Vol. 1: *Synthesis* (2003), pp. 76–90, 346–62; Ptolemy, *Geography* 1. 10.

13 Tacitus, *Hist.* 4. 50, Ptolemy, *Geog.* 1. 8.

14 Mattingly (2003), pp. 85, 88–9, 355–62.

15 In general see Wells (2013), *passim*, and (1999), pp. 224–58, M. Todd, *The Early Germans* (2nd edn, 2004), pp. 84–102; on bog finds see J. Ilkjaer, 'Danish war booty sacrifices', in B. Stoorgard & L. Thomsen (eds), *The Spoils of Victory. The North in the Shadow of the Roman Empire* (2003), pp. 44–65.

16 Tacitus, *Ann.* 13. 57; X. Jensen, L. Jørgensen & U. Hansen, 'The Germanic army: warriors, soldiers and officers', in Stoorgard & Thomsen (2003), pp. 310–28.

17 Tacitus, *Germania* 5, with Todd (2004), pp. 98–102; F. Hunter, 'Iron age hoarding in Scotland and northern Britain', in A. Gwilt & C. Haselgrove (eds), *Reconstructing Iron Age Societies* (1997), pp. 108–33.

18 See D. Harding, *The Iron Age in Northern Britain. Celts, Romans, Natives and Invaders* (2004), pp. 179–99, F. Hunter, 'Roman and native in Scotland: new approaches', *JRA* 14 (2001), pp. 289–309 and 'The lives of Roman objects beyond the frontier', in Wells (2013), pp. 15–28; Friensted, see C. Schmidt, 'Just recycled? New light on the Roman imports at the "central farmstead" of Fienstedt (central Germany)', in Wells (2013), pp. 57–70.

19 Todd (2004), p. 91.

20 Todd (2004), pp. 94–5.

21 Digest 49. 15. 6, *RIB* 2174–8 with E. Birley, 'Marcus Cocceius Firmus: an epigraphic study', in E. Birley (ed.), *Roman Britain and the Roman Army. Collected papers* (1953), pp. 87–103; on raiding for slaves to sell to the Romans see B. Cunliffe, *Greeks, Romans and Barbarians: Spheres of Interaction* (1988), pp. 171–89.

22 Tacitus, *Ann.* 2. 52, 11. 16–17, with Todd (2004), pp. 84–7.

23 Wells (1999), pp. 246–56, Todd (2004), pp. 62–80, 97–8.

24 A. Jørgensen, 'Fortifications and the control of land and sea traffic in the Pre-Roman and Roman Iron Age', in Stoorgard & Thomsen (2003), pp. 194–209; Tacitus, *Ann.* 2. 19.

25 For a fuller narrative of this later period there is A. Goldsworthy, *The Fall of the West* (= *How Rome Fell*) (2009).

26 Drinkwater (2007), pp. 117–44 on society and population.

27 *AE* 1993, 1231; see R. MacMullen, *Enemies of the Roman Order* (1966), pp. 196–234 and *Roman Government's Response to Crisis AD 235–337* (1976).

CONCLUSION – PEACE AND WAR

1 Caesar, *BG* 8. 44.

2 G. de la Bédoyère review of D. Mattingly, *An Imperial Possession. Britain in the Roman Empire 54 BC–AD 409* (2006), in *History Today* (August 2006), p. 62, with reply in D. Mattingly, *Imperialism, Power, and Identity. Experiencing the Roman Empire* (2011), p. 274, fn. 3.

INDEX